McDougal Littell

Math Intervention

Teacher's Edition
for Books 1–7

McDougal Littell
A DIVISION OF HOUGHTON MIFFLIN COMPANY
Evanston, Illinois • Boston • Dallas

ISBN-13: 978-0-618-90519-5
ISBN-10: 0-618-90519-7

123456789—PBO—11 10 09 08 07

CONTENTS — Teacher's Edition for Books 1–7

PROGRAM OVERVIEW

- The *Math Intervention* program includes seven student books covering a wide range of mathematical topics needed for success in middle and high school mathematics. Student books are available in both English and Spanish.

- You may find this program helpful for use with students as spot remediation within a regular class setting, or as a more complete course in an after-school program, follow-up remediation class, or summer school environment.

- The materials in these books can be used to help bring students up to grade-level expectations. Students with broad areas of weakness may benefit from completing all seven books. Other students may only need to work on selected books or lessons.

- Lessons in the student books include worked-out Examples and Practice exercises to help build understanding of a topic and develop math skills. Problem solving lessons suggest strategies for approaching real-world problem-solving situations and promote the use of estimation to check reasonableness of solutions. Activities build understanding of a topic through the use of models and games. Mixed Practice sections include practice of vocabulary, skills, and problem-solving methods covering a group of lessons.

- This Teacher's Edition contains assessment materials covering the topics of the seven student books. A Pre-Course Diagnostic Test with a detailed item-analysis helps you identify the math content areas your students may need to practice. You may wish to direct your students to complete the work in selected lessons, or cover a given book as a whole. Tests are provided on each of the student Books 1–7. You may also wish to use these book tests as diagnostic tools to identify student review needs. Assessment materials are provided in both English and Spanish.

- This Teacher's Edition includes blackline masters for use with many of the activities in Books 1–7.

- Answers for all assessment materials in this Teacher's Edition as well as for all the exercises in the student Books 1–7 are provided at the back of this Teacher's Edition.

 **Book 1: Whole Numbers**

Multiplication and Division of Whole Numbers

CONTENTS · Book 2: Fractions and Decimals

Understanding Decimals

Operations with Decimals

Book 4: Ratios, Rates, Proportions, and Percents

Ratios, Rates, and Proportions

Percents, Interest, and Probability

 # CONTENTS   Book 5: Algebraic Thinking

Basic Concepts and Properties

Functional Relationships Between Two Quantities

CONTENTS — Book 6: Data Analysis and Geometry

Data Analysis

Length and Area

Surface Area and Volume

Other Geometry Concepts

Solving Multi-Step Equations and Inequalities

Properties of Exponents

Name _____   Date _____

Pre-Course Diagnostic Test *For use before Math Intervention Books 1–7*

Whole Numbers

Whole Number Concepts

1. Which number is missing on this number line?

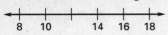

  8 10   14 16 18

(A) 11   (B) 12   (C) 13   (D) 15

2. Which place-value chart does the model represent?

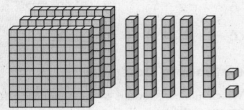

(A)

Hundreds	Tens	Ones
3	6	2

(B)

Hundreds	Tens	Ones
5	3	2

(C)

Hundreds	Tens	Ones
2	5	3

(D)

Hundreds	Tens	Ones
3	5	2

3. Which number is 16,372 rounded to the hundreds' place?

(A) 16,000 (B) 16,300 (C) 16,400 (D) 17,000

Addition and Subtraction of Whole Numbers

4. Which subtraction fact corresponds to the addition fact $14 + 3 = 17$?

(A) $17 - 3 = 14$ (B) $14 - 3 = 11$

(C) $17 - 17 = 0$ (D) $17 + 14 = 31$

5. This month, Jackson earned $1500. He spent $678 on rent and $312 on utilities. How much does he have left from his earnings?

(A) $410   (B) $510

(C) $520   (D) $1134

6. Which strategy could you use to find $15 + 67$?

(A) Count on by 1s seven times to go from 15 to 22. Then count on by 10s six times.

(B) Count on by 5s two times to go from 15 to 25. Then count on by 10s six times.

(C) Count on by 1s five times to go from 15 to 20. Then count on by 10s six times.

(D) Count on by 2s six times to go from 15 to 21. Then count on by 10s two times.

Multiplication and Division of Whole Numbers

7. A vendor at a music convention sold 135 CDs at $12 each. How much did the vendor collect from these sales?

(A) $270 (B) $405 (C) $1485 (D) $1620

8. Mrs. Shipman bought 115 treats to divide equally among the 28 students in her class. How many treats will each student receive?

(A) 3 treats each with 4 treats remaining

(B) 3 treats each with 12 treats remaining

(C) 4 treats each with 3 treats remaining

(D) 4 treats each with 13 treats remaining

9. Which expression is true?

(A) $6 + 9 \cdot 2^2 - 5 = 55$

(B) $40 \div 8 + 4 \cdot 3^2 = 81$

(C) $(5 + 2) \cdot 4 - 1 = 21$

(D) $12 - 8 \div 2^2 + 7 = 17$

Fractions and Decimals

Number Concepts

10. What is the prime factorization of 252?

(A) $2^2 \times 3^2 \times 7$ (B) $2^2 \times 3^2 \times 7^2$

(C) $2 \times 3^2 \times 7$ (D) $2^2 \times 3 \times 7$

11. Sal has 18 green and 42 red beads. She is dividing the beads into equal groups without mixing colors. How many are in each group?

(A) 4   (B) 5

(C) 6   (D) 7

Pre-Course Diagnostic Test *continued*

12. What is the least common multiple of 8, 16, and 20?

Ⓐ 20 Ⓑ 80 Ⓒ 128 Ⓓ 2560

Understanding Fractions

13. Which fraction is equivalent to the fraction represented in the model?

Ⓐ $\frac{10}{12}$ Ⓑ $\frac{15}{20}$ Ⓒ $\frac{9}{16}$ Ⓓ $\frac{4}{8}$

14. Which comparison is true?

Ⓐ $\frac{2}{5} < \frac{3}{10}$

Ⓑ $\frac{4}{7} < \frac{2}{9}$

Ⓒ $\frac{2}{3} > \frac{9}{11}$

Ⓓ $\frac{5}{12} > \frac{3}{8}$

15. The table shows the lengths of four paths. Which list correctly orders the paths from least length to greatest length?

Path A	$\frac{15}{7}$ miles
Path B	$2\frac{3}{7}$ miles
Path C	$\frac{25}{14}$ miles
Path D	$2\frac{9}{14}$ miles

Ⓐ Path C, Path D, Path A, Path B

Ⓑ Path C, Path B, Path A, Path D

Ⓒ Path D, Path B, Path C, Path A

Ⓓ Path C, Path A, Path B, Path D

Operations with Fractions

16. What is the sum $\frac{7}{9} + \frac{1}{6}$?

Ⓐ $\frac{8}{15}$ Ⓑ $\frac{5}{9}$

Ⓒ $\frac{17}{18}$ Ⓓ $\frac{5}{6}$

17. Lydia has $8\frac{1}{3}$ cups of flour in a bag. She uses $5\frac{3}{4}$ cups of flour to make biscuits. How much flour does she have left in the bag?

Ⓐ $2\frac{1}{4}$ cups Ⓑ $2\frac{7}{12}$ cups

Ⓒ $2\frac{11}{12}$ cups Ⓓ $3\frac{1}{2}$ cups

18. Which statement is true?

Ⓐ $4\frac{1}{2} \div \frac{7}{8} = 5\frac{1}{7}$ Ⓑ $4\frac{1}{2} \times \frac{7}{8} = 5\frac{1}{7}$

Ⓒ $\frac{7}{8} \div 4\frac{1}{2} = 5\frac{1}{7}$ Ⓓ $\frac{7}{8} \times 4\frac{1}{2} = 1\frac{3}{4}$

Understanding Decimals

19. Which number shown is 14.748 rounded to the nearest tenth?

Ⓐ 15 Ⓑ 14.8

Ⓒ 14.75 Ⓓ 14.7

20. Mallim has a card that is 3.875 inches long. Which envelope length could Mallim use to hold his card?

Ⓐ 3.86 in. Ⓑ 3.79 in.

Ⓒ 3.9 in. Ⓓ 3.871 in.

21. Which number line is labeled correctly?

Ⓐ

Ⓑ

Ⓒ

Ⓓ

Operations with Decimals

22. Which sum is the correct way to write 4.5215 + 332.3 in a column?

Ⓐ
$$\begin{array}{r} 332.3 \\ + \, 4.5215 \\ \hline \end{array}$$

Ⓑ
$$\begin{array}{r} 3323 \\ + \, 45215 \\ \hline \end{array}$$

Ⓒ
$$\begin{array}{r} 332.30 \\ + \, 4.5215 \\ \hline \end{array}$$

Ⓓ
$$\begin{array}{r} 332.3 \\ + \quad 4.5215 \\ \hline \end{array}$$

Pre-Course Diagnostic Test *continued*

23. Which number is the product 2.9481 × 1000?

  (A) 2948.1   **(B)** 294.81

  (C) 29.481   **(D)** 2.9481

24. Joy paid $4.83 for 4.2 pounds of fruit. How much did she pay per pound?

  (A) $.12   **(B)** $.58   **(C)** $1.15   **(D)** $11.50

Integers and Rational Numbers

Basic Concepts

25. Which value is equivalent to $|-8|$?

  (A) 8   **(B)** the opposite of 8

  (C) 8 squared   **(D)** -8

26. Which number is a rational number?

  (A) 1.47526…   **(B)** 8.01404…

  (C) 2.99999…   **(D)** 4.15158…

27. Which list shows the numbers in order from least to greatest?

  (A) $-7.45, -7\frac{7}{9}, -7\frac{1}{9}, 7.01$

  (B) $-7\frac{1}{9}, -7\frac{7}{9}, -7.45, 7.01$

  (C) $7.01, -7.45, -7\frac{7}{9}, -7\frac{1}{9}$

  (D) $-7\frac{7}{9}, -7.45, -7\frac{1}{9}, 7.01$

Operations with Integers and Rational Numbers

28. Which number line models $-2 - (-6)$?

  (A)

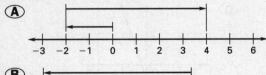

  (B)

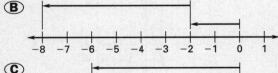

  (C)

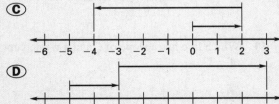

  (D)

29. What do the product -12×6 and the quotient $12 \div -6$ have in common?

  (A) When you take the absolute value of each result, you get the same number.

  (B) Both involve using the opposite of 12 and the absolute value of 6.

  (C) The resulting sign for both is positive.

  (D) The resulting sign for both is negative.

30. Find the sum $-2\frac{7}{10} + 0.06$.

  (A) -2.76 **(B)** -2.64 **(C)** 2.64 **(D)** 2.76

Ratios, Rates, Proportions, and Percents

Ratios, Rates, and Proportions

31. George's store has 3 manual lawn mowers out of 24 lawn mowers. The ratio of manual mowers to all mowers at Arnie's store is 4 : 40. Which statement is true?

  (A) There is a higher portion of manual lawn mowers at George's store than at Arnie's store.

  (B) There is a higher portion of manual lawn mowers at Arnie's store than at George's store.

  (C) The ratio of manual lawn mowers to all lawn mowers is the same at both stores.

  (D) The ratio of manual lawn mowers to all lawn mowers at George's store is 1 : 10.

32. A machine fills 750 water bottles in 3 hours. Which is the machine's hourly rate?

  (A) 150 water bottles per hour

  (B) 250 water bottles per hour

  (C) 750 water bottles per hour

  (D) 2250 water bottles per hour

33. Which value of a makes the proportion $\frac{7}{14} = \frac{9}{a}$ true?

  (A) 12   **(B)** 14   **(C)** 18   **(D)** 27

Percents, Interest, and Probability

34. Which fraction is equivalent to 40%?

  (A) $\frac{1}{25}$ **(B)** $\frac{1}{4}$ **(C)** $\frac{2}{5}$ **(D)** $\frac{3}{5}$

Pre-Course Diagnostic Test *continued*

35. Riley deposits $400 in a savings account that pays 5.2% simple interest on the same day that Miguel deposits $400 in a savings account that pays 4.8% compound interest. Which statement is true?

Ⓐ In 3 years Riley will have more in her account than Miguel will have in his.

Ⓑ In 3 years Miguel will have more in his account than Riley will have in hers.

Ⓒ In 3 years Riley and Miguel will have the same amount of money in their accounts.

Ⓓ In 3 years the combined amount in both accounts will be $924.80.

36. What is the probability that the spinner *will not* land on an even number?

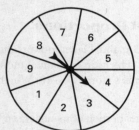

Ⓐ $\frac{1}{3}$ Ⓑ $\frac{2}{3}$

Ⓒ $\frac{4}{9}$ Ⓓ $\frac{5}{9}$

Algebraic Thinking

Basic Concepts and Properties

37. Which rule describes the pattern 4, 8, 12, 16, 20, . . .?

Ⓐ Start with 4. Then multiply a term by 2 to get the next term.

Ⓑ Start with 4. Then multiply a term by 3 to get the next term.

Ⓒ Start with 4. Then add 3 to a term to get the next term.

Ⓓ Start with 4. Then add 4 to a term to get the next term.

38. "Twelve more than twice the number of books" is represented by which expression?

Ⓐ $12b + 2$ Ⓑ $2b + 12$

Ⓒ $2(b + 12)$ Ⓓ $(b + 2) + 12$

39. What is the solution of $n - 9 = -4$?

Ⓐ -13 Ⓑ -5 Ⓒ 5 Ⓓ 13

Functional Relationships Between Two Quantities

40. Which graph shows the line $y = 3x - 1$?

Ⓐ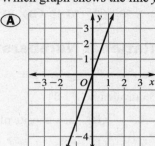

Ⓑ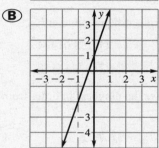

Ⓒ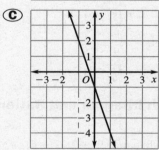

Ⓓ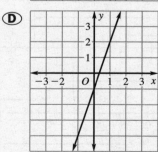

41. Which line has a slope of $\frac{1}{3}$ and a y-intercept of -3?

Ⓐ $y = \frac{1}{3}x - 3$ Ⓑ $y = -3x + \frac{1}{3}$

Ⓒ $y = -\frac{1}{3}x + 3$ Ⓓ $y = -\frac{1}{3}x - 3$

Pre-Course Diagnostic Test *continued*

42. Which relationship between wages and hours is represented in the graph?

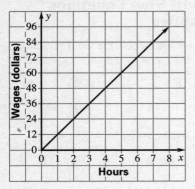

(A) Geneveve makes $6 for every hour she works.

(B) Geneveve makes $8 for every hour she works.

(C) Geneveve makes $12 for every hour she works.

(D) Geneveve makes $24 for every hour she works.

Data Analysis and Geometry

Data Analysis

43. Which list names objects that are all paper products?

(A) newsletter, pencil, camera, dish

(B) envelope, newsletter, business card, notepad

(C) envelope, toner, tissue, watermelon

(D) label, bottle, construction paper, paper towels

44. According to the list of shirt sizes for the girls' basketball team, how many girls on the team wear a size medium (M) shirt?

Shirt sizes: S, M, M, M, L, M, L, S, M L, S, M, L, L, L, M, S, S, M, M, S, S, L, L, M

(A) 7   **(B)** 8   **(C)** 9   **(D)** 10

45. The tally chart shows the results of a probability experiment that tosses a coin 50 times. What is the experimental probability of tossing tails?

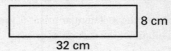

Heads	卌 卌 卌 卌 卌 III
Tails	卌 卌 卌 卌 II

(A) $\frac{1}{2}$ **(B)** $\frac{11}{25}$ **(C)** $\frac{14}{25}$ **(D)** $\frac{21}{50}$

Length and Area

46. What is the perimeter of the rectangle?

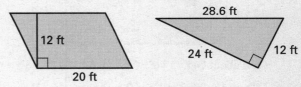

(A) 72 cm   **(B)** 80 cm

(C) 160 cm   **(D)** 256 cm

47. The dimensions of a parallelogram and a triangle are shown. Which statement is true?

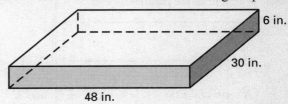

(A) The area of the parallelogram is 120 ft².

(B) The area of the triangle is 288 ft².

(C) The area of the parallelogram is 64 ft².

(D) The area of the triangle is 144 ft².

48. A circle has a diameter of 18 meters. What is the area of the circle?

(A) 9π m²   **(B)** 18π m²

(C) 81π m²   **(D)** 324π m²

Surface Area and Volume

49. What is the surface area of the rectangular prism?

(A) 3816 in.²   **(B)** 3996 in.²

(C) 4752 in.²   **(D)** 8640 in.²

Pre-Course Diagnostic Test *continued*

50. The dimensions of two prisms are shown. Which statement is true?

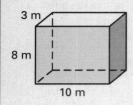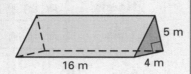

3 m
8 m
10 m
16 m
5 m
4 m

(A) The volumes of both prisms are equal.

(B) The volume of the rectangular prism is less than the volume of the triangular prism.

(C) The volume of the rectangular prism is greater than the volume of the triangular prism.

(D) The volume of the triangular prism is 320 m³.

51. What is the volume of the cylinder?

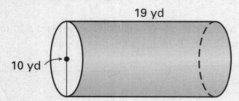

19 yd

10 yd

(A) about 745.75 yd³   **(B)** about 1491.5 yd³

(C) about 2983 yd³   **(D)** about 5966 yd³

Other Geometry Concepts

52. Two angles are supplementary. One angle measures 46°. What is the measure of the other angle?

(A) 44°   **(B)** 90°   **(C)** 104°   **(D)** 134°

53. Which values could be the side lengths of a right triangle in inches?

(A) 7, 24, and 25   **(B)** 16, 25, and 34

(C) 8, 15, and 20   **(D)** 6, 8, and 12

54. Which lines are parallel?

E   F
H   G

(A) $\overleftrightarrow{EF}$ and $\overleftrightarrow{FG}$ **(B)** $\overleftrightarrow{EF}$ and $\overleftrightarrow{EH}$

(C) $\overleftrightarrow{HG}$ and $\overleftrightarrow{EH}$ **(D)** $\overleftrightarrow{EH}$ and $\overleftrightarrow{FG}$

Getting Ready for Algebra

Solving Multi-Step Equations and Inequalities

55. Which equation models the word sentence "*Seven less than five times a number is eighteen*"?

(A) $5x - 18 = 7$ **(B)** $7 - 5x = 18$

(C) $5x - 7 = 18$ **(D)** $18 - 5x = 7$

56. What is the solution of $2x + 8 = 14$?

(A) 3   **(B)** 6   **(C)** 7   **(D)** 8

57. As a fitness goal, Ned challenges himself to accumulate 1500 pushups on his workout calendar by doing 20 pushups a day. He has already accumulated 300 pushups. Which equation can you use to find the number of days d he has left to reach his goal?

(A) $300 - 20d = 1500$

(B) $300 + 20d = 1500$

(C) $300d - 20 = 1500$

(D) $300d + 20 = 1500$

Properties of Exponents

58. What is the value of 5^0?

(A) 0   **(B)** 1   **(C)** 5   **(D)** 10

59. Which expression is equivalent to $(x^4)^8$?

(A) $x^{(4+8)}$

(B) $x^8 \cdot x^8 \cdot x^8 \cdot x^8$

(C) $x^4 \cdot x^4 \cdot x^4 \cdot x^4 \cdot x^4 \cdot x^4 \cdot x^4 \cdot x^4$

(D) $x^4 + x^{32}$

60. Which equation is true?

(A) $\dfrac{8a^4b^4}{8a^2b^2} = 8a^2b^2$

(B) $\dfrac{16a^5b^4}{a^4b^5} = \dfrac{16b}{a}$

(C) $\dfrac{2ab}{4ab} = \dfrac{ab}{2}$

(D) $\dfrac{12a^2b^4}{3a^5b} = \dfrac{4b^3}{a^3}$

Teacher's Commentary for Pre-Course Diagnostic Test

The 60 items on the Pre-Course Diagnostic Test shown on pages 1–6 cover the materials across Books 1–7 of the *Math Intervention* program. After you have given a student or group of students the Pre-Course Diagnostic Test, you can use the following chart to determine which mathematical topics are causing the student or students difficulty. If the students miss item 10, for example, on the Pre-Course Test, then you may want the students to complete the materials in Math Intervention Book 2, Lesson 2-1.

You can use this chart to decide which lessons or complete books in the *Math Intervention* program would be most helpful to your students.

Item Analysis

If a student misses the Pre-Course Test item:	then the student has trouble with:	Have the student go to Book:	to work on Lesson(s):
1	identifying and ordering whole numbers	1	1-2, 1-3, and 1-5
2	place value and expanded notation	1	1-4
3	rounding whole numbers	1	1-6
4	addition and subtraction facts	1	1-9
5	adding and subtracting whole numbers	1	1-11 to 1-13 and 1-15 to 1-18
6	mental math strategies for addition	1	1-19
7	multiplying whole numbers	1	1-24 to 1-27 and 1-34
8	dividing whole numbers	1	1-28 to 1-30 and 1-34
9	exponents and/or order of operations	1	1-32 to 1-33
10	prime factorization	2	2-1
11	greatest common factor	2	2-2
12	least common multiple	2	2-3
13	equivalent fractions and/or simplifying fractions	2	2-4 to 2-6
14	comparing and ordering fractions	2	2-7
15	comparing and ordering mixed numbers and improper fractions	2	2-8 to 2-9
16	adding fractions	2	2-10 to 2-12

If a student misses the Pre-Course Test item:	then the student has trouble with:	Have the student go to Book:	to work on Lesson(s):
17	subtracting mixed numbers	2	2-13 and 2-17
18	multiplying and dividing fractions and mixed numbers	2	2-14 to 2-16
19	rounding decimals	2	2-18 to 2-19
20	comparing and ordering decimals	2	2-20
21	converting between decimals and fractions	2	2-21 to 2-22
22	adding decimals	2	2-23
23	multiplying decimals	2	2-24 to 2-26
24	dividing decimals	2	2-27 to 2-28 and 2-30
25	absolute value	3	3-2
26	rational numbers	3	3-4
27	ordering rational numbers	3	3-5
28	adding and subtracting integers	3	3-7 to 3-8
29	multiplying and dividing integers	3	3-9 to 3-10
30	rational number operations	3	3-12
31	ratios	4	4-1
32	unit rates	4	4-2
33	solving proportions	4	4-7
34	percents	4	4-9 to 4-10
35	interest	4	4-14 to 4-15
36	probability	4	4-17
37	patterns	5	5-1 to 5-2
38	writing algebraic expressions	5	5-4
39	solving addition and subtraction equations	5	5-8
40	graphing linear equations	5	5-12 to 5-15
41	slope and y-intercept	5	5-16 and 5-18
42	direct variation	5	5-17
43	sorting objects and data	6	6-1
44	recording and representing data	6	6-2 to 6-3

If a student misses the Pre-Course Test item:	then the student has trouble with:	Have the student go to Book:	to work on Lesson(s):
45	probability experiments	6	6-5
46	finding perimeter	6	6-7
47	finding the area of a parallelogram and a triangle	6	6-9 to 6-10
48	finding the area of a circle	6	6-13
49	finding the surface area of a rectangular prism	6	6-15
50	finding the volume of a rectangular prism and a triangular prism	6	6-16 to 6-17
51	finding the volume of a cylinder	6	6-18
52	complementary and supplementary angles	6	6-21
53	the Pythagorean Theorem	6	6-26 to 6-27
54	parallel and perpendicular lines	6	6-28
55	writing equations	7	7-1
56	solving multi-step equations	7	7-2
57	solving problems with multi-step equations	7	7-3
58	zero and negative exponents	7	7-7
59	finding the power of a power	7	7-9
60	finding the quotient of powers	7	7-11

Name _____   Date _____

Answer Sheet for Pre-Course Diagnostic Test

Mark your answer sheet carefully. Take a moment to make sure you mark your answer in the correct place. This is especially important if you skip one or more problems. When answering multiple-choice tests, be sure to fill in the bubble completely and, if you change an answer, to erase all traces of your old mark.

Sample answer: Ⓐ Ⓑ ● Ⓓ

1. Ⓐ Ⓑ Ⓒ Ⓓ	21. Ⓐ Ⓑ Ⓒ Ⓓ	41. Ⓐ Ⓑ Ⓒ Ⓓ
2. Ⓐ Ⓑ Ⓒ Ⓓ	22. Ⓐ Ⓑ Ⓒ Ⓓ	42. Ⓐ Ⓑ Ⓒ Ⓓ
3. Ⓐ Ⓑ Ⓒ Ⓓ	23. Ⓐ Ⓑ Ⓒ Ⓓ	43. Ⓐ Ⓑ Ⓒ Ⓓ
4. Ⓐ Ⓑ Ⓒ Ⓓ	24. Ⓐ Ⓑ Ⓒ Ⓓ	44. Ⓐ Ⓑ Ⓒ Ⓓ
5. Ⓐ Ⓑ Ⓒ Ⓓ	25. Ⓐ Ⓑ Ⓒ Ⓓ	45. Ⓐ Ⓑ Ⓒ Ⓓ
6. Ⓐ Ⓑ Ⓒ Ⓓ	26. Ⓐ Ⓑ Ⓒ Ⓓ	46. Ⓐ Ⓑ Ⓒ Ⓓ
7. Ⓐ Ⓑ Ⓒ Ⓓ	27. Ⓐ Ⓑ Ⓒ Ⓓ	47. Ⓐ Ⓑ Ⓒ Ⓓ
8. Ⓐ Ⓑ Ⓒ Ⓓ	28. Ⓐ Ⓑ Ⓒ Ⓓ	48. Ⓐ Ⓑ Ⓒ Ⓓ
9. Ⓐ Ⓑ Ⓒ Ⓓ	29. Ⓐ Ⓑ Ⓒ Ⓓ	49. Ⓐ Ⓑ Ⓒ Ⓓ
10. Ⓐ Ⓑ Ⓒ Ⓓ	30. Ⓐ Ⓑ Ⓒ Ⓓ	50. Ⓐ Ⓑ Ⓒ Ⓓ
11. Ⓐ Ⓑ Ⓒ Ⓓ	31. Ⓐ Ⓑ Ⓒ Ⓓ	51. Ⓐ Ⓑ Ⓒ Ⓓ
12. Ⓐ Ⓑ Ⓒ Ⓓ	32. Ⓐ Ⓑ Ⓒ Ⓓ	52. Ⓐ Ⓑ Ⓒ Ⓓ
13. Ⓐ Ⓑ Ⓒ Ⓓ	33. Ⓐ Ⓑ Ⓒ Ⓓ	53. Ⓐ Ⓑ Ⓒ Ⓓ
14. Ⓐ Ⓑ Ⓒ Ⓓ	34. Ⓐ Ⓑ Ⓒ Ⓓ	54. Ⓐ Ⓑ Ⓒ Ⓓ
15. Ⓐ Ⓑ Ⓒ Ⓓ	35. Ⓐ Ⓑ Ⓒ Ⓓ	55. Ⓐ Ⓑ Ⓒ Ⓓ
16. Ⓐ Ⓑ Ⓒ Ⓓ	36. Ⓐ Ⓑ Ⓒ Ⓓ	56. Ⓐ Ⓑ Ⓒ Ⓓ
17. Ⓐ Ⓑ Ⓒ Ⓓ	37. Ⓐ Ⓑ Ⓒ Ⓓ	57. Ⓐ Ⓑ Ⓒ Ⓓ
18. Ⓐ Ⓑ Ⓒ Ⓓ	38. Ⓐ Ⓑ Ⓒ Ⓓ	58. Ⓐ Ⓑ Ⓒ Ⓓ
19. Ⓐ Ⓑ Ⓒ Ⓓ	39. Ⓐ Ⓑ Ⓒ Ⓓ	59. Ⓐ Ⓑ Ⓒ Ⓓ
20. Ⓐ Ⓑ Ⓒ Ⓓ	40. Ⓐ Ⓑ Ⓒ Ⓓ	60. Ⓐ Ⓑ Ⓒ Ⓓ

Name _____   Date _____

 BOOK 1 **Test on *Whole Numbers***

Vocabulary Questions

Fill in the missing word(s).

1. The statement $5 + 8 = 8 + 5$ shows the _____ property of addition.

2. The statement $(3 \cdot 9) \cdot 2 = 3 \cdot (9 \cdot 2)$ shows the _____ property of multiplication.

Match the word with its mathematical meaning and everyday meaning.

3. count on   4. expression   5. dividend

Mathematical meaning	**Everyday meaning**
A. to add	**X.** money paid to a shareholder
B. the number you divide	**Y.** a common saying
C. a combination of numbers, powers, and mathematical symbols	**Z.** to rely on

Answers

1. _____
2. _____
3. _____
4. _____
5. _____
6. _____
7. _____
8. _____
9. _____
10. See graph. _____
11. _____

Whole Number Concepts

Write the expanded form as a number.

6. 4 tens + 8

7. 3 hundreds + 6 tens + 2

Write how many.

8.

Hundreds	Tens	Ones

9.

Hundreds	Tens	Ones

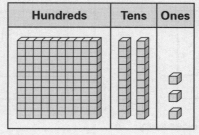

10. Fill in the missing numbers on the number line.

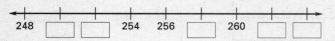

248 ☐ ☐ 254 256 ☐ 260 ☐ ☐

11. What is the value of 6 nickels?

   A. 25¢   **B.** 30¢   **C.** 35¢   **D.** 40¢

Test *continued*

BOOK 1 TEST

Write the value in expanded form.

12. 5240   **13.** 306   **14.** 42

Write the numbers in order from least to greatest.

15. 435, 431, 433, 432   **16.** 876, 768, 678, 786

Round the number to the place value of the digit that is underlined.

17. 5,633,456   **18.** 31,712   **19.** 428

Addition and Subtraction of Whole Numbers

20. Skip count to find the value of 7 dimes. Then subtract 5 dimes. What is the new value?

21. Use the numbers 4, 12, and 16 to write two addition facts and two subtraction facts.

22. Illustrate the fact family.

$8 + 6 = 14$

$6 + 8 = 14$

$14 - 6 = 8$

$14 - 8 = 6$

Find the sum or difference.

23. $0 + 95$ **24.** $17 - 0$ **25.** $6 + 2 + 4 + 8$

Write the sum.

26.

Tens	Ones
8	2
+ 1	6

27.

Tens	Ones
3	0
+ 4	3

Add. Regroup if necessary.

28.

2	8
+ 2	4

29.

1	5
+ 7	5

Find the sum.

30. $269 + 714$ **31.** $15,040 + 9542$

Answers

12. _____

13. _____

14. _____

15. _____

16. _____

17. _____

18. _____

19. _____

20. _____

21. _____

_____

_____

_____

22. See left.

23. _____

24. _____

25. _____

26. See left.

27. See left.

28. See left.

29. See left.

30. _____

31. _____

Name _____   Date _____

  Test *continued*

Subtract to find how many more or how many fewer tapes there are than cases.

Answers

32.    **33.**

32. _____

33. _____

34. _____

35. See left. _____

36. See left. _____

37. _____

38. _____

39. _____

34. Use the model to find $100 - 30$.

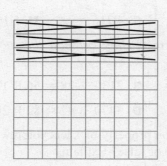

40. _____

41. _____

42. _____

43. _____

Subtract. Regroup if necessary.

35.

Hundreds	Tens	Ones
3	4	4
−	8	7

36.

Hundreds	Tens	Ones
7	2	0
−	4	5

Which of A, B, C, or D shows the correct difference?

37. $62 - 38$

    A. 24   **B.** 26   **C.** 34   **D.** 36

38. $14,562 - 1897$

    A. 12,565   **B.** 12,665   **C.** 12,765   **D.** 13,335

Find the sum or difference.

39. $19 + 64$ **40.** $80 - 50$

41. $12 + 48 + 7$ **42.** $17 + 54 + 23$

Multiplication and Division of Whole Numbers

43. You have 18 tokens. You give 3 tokens at a time to your friends until all your tokens are gone. Which fact models this situation?

    A. $18 - 3 = 15$ **B.** $6 \div 3 = 2$ **C.** $18 \times 3 = 54$ **D.** $18 \div 3 = 6$

Name _____ Date _____

BOOK 1 **Test** *continued*

44. Give the first 8 multiples of 6. Then find 7×6.

_____

45. 3 times what number is 27?

Find the product or quotient.

46. 32×4	**47.** 26×8	**48.** $9,400,000 \div 1000$
49. 157×100	**50.** 24×15	**51.** 341×50
52. 3542×141	**53.** $14,934 \div 6$	**54.** $4000 \div 8$

55. Which division problem has a dividend that is an exact multiple of the divisor?

   A. $6\overline{)458}$ **B.** $9\overline{)813}$ **C.** $4\overline{)716}$ **D.** $5\overline{)102}$

56. Which division statement is correct? *Hint: Estimate the quotients to check for reasonableness.*

   A. $1520 \div 35 = 63$ R 15 **B.** $2130 \div 28 = 56$ R 12

   C. $2440 \div 48 = 45$ R 40 **D.** $3470 \div 42 = 82$ R 26

57. Sarah says that the multiplication property of 1 lets you rewrite $4 \cdot (1 \cdot 14)$ as $4 \cdot 1$. Is this true or false? Explain.

_____

_____

58. Write the product $3^5 \cdot 3^8$ as a single power.

59. What should you do first to simplify $8 \cdot 9 \div 3(2 - 1) + 6^2$?

   A. Evaluate $2 - 1$.   **B.** Evaluate 6^2.

   C. Evaluate $9 \div 3$.   **D.** Evaluate $8 \cdot 9$.

60. There are 12 boxes. Each box contains 16 teabags. Which operation should you use to find the total number of teabags?

   A. $16 - 12$ **B.** 16×12 **C.** $16 \div 12$ **D.** $16 + 12$

61. Jacklyn has 79 buttons to sew onto shirts. She plans to sew 3 buttons at the top of each shirt. She figures that $79 \div 3 = 26$ R 1, so she can sew buttons onto 26 shirts with 1 button remaining. Show how you can check Jacklyn's quotient by writing an addition problem.

_____

_____

62. Describe 3^6 in words. Then show how to evaluate the power.

_____

_____

Answers

44. See left. _____

_____

45. _____

46. _____

47. _____

48. _____

49. _____

50. _____

51. _____

52. _____

53. _____

54. _____

55. _____

56. _____

57. See left. _____

58. _____

59. _____

60. _____

61. See left. _____

62. See left. _____

BOOK 1 **Test** *continued*

Problem Solving with Whole Numbers

63. A school sells ice cream cakes to help raise money for the PTA. The school earns $12 for each cake that is sold. Students sell 722 cakes. Explain how to find the total amount of money the school earns.

_____

_____

64. Four friends send out holiday cards. Sheila sends 37 cards, Helen 42, Catherine 36, and Mel sends 40 cards. Write the friends in order from least number of cards sent to greatest number sent.

_____

65. Quentin sells 4682 boxes of raisins in June and 4619 boxes of raisins in July. When these amounts are rounded to the nearest hundred are they the same? Why or why not?

_____

_____

66. Rhonda is buying erasers. Her total at the register is 72 cents. Rhonda has several pennies, dimes, nickels, and quarters. Draw pictures to show four different ways Rhonda can pay for the erasers using at least 1 nickel.

67. A construction team builds 18 new houses in a community. A realtor sells 7 of these houses. Explain how to find the number of houses that are still left to sell.

_____

_____

68. Eliza had a deck built for $3560 and a fence installed for $2840. Then she spent $1150 to put new blinds on all her windows. Explain how you can find the total amount Eliza spent on these three home improvement projects.

_____

_____

Answers

63. See left. _____

64. See left. _____

65. See left. _____

66. See left. _____

67. See left. _____

68. See left. _____

Name _____ Date _____

BOOK 2 # Test on *Fractions and Decimals*

Vocabulary Questions

Fill in the missing word(s).

1. A _____ number has no factors other than itself and 1.

2. The _____ of a fraction refers to the equal parts out of a set or whole.

3. When you write a mixed number as an improper fraction, you keep the same _____ as the mixed number. When you write a mixed number as a decimal, you must first write the mixed number as an _____ _____ and then divide the _____ by the _____.

Match the item with its description.

4. $7\frac{4}{9}$ **A.** terminating decimal

5. $\frac{5}{2}$ **B.** repeating decimal

6. 0.98   **C.** improper fraction

7. $0.\overline{5}$ **D.** mixed number

Answers

1. _____

2. _____

3. _____

   _____

   _____

4. _____

5. _____

6. _____

7. _____

8. _____

9. _____

10. _____

11. _____

12. _____

Number Concepts

Write the prime factorization of the number.

8. 16   9. 140   10. 515

11. What is the greatest common factor of 21 and 45?

    A. 3   **B.** 5   **C.** 7   **D.** 9

12. How can you find the least common multiple of 14 and 18?

    A. List all the factors of 14 and 18, and identify the greatest factor that appears in both lists.

    B. List all the factors of 14 and 18, and identify the smallest factor that appears in both lists.

    C. Find the sum of all the prime factors of both 14 and 18, using each common factor only once.

    D. Find the product of all the prime factors of both 14 and 18, using each common factor only once.

Name _____   Date _____

Understanding Fractions

Write the fraction that is represented by the model.

13.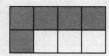

14.

Write three fractions that are equivalent to the fraction.

15. $\frac{1}{6}$ 16. $\frac{4}{5}$ 17. $\frac{3}{14}$

Write the fraction in simplest form.

18. $\frac{10}{18}$ 19. $\frac{9}{9}$ 20. $\frac{24}{32}$

21. Which statement is true?

    A. $\frac{3}{5} > \frac{6}{7}$ **B.** $\frac{9}{10} > \frac{2}{3}$ **C.** $\frac{1}{4} < \frac{1}{8}$ **D.** $\frac{1}{2} < \frac{2}{9}$

22. Order the fractions $\frac{5}{12}, \frac{4}{17},$ and $\frac{3}{8}$ from least to greatest.

Use the model to write the mixed number as an improper fraction.

23. $1\frac{2}{3}$

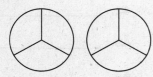

24. $2\frac{1}{5}$

Write the improper fraction as a mixed number.

25. $\frac{7}{3}$ 26. $\frac{49}{9}$ 27. $\frac{20}{11}$

28. Which list of numbers is in order from least to greatest?

    A. $2\frac{4}{7}, \frac{14}{5}, 2\frac{1}{2}$ **B.** $2\frac{1}{2}, 2\frac{4}{7}, \frac{14}{5}$

    C. $\frac{14}{5}, 2\frac{4}{7}, 2\frac{1}{2}$ **D.** $2\frac{1}{2}, \frac{14}{5}, 2\frac{4}{7}$

29. Write a true statement using <, >, or = with the numbers $6\frac{8}{9}$ and $\frac{64}{9}$.

Answers

13. _____

14. _____

15. _____

16. _____

17. _____

18. _____

19. _____

20. _____

21. _____

22. _____

23. See left. _____

_____

24. See left. _____

_____

25. _____

26. _____

27. _____

28. _____

29. _____

BOOK 2 **Test** *continued*

Operations with Fractions

Answers

Find the sum.

30. $\frac{4}{9} + \frac{1}{9}$ **31.** $\frac{5}{12} + \frac{7}{12}$ **32.** $\frac{2}{15} + \frac{8}{15}$

33. What is the difference $\frac{11}{16} - \frac{9}{16}$?

     A. 2   **B.** $\frac{1}{4}$ **C.** $\frac{3}{16}$ **D.** $\frac{1}{8}$

Find the difference.

34. $\frac{5}{6} - \frac{4}{9}$ **35.** $\frac{7}{8} - \frac{1}{4}$ **36.** $\frac{2}{3} - \frac{8}{15}$

37. What is the sum $\frac{3}{4} + \frac{3}{5}$?

     A. $\frac{2}{3}$ **B.** $1\frac{1}{5}$ **C.** $1\frac{3}{10}$ **D.** $1\frac{7}{20}$

Find the sum.

38. $3\frac{1}{4} + 3\frac{5}{6}$ **39.** $4\frac{2}{3} + 1\frac{7}{12}$ **40.** $1\frac{5}{8} + 2\frac{9}{20}$

Find the difference.

41. $3\frac{2}{5} - 1\frac{1}{15}$ **42.** $5\frac{1}{2} - 3\frac{7}{10}$ **43.** $8\frac{1}{3} - 5\frac{3}{4}$

44. Which multiplication problem does this model represent?

     A. $\frac{3}{5} \times 10$ **B.** $\frac{3}{5} \times 4$ **C.** $\frac{2}{3} \times 10$ **D.** $\frac{1}{6} \times 4$

Find the product.

45. $4 \times \frac{5}{7}$ **46.** $\frac{2}{3} \times \frac{9}{14}$ **47.** $\frac{1}{8}$ of $\frac{3}{11}$

48. What is the first step when finding the quotient $\frac{2}{9} \div \frac{2}{3}$?

     A. $\frac{2}{9} \div \frac{2}{3} = \frac{4}{27}$ **B.** $\frac{2}{9} \div \frac{2}{3} = \frac{2}{9} \times \frac{2}{3}$

     C. $\frac{2}{9} \div \frac{2}{3} = \frac{9}{2} \times \frac{2}{3}$ **D.** $\frac{2}{9} \div \frac{2}{3} = \frac{2}{9} \times \frac{3}{2}$

49. What is the first step when finding the product $1\frac{9}{11} \times \frac{4}{5}$?

     A. $1\frac{9}{11} \times \frac{4}{5} = 1\frac{45}{55} \times \frac{44}{55}$ **B.** $1\frac{9}{11} \times \frac{4}{5} = \frac{20}{11} \times \frac{4}{5}$

     C. $1\frac{9}{11} \times \frac{4}{5} = 1\frac{9}{11} \times \frac{5}{4}$ **D.** $1\frac{9}{11} \times \frac{4}{5} = \frac{4}{5} \times 1\frac{9}{11}$

Answers

30. _____
31. _____
32. _____
33. _____
34. _____
35. _____
36. _____
37. _____
38. _____
39. _____
40. _____
41. _____
42. _____
43. _____
44. _____
45. _____
46. _____
47. _____
48. _____
49. _____

BOOK 2 **Test** *continued*

Find the quotient.

50. $\frac{6}{7} \div \frac{3}{14}$ **51.** $2\frac{1}{4} \div \frac{5}{16}$ **52.** $2\frac{8}{9} \div 1\frac{1}{9}$

Understanding Decimals

53. In the number 148.723, which digit is in the hundredths' place?

    A. 1   **B.** 2   **C.** 3   **D.** 4

54. What number is the result of rounding 34.218 to the tenths' place?

    A. 34.2   **B.** 34.3   **C.** 34.21   **D.** 34.22

55. Which is a true statement?

    A. 3.78 < 3.76   **B.** 4.1415 > 4.1425

    C. 0.45 < 0.39   **D.** 72.48 < 72.51

56. Write 0.76 as a fraction in simplest form.

57. Write $2\frac{4}{5}$ as a decimal.

Operations with Decimals

58. Use the space provided to write 104.25 + 218.04 in a column. Then find the sum.

59. What is the sum 14.08 + 9.3168?

    A. 23.3968   **B.** 94.576   **C.** 107.248   **D.** 150.1168

60. What is the difference 5.048 − 2.987?

    A. 2.051   **B.** 2.061   **C.** 2.941   **D.** 3.941

61. Use the space provided to write 17.74 − 12.0183 in a column. Then find the difference.

Find the product.

62. 0.04 × 8   **63.** 1.2 × 0.15   **64.** 0.09 × 0.76

Find the quotient.

65. 0.49 ÷ 7   **66.** 4.2 ÷ 0.14   **67.** 80 ÷ 0.16

Answers

50. _____

51. _____

52. _____

53. _____

54. _____

55. _____

56. _____

57. _____

58. See left. _____

_____

59. _____

60. _____

61. See left. _____

_____

62. _____

63. _____

64. _____

65. _____

66. _____

67. _____

BOOK 2 **Test** *continued*

Problem Solving with Fractions and Decimals

Answers

68. _____

69. _____

70. _____

71. See left. _____

68. You open a new container of almonds and scoop out 7 servings. Each serving is $\frac{1}{4}$ cup. There are $2\frac{1}{4}$ cups of almonds left in the container. What strategy can you use to find the original amount of almonds in the container?

   A. Multiply $\frac{1}{4}$ by 7. Then subtract $2\frac{1}{4}$.

   B. Multiply $\frac{1}{4}$ by 7. Then add $2\frac{1}{4}$.

   C. Divide 7 by $\frac{1}{4}$. Then add $2\frac{1}{4}$.

   D. Divide 7 by $\frac{1}{4}$. Then subtract $2\frac{1}{4}$.

69. Lang says that $2.97 + 5.341 = 8.311$. Which method can be used to check the reasonableness of Lang's solution?

   A. $2 + 5 = 7$; Since 7 is not close to 8.311, the answer is not reasonable.

   B. $3 + 6 = 9$; Since 9 is not close to 8.31, the answer is not reasonable.

   C. $2 + 6 = 8$; Since 8 is close to 8.31, the answer is reasonable.

   D. $3 + 5 = 8$; Since 8 is close to 8.31, the answer is reasonable.

70. Paolo worked 5 days last week and made $112.50. He worked 4 days this week and made $142.50. What additional information do you need to find Paolo's hourly pay?

   A. Paolo worked a total of 34 hours in the two-week period.

   B. Paolo worked 6 hours on Saturday.

   C. Paolo worked another 3 days and made $75.

   D. No additional information is necessary.

71. Rhythm Techniques Dance School is participating in a parade. The school has 18 dance team members and 78 students. Mrs. Gregg wants to line up the participants in equal rows so that team members and students are not mixed. What is the greatest number of participants Mrs. Gregg can assign to a row? Explain your reasoning.

   _____

   _____

   _____

BOOK 2 **Test** *continued*

72. The top shelf of a bookcase contains 16 books. Of those, 7 are paperback. There are 14 paperback books on the second shelf. This shelf has the same fraction of paperback books as the top shelf. How many books does the second shelf contain? Explain.

_____

_____

_____

73. Two wooden planks are each $5\frac{3}{8}$ inches long. To find the total length when these planks are joined at the ends, Kirk multiplies $2 \times 5\frac{3}{8}$ to get $10\frac{6}{16}$ and then simplifies to get $10\frac{3}{8}$ inches. Is he correct? Explain why or why not.

_____

_____

74. Birdseed at your local Feed and Seed costs $1.15 per pound. Three prepared sacks on a shelf weigh 3.46 pounds, 3.48 pounds, and 3.47 pounds. Tell how you can find the *least* amount that you can pay for one of these sacks.

_____

_____

75. You are buying a coaxial cable for your television set. You want the longer of two cables that measure 15.75 feet and $15\frac{5}{8}$ feet. Explain how to decide which cable you should buy.

_____

_____

76. Dipa has $142.75. She spends $62.12 on groceries and then purchases 3 shirts at $7.51 each. She then puts half of the remaining money in her savings account. Explain how to find the amount of money that Dipa has left.

_____

_____

_____

Answers

72. See left. _____

73. See left. _____

74. See left. _____

75. See left. _____

76. See left. _____

BOOK 3 # Test on *Integers and Rational Numbers*

Vocabulary Questions

Fill in the missing word.

1. To subtract an integer, you can add its _____ .

2. A _____ integer is to the left of zero on a number line.

Match the word with its mathematical meaning and everyday meaning.

3. positive   4. base   5. operation

Mathematical meaning

A. describes an integer greater than zero

B. addition, subtraction, multiplication, or division

C. the repeated factor in a power

Everyday meaning

X. the bottom support of something

Y. certain

Z. a process that a machine performs

Answers

1. _____
2. _____
3. _____
4. _____
5. _____
6. See graph. _____
7. _____
8. _____
9. _____
10. _____

Basic Concepts

6. Place the integers 3, −1, −5, and 4 on the number line.

7. Which numbers in the list are integers?

   $\frac{4}{5}$, −9.6, 2.14, 0, −7, −$\frac{1}{2}$

   A. −$\frac{1}{2}$, $\frac{4}{5}$, 0, −7   B. 0, −7

   C. −9.6, 2.14, 0, −7   D. $\frac{4}{5}$, −9.6, 2.14, 0, −7, −$\frac{1}{2}$

8. Which expression equals −45?

   A. opposite of −45   B. opposite of 45

   C. |−45| D. |45|

9. Name two integers that could have an absolute value of 19.

10. Order the integers 14, −12, 15, and −16 from least to greatest.

Name _____   Date _____

BOOK 3 **Test** *continued*

11. Which statement is true?

    A. $-25 > -26$ **B.** $32 < -36$ **C.** $-40 < -48$ **D.** $-57 > 53$

12. Which number is a rational number?

    A. $28.2875\ldots$ **B.** $3.1428\ldots$ **C.** $1.4444\ldots$ **D.** $4.2227\ldots$

13. Place the rational numbers $-3\frac{1}{4}$, -2.65, 0.83, and $2\frac{5}{8}$ on a number line.

14. Order the numbers $-15\frac{2}{9}$, 15.408, $15\frac{4}{5}$, and -15.69 from least to greatest.

Operations with Integers and Rational Numbers

15. Use the number line to find the sum $-3 + 6$.

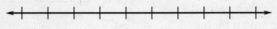

Find the sum using absolute values.

16. $-15 + (-6) + (-14)$ **17.** $-50 + (-70)$

18. Use the number line to find the difference $-12 - (-5)$.

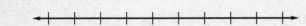

Find the difference using the subtraction rule.

19. $60 - (-8)$ **20.** $5 - 18$ **21.** $-24 - 14$

22. Which method correctly uses *repeated addition* to find the product $8(-3)$?

    A. Since $8(3)$ is 24, then $8(-3) = -24$.

    B. $8 + 8 + 8 = 24$

    C. $-3 + (-3) + (-3) + (-3) + (-3) + (-3) + (-3) + (-3) = -24$

    D. $8 + (-3) = 5$

Find the product.

23. $9(-4)$ **24.** $(-12)(-2)$ **25.** $3(-5)(-6)$

Answers

11. _____

12. _____

13. See graph. _____

14. _____

15. See graph. _____

    _____

16. _____

17. _____

18. See graph. _____

    _____

19. _____

20. _____

21. _____

22. _____

23. _____

24. _____

25. _____

26. Which multiplication problem is the same as $-135 \div (-9)$?

    A. $\underline{\ ?\ } \times (-15) = -135$ **B.** $\underline{\ ?\ } \times (-135) = -9$

    C. $135 \times (-9) = \underline{\ ?\ }$ **D.** $\underline{\ ?\ } \times (-9) = -135$

Find the quotient.

27. $64 \div (-4)$ **28.** $-70 \div -14$ **29.** $-36 \div 9$

30. Each of 18 students in a class gives \$3 toward refreshments for a holiday party. Which method finds the total amount given by the students?

    A. Add 18 and 3 to get \$21.   **B.** Subtract 3 from 18 to get \$15.

    C. Multiply 18 by 3 to get \$54.   **D.** Divide 18 by 3 to get \$6.

Identify the operation suggested by the phrase.

31. a difference in two heights   **32.** forty-three points higher

Find the sum, difference, product, or quotient.

33. $12\frac{3}{10} + \left(-8\frac{1}{5}\right)$ **34.** $-14.9 - 7.08$

35. $-10.05 \times (-1.4) \times (-0.2)$ **36.** $-2\frac{4}{9} \div -\frac{11}{15}$

37. What is the *expanded form* of $\left(\frac{2}{5}\right)^4$?

    A. $2 \times 2 \times 2 \times 2 + 5 \times 5 \times 5 \times 5$ **B.** $\frac{2}{5} \times \frac{2}{5} \times \frac{2}{5} \times \frac{2}{5}$

    C. $\frac{2}{5} + \frac{2}{5} + \frac{2}{5} + \frac{2}{5}$ **D.** $\frac{2}{5} \times 4$

Evaluate the power.

38. 7^3 **39.** $\left(\frac{2}{3}\right)^5$ **40.** $(4.3)^3$

Problem Solving with Integers and Rational Numbers

41. Lindsay scored 15 baskets during the game on Thursday and 9 baskets during the game on Friday. Explain how to use an integer to represent the change in the number of baskets Lindsay scored.

_____

_____

Answers

26. _____

27. _____

28. _____

29. _____

30. _____

31. _____

32. _____

33. _____

34. _____

35. _____

36. _____

37. _____

38. _____

39. _____

40. _____

41. See left. _____

Test *continued*

BOOK 3

42. How can you show that 11 is a rational number? Explain.

_____

_____

43. Bryant tries to fit a picture into a frame that is $3\frac{5}{8}$ inches wide, but the frame is too small. Should she try a frame that is $3\frac{4}{9}$ inches wide or 3.65 inches wide? Explain your reasoning.

_____

_____

44. Milo and Deanna are in a subway station. Milo finds a jacket on a stairwell located 15 feet below ground and takes it to Deanna at a turnstile located 40 feet below ground. Tell how to find the change in elevation from the point where Milo finds the jacket to the turnstile.

_____

_____

45. Henry spends $4 in tolls when he travels to visit his uncle. Write a product expression to represent how much Henry deducts from his toll account after making 12 trips to visit his uncle. Simplify the expression and explain what the answer means.

_____

46. Will the quotient of $-1075 \div 215$ be positive or negative? Explain.

_____

_____

47. There are 15 students in Mrs. Jerraro's class. Of these students, 9 turn in term papers on time. After Mrs. Jerraro grades 7 of those papers, the remaining students turn in their term papers. Explain how to find the number of term papers Mrs. Jerraro has yet to grade.

_____

_____

48. Janice and Ron are mailing business packages. Janice's package weighs 14 pounds. The weight of Ron's package is $3\frac{1}{8}$ times the weight of Janice's package. Tell how to find the weight of Ron's package.

_____

_____

Answers

42. See left. _____

43. See left. _____

44. See left. _____

45. See left. _____

46. See left. _____

47. See left. _____

48. See left. _____

Math Intervention
Teacher's Edition **25**

BOOK 4 # Test on *Ratios, Rates, Proportions, and Percents*

Answers

Vocabulary Questions	1. _____
Fill in the missing word(s).	
1. When you are converting from centimeters to kilometers, you _____ by a power of 10.	2. _____
	3. _____
2. To write 72% as a decimal, you would move the decimal point two places to the _____.	4. _____
3. You can use multiplication, or _____ _____, to solve a proportion.	5. _____
	6. _____

Match the word with the item it best describes.

4. ratio   5. unit rate   6. rate

A. $\dfrac{150 \text{ miles}}{3 \text{ hours}}$ B. $\dfrac{18 \text{ green beans}}{90 \text{ total beans}}$ C. $\dfrac{6 \text{ pages}}{1 \text{ minutes}}$

7. _____

_____

8. _____

Ratios, Rates, and Proportions

9. _____

7. Write the ratio 14 : 19 in two other ways.

10. _____

Write the rate in simplest form.

11. _____

8. 18 books in 6 months   9. 630 lamps in 9 hours

12. _____

Write the expression(s) needed to make the conversion.

13. _____

10. How many milligrams are in 42 hectograms?

14. _____

11. How many meters are in 1400 centimeters?

15. _____

12. How many deciliters are in 250 milliliters?

16. _____

13. How many hours are in 540 minutes?

14. How many yards are in 8 miles?

17. _____

15. How many fluid ounces are in 3 quarts?

18. _____

Compare the units.

16. Which is colder, 12°C or 50°F?

17. Which is greater, 140 cubic feet or 3 cubic meters?

18. What are the cross products of $\dfrac{25}{x} = \dfrac{15}{18}$?

     A. 450 and $15x$ **B.** 375 and $15x$

     C. 375 and $18x$ **D.** 270 and $25x$

19. What is the solution of $\frac{4}{20} = \frac{x}{45}$?

A. 2 **B.** 8 **C.** 9 **D.** 36

20. The largest natural bridge in the world is the Rainbow Bridge in Utah. It stands 290 feet tall. Amber used a scale of 1 inch : 20 feet to make a model of this bridge. Which proportion can you use to find the height of Amber's model?

A. $\frac{1 \text{ inch}}{20 \text{ feet}} = \frac{290 \text{ feet}}{x \text{ inches}}$ **B.** $\frac{x \text{ inches}}{20 \text{ feet}} = \frac{1 \text{ inch}}{290 \text{ feet}}$

C. $\frac{1 \text{ inch}}{20 \text{ feet}} = \frac{x \text{ inches}}{290 \text{ feet}}$ **D.** $\frac{1 \text{ inch}}{290 \text{ feet}} = \frac{20 \text{ feet}}{x \text{ inches}}$

Percents, Interest, and Probability

21. Write a simplified fraction that is equivalent to 28%.

22. Write a decimal that is equivalent to 7%.

Write the decimal as a percent.

23. 0.45 **24.** 0.72 **25.** 0.02

Write the fraction as a percent.

26. $\frac{17}{20}$ **27.** $\frac{1}{8}$ **28.** $\frac{11}{32}$

Find the percent of the number.

29. 30% of 50 **30.** 48% of 175

Tell whether the percent of change is an *increase* or *decrease*. Then find the percent of change.

31. Original amount: 65
New amount: 26

32. Original amount: 40
New amount: 54

33. Your food bill at a diner is $15.40. You leave an 18% tip. Which expression can you use to find the total cost of your meal?

A. $15.40 + 0.18$ **B.** $\frac{18}{100} = \frac{x}{15.40}$

C. $15.40 - \left(\frac{18}{100} \times 15.40\right)$ **D.** $15.40 + (0.18)(15.40)$

34. An electronics store is offering a 15% discount on a laptop computer that originally cost $1260. What is the sale price of the computer?

A. $189 **B.** $1071 **C.** $1197 **D.** $1449

Answers

19. _____
20. _____
21. _____
22. _____
23. _____
24. _____
25. _____
26. _____
27. _____
28. _____
29. _____
30. _____
31. _____
_____
32. _____
_____
33. _____
34. _____

BOOK 4 TEST

Test *continued*

35. Utoya paid a wholesale price of $12 each for long-sleeved shirts. She plans to mark them up 60% to sell in her clothing store. What will be the retail price for one of these shirts?

    A. $12.60   **B.** $16.80   **C.** $19.20   **D.** $60.00

Find the simple interest earned.

36. Principal: 625
Annual rate: 6%
Time: 2 years

37. Principal: 4225
Annual rate: 3.1%
Time: 42 months

38. John deposits $560 in an account that pays 5.8% interest compounded annually. What is the balance in the account after 4 years?

    A. $592.48   **B.** $663.20   **C.** $701.67   **D.** $742.36

For Exercises 39 and 40, use the table below. The table shows the contents of a sock bin. A customer reaches in and pulls out a pair of socks at random. Find the probability of the event.

White pairs	12
Blue pairs	15
Black pairs	14
Gray pairs	9

39. selecting a white pair

40. selecting a gray pair

Problem Solving with Ratios, Rates, Proportions, and Percents

41. Van's Office Supply sells 75 different items, 15 of which are different kinds of envelopes. The ratio of envelopes to all items at Jim's Office Supply is 10 : 25. Tell how to determine which supply company has the greater ratio of envelopes to all items.

_____

_____

42. Karlie purchases 60 meters of red material. Explain how to find the number of millimeters of red material she bought.

_____

_____

43. Mae gives Henao 144 pints of filtered water. Explain how to find the amount of water Henao received in gallons.

_____

_____

Answers

35. _____

36. _____

37. _____

38. _____

39. _____

40. _____

41. See left.

42. See left.

43. See left.

44. The ratio of boys to girls in Mr. Janson's class is 5 boys : 9 girls. Mrs. Reid's class has an equivalent ratio of boys to girls. Tell how to write and solve a proportion to find the number of boys in Mrs. Reid's class if there are 27 girls in the class.

_____

_____

45. Dee has a collection of 415 stamps. She says that friends contributed 60% of her collection. Describe how to use a proportion to find the number of stamps that were given to her by friends.

_____

_____

46. Last year 150 students enrolled in a martial arts school. This year's enrollment is 186. Tell whether the percent of change is an increase or a decrease. Then determine the percent of change. Explain your answer.

_____

_____

47. Nyliam makes a 3% commission on each house that she sells. Last weekend, she sold a house for $152,500. Tell how to find the amount of commission she earned.

_____

_____

48. Kirsten borrowed $7000 to buy a used car. She will pay the money back in 3 years at 8% simple interest. Explain how to find the amount of money Kirsten will pay in interest.

_____

_____

49. Leonard deposits $815 in an account that pays 3.5% interest compounded annually. Tell how to use the compound interest formula to find the amount of money in Leonard's account after 5 years.

_____

_____

50. You roll an 8-sided number cube with sides numbered 1–8. Explain how to find the probability that you do *not* roll an even number.

_____

_____

Answers

44. See left. _____

45. See left. _____

46. See left. _____

47. See left. _____

48. See left. _____

49. See left. _____

50. See left. _____

BOOK 5 — Test on *Algebraic Thinking*

Vocabulary Questions

Fill in the missing word.

1. To solve the equation $4x = 36$, you can use the _____ property of equality to divide each side by 4.

2. Since you can use addition to "undo" subtraction, addition is called the _____ operation of subtraction.

Match the word with its mathematical meaning and everyday meaning.

3. rule   4. origin   5. intercept

Mathematical meaning	**Everyday meaning**
A. the point where the horizontal and vertical axes intersect	**X.** an instruction that is to be followed
B. a statement that describes a pattern	**Y.** to stop or interrupt
C. the point where a line crosses an axis	**Z.** the beginning

Answers

1. _____
2. _____
3. _____
4. _____
5. _____
6. _____
7. _____
8. _____
9. _____
10. _____
11. _____

Basic Concepts and Properties

Write the next two numbers or shapes in the pattern.

6. 1, 6, 11, 16, . . .

7. △ □ ○ △ □ □ ○ △ □ . . .

8. Which rule describes the pattern?

   70, 67, 64, 61, . . .

   A. Start with 70 and subtract 2 from each term.

   B. Start with 70 and subtract 3 from each term.

   C. Start with 70 and add 3 to each term.

   D. Start with 70 and add 7 to each term.

9. Find the 8th term of the pattern: 12, 16, 20, 24, . . .

Substitute and use the order of operations to evaluate the expression.

10. $(3a - c) + 4b$ when $a = 4$, $b = 1$, and $c = 5$

11. $a^2 - (c + 2b) \cdot 6$ when $a = 12$, $b = 10$, and $c = 3$

BOOK 5 **Test** *continued*

12. Emilio has three less than four times the number of pears in a crate. Write an algebraic expression for this situation.

13. What operation would you use in an algebraic expression for the words *decreased by*?

A. addition   **B.** subtraction   **C.** division   **D.** multiplication

14. Which statement is an example of the *commutative property of addition*?

A. $8 + 6 = 6 + 8$

B. $(5 + 3) + 1 = 5 + (3 + 1)$

C. $14 + 0 = 14$

D. $25 + (-25) = 0$

15. Which statement is an example of the *identity property of multiplication*?

A. $9 \cdot 2 = 2 \cdot 9$

B. $4(10 \cdot 7) = (4 \cdot 10)7$

C. $528 \cdot 1 = 528$

D. $9 \cdot \frac{1}{9} = 1$

Use the distributive property to write the expression another way. Then simplify the expression.

16. $12(2 + 4 + 8)$

17. $9(14) + 9(5) + 9(11)$

18. What is the coefficient of x in the expression $4x^3 + 6x + 5$?

A. 3   **B.** 4   **C.** 5   **D.** 6

19. Simplify the expression $3(x^2 + 8x) + 5x^2 - 2x - 5$.

Solve the equation.

20. $-1.3 = x + 14.5$

21. $y - 27 = -18$

22. $\frac{a}{8} = 4$

23. $-6b = 54$

24. Julianne has 24 paint pens. This is 3 times the number of paint pens Braylon has. Which equation can you use to find the number of paint pens p that Braylon has?

A. $24p = 3$ **B.** $\frac{p}{24} = 3$ **C.** $\frac{p}{3} = 24$ **D.** $3p = 24$

25. Which value is a solution of $a > -12$?

A. -15 **B.** -13 **C.** -12 **D.** -10

26. Which graph shows the solution of $m - 4 \geq 20$?

A.
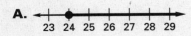

B.

C.

D.

Answers

12. _____

13. _____

14. _____

15. _____

16. _____

_____

17. _____

_____

18. _____

19. _____

20. _____

21. _____

22. _____

23. _____

24. _____

25. _____

26. _____

BOOK 5 TEST

BOOK 5 **Test** *continued*

Functional Relationships Between Two Quantities

27. Write a rule that shows how *y* relates to *x*.

x	−1	0	1	2
y	3	0	−3	−6

Plot the point.

28. $A(-1, -2)$

29. $B(2, 3)$

30. $C(4, 1)$

31. $D(-1, 2)$

32. $E(2, -2)$

33. $F(-2, -4)$

34. Complete the table of values to draw the graph of $y = 2x - 3$.

x	−1	0	1	2
y				

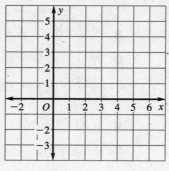

35. Find the slope of the line.

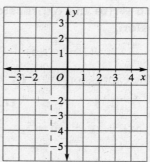

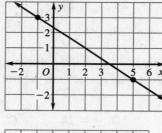

36. Suppose a printer can print 15 pages per minute. Graph the relationship between minutes and the number of printed pages.

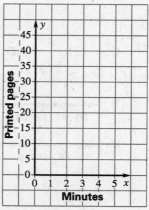

Answers

27. _____

28. See graph.

29. See graph.

30. See graph.

31. See graph.

32. See graph.

33. See graph.

34. See table.

See graph.

35. _____

36. See graph.

Name _____   Date _____

37. Which graph shows the line $y = -\frac{1}{3}x + 1$?

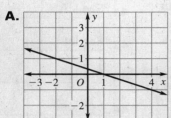

A.

B.

C.

D.

Answers

37. _____

38. _____

39. See table. _____

See graph. _____

40. See left. _____

38. The graph shows the amount Neill earns when he works a certain number of hours. Use the graph to estimate Neill's earnings when he works 6 hours.

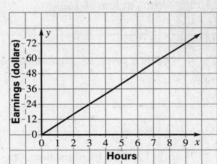

39. Complete the table of values to draw the graph of $y = \frac{1}{2}x^2$.

x	−2	−1	0	1	2
y					

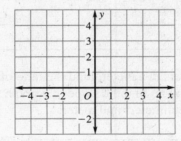

Problem Solving with Algebraic Thinking

40. Kerr is increasing her vocabulary by learning new words in her dictionary. After the first month, she knows 6 new words. By the end of the second month, she knows a total of 24 words, the third month 96 words, and after the fourth month she knows a total of 384 words. If her pattern continues, explain how to find the total number of words Kerr will have learned after the sixth month.

_____

_____

BOOK 5 **Test** *continued*

41. Vladimir sold 114 ties this week, which is 6 more ties than he sold last week. Write and solve an equation to find the number of ties Vladimir sold last week. Explain your reasoning.

_____

_____

42. A karate instructor hands out coupons to each of 15 students in his class. Each student gets 3 coupons. How many coupons did the karate instructor start with? Suppose you solved this problem and got 5 coupons. Is your answer reasonable? Explain.

_____

_____

43. The equation $d = l - 4$ describes the number of laps l Keith swims and the number of times he practices his dives d. Write four ordered pairs that make the rule true if Keith swims at least 6 laps.

_____

44. Tell whether the graph of $y = -15$ is a *vertical*, *horizontal*, or *diagonal* line. Explain your reasoning.

_____

_____

45. A line passes through $(-2, 7)$ and $(12, 15)$. Explain how you can find the slope of this line without graphing.

_____

_____

46. There are 100 centimeters in a meter. Find the ratio of centimeters to meters. Then explain how to find the slope of a graph that shows the relationship between centimeters and meters.

_____

_____

47. Tell whether the graph of $y = -\frac{3}{4}x^3$ is a *line*, a *parabola*, or a *curve*. Explain your reasoning.

_____

_____

Answers

41. See left.

42. See left.

43. See left.

44. See left.

45. See left.

46. See left.

47. See left.

Name _____   Date _____

BOOK 6 Test on *Data Analysis and Geometry*

Vocabulary Questions

Fill in the missing word(s).

1. To find the _____ of a prism, you need to find the total area of all the faces.

2. The number 25 is a _____ because it is the square of a positive integer.

Match the word with its mathematical meaning and everyday meaning.

3. event   4. segment   5. acute

Mathematical meaning

A. a part of a line with definite length

B. describes an angle with a measure less than 90°

C. something that may happen

Everyday meaning

X. an occurrence

Y. a part into which something separates or divides

Z. sharp or severe

Answers

1. _____
2. _____
3. _____
4. _____
5. _____
6. _____
7. See left.

Data Analysis

6. Which person has correctly assembled a group of all the even numbers greater than 15 from the list below?

   10, 15, 14, 18, 16, 19, 20, 21, 4, 48, 7, 12, 33

   Maisie: 4, 10, 12, 14, 16, 18, 20, 48

   Jerome: 19, 21, 33

   Carlo: 16, 18, 20, 48

   Laine: 16, 18, 19, 20, 21, 33, 48

   A. Maisie   **B.** Jerome   **C.** Carlo   **D.** Laine

7. Record the frequencies of the odd numbers in the list.

   3, 8, 8, 5, 4, 8, 5, 2, 8, 5, 3, 1, 2

   _____

   _____

BOOK 6 **Test** *continued*

8. A store bin contains 5 bags of walnuts, 8 bags of pecans, 11 bags of hazelnuts, and 12 bags of almonds. Represent the data as a tally chart.

9. A copying room has 15 packs of white paper, 21 packs of yellow paper, and 46 packs of pink paper. Write a fraction that shows how the packs of white paper compare to the total packs of paper.

10. The bar graph shows the results of rolling a number cube 75 times. Use the results to find the probability of rolling a number greater than 3 on the next roll.

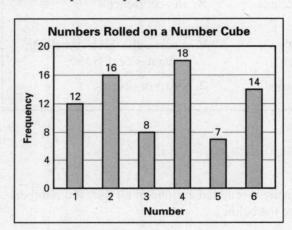

Numbers Rolled on a Number Cube

Answers

8. See chart.

9. _____

10. _____

11. _____

12. _____

Length and Area

11. Each unit in the coordinate grid represents one inch. Calculate the length of the line segment in inches from point *A* to point *B*.

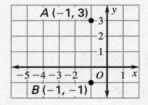

12. Find the perimeter of the rectangle.

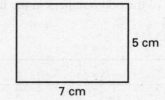

5 cm

7 cm

BOOK 6 **Test** _continued_

13. **a.** Using a customary ruler, draw and label a rectangle that is 4 inches long and 2.5 inches wide.

Answers

13. **a.** See left. _____

b. _____

14. _____

15. _____

16. **a.** _____

b. _____

17. **a.** _____

b. _____

b. Calculate the area of the rectangle you drew in square inches.

14. Find the area of the parallelogram.

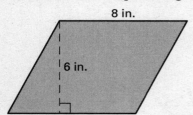
8 in.

6 in.

15. What is the area of a triangle that has a height of 10 cm and a base of 12 cm?

16. Find the circumference of the circle. Use $\pi \approx 3.14$.

a.

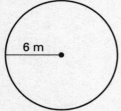
6 m

b.

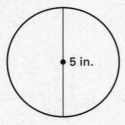
5 in.

17. Find the area of the circle. Use $\pi \approx 3.14$.

a.

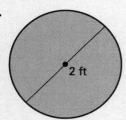
2 ft

b.

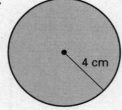
4 cm

BOOK 6 TEST

BOOK 6 **Test** *continued*

Surface Area and Volume

18. Find the surface area of the cube formed by this pattern.

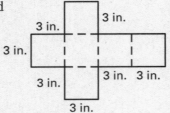

18. _____

19. **a.** See left.

b. _____

20. **a.** _____

b. _____

21. _____

22. **a.** _____

b. _____

23. **a.** _____

b. _____

19.

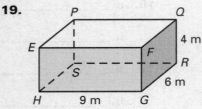

a. Name the faces of the rectangular prism.

_____

b. Find the surface area of the prism.

20. Find the volumes of the rectangular prism and triangular prism.

a. 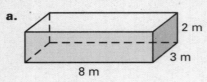   **b.**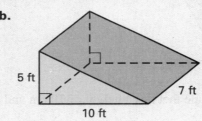

21. What is the volume of a cylinder with a radius of 8 cm and a height of 3 cm? Give your answer in terms of π.

Other Geometry Concepts

22. Measure the angle with a protractor.

a. 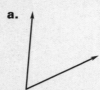   **b.**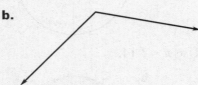

23. Classify the angle as acute, right, obtuse, or straight.

a. 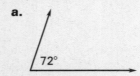   **b.**

Name _____   Date _____

BOOK 6   **Test** *continued*

24. Find the measures of the complement and the supplement of the angle, if possible.

    a. 14°   **b.** 118°   **c.** 29°   **d.** 86°

25. Classify the triangle as acute, right, or obtuse.

    a.

    b.

26. A triangle has sides of length 34 centimeters, 15 centimeters, and 34 centimeters. Is this triangle equilateral, isosceles, or scalene?

27. Find the measure of the third angle of the triangle.

    a. 15°, 34°   **b.** 102°, 58°   **c.** 95°, 75°

28. Find the measure of the fourth angle of the quadrilateral.

    a. 200°, 12°, 56°   **b.** 94°, 92°, 36°   **c.** 116°, 124°, 70°

29. Find the square root. If necessary, round your answers to the nearest tenth.

    a. $\sqrt{25}$ **b.** $-\sqrt{63}$ **c.** $-\sqrt{114}$ **d.** $\sqrt{96}$

30. Find *x*. Round to the nearest tenth if necessary.

    a.
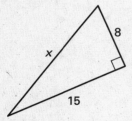
    b.
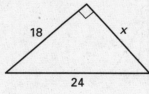

31. A triangle has sides of length 16 inches, 30 inches, and 34 inches. Tell whether the triangle is a right triangle.

32. Tell whether the lines are parallel, perpendicular, or neither.

    a.
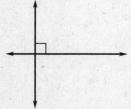
    b.
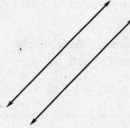

Answers

24. a. _____

    b. _____

    c. _____

    d. _____

25. a. _____

    b. _____

26. _____

27. a. _____

    b. _____

    c. _____

28. a. _____

    b. _____

    c. _____

29. a. _____

    b. _____

    c. _____

    d. _____

30. a. _____

    b. _____

31. _____

32. a. _____

    b. _____

Name _____   Date _____

33. Which figure is congruent to the one shown?

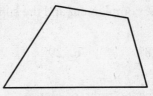

Answers

33. _____

34. _____

35. _____

36. See left. _____

A.

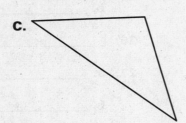

B.

C.

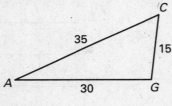

D.

34. Suppose $\triangle KLM \cong \triangle EFG$. Which list correctly names pairs of corresponding angles?

   A. $\angle M \cong \angle E$, $\angle L \cong \angle F$, $\angle K \cong \angle G$

   B. $\angle K \cong \angle E$, $\angle L \cong \angle F$, $\angle M \cong \angle G$

   C. $\angle K \cong \angle G$, $\angle L \cong \angle E$, $\angle M \cong \angle F$

   D. $\angle M \cong \angle L$, $\angle L \cong \angle K$, $\angle K \cong \angle M$

35. Given $\triangle ACG \sim \triangle HJP$, which is the correct measure for JP?

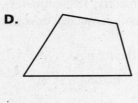

  A. 6   **B.** 8   **C.** 12   **D.** 16

Problem Solving with Data Analysis and Geometry

36. A department store sells linens. The store has two different displays that contain washcloths, hand towels, and bath towels. The number of each type is shown in the lists. Explain how you can find the total fraction of hand towels in these displays.

Display 1: 12 washcloths, 17 hand towels, 8 bath towels
Display 2: 9 washcloths, 18 hand towels, 6 bath towels

_____

_____

Name _____   Date _____

37. A rectangular construction site is 24 meters wide and 28 meters long. How can you find the perimeter and area of this site?

_____

_____

38. Mark draws a parallelogram with a base of 14 centimeters and a height of 3 centimeters. Holly draws a parallelogram with the same area. If the base of Holly's parallelogram is 7 centimeters, explain how to find the height of Holly's parallelogram.

_____

_____

39. A deli worker cuts a wedge of cheese in the shape of a triangular prism. The area of the prism's base is 14 square inches. Explain how to find the volume of the cheese if the height of the prism is 8 inches.

_____

_____

40. You know that a triangle has two acute angles. Is this enough information for you to classify it as an acute triangle? Use examples to explain.

_____

_____

41. Can a quadrilateral have angles that measure 90°, 90°, 30°, and 140°? Why or why not?

_____

_____

42. A rectangular parking lot is 50 feet long and 30 feet wide. Miriam walks from one corner of the lot straight across to the opposite corner. Describe how to find the distance that she walks. Round the distance to the nearest tenth of a foot, if necessary.

_____

_____

43. The rectangles are similar. The lengths of a pair of corresponding sides are labeled. Explain how to find the ratio of similarity.

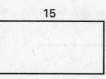
15

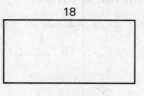
18

_____

_____

Answers

37. See left.

38. See left.

39. See left.

40. See left.

41. See left.

42. See left.

43. See left.

BOOK 7 — Test on *Getting Ready for Algebra*

Vocabulary Questions

Fill in the missing word(s).

1. In the expression $3^{\frac{1}{2}}$ the $\frac{1}{2}$ is called a(n) _____ exponent.

2. In the expression $3x - 12 = 15$, the 3 is called a(n) _____.

3. A(n) _____ exponent makes a power equal to 1.

4. To find the product $a^3 \cdot a^8$, you need to _____ the exponents.

Match the word with the item it describes.

5. quotient   6. linear inequality   7. multi-step equation

A. $8x - 9 = 24$ B. $\frac{x}{8}$ C. $7x > 21$

Solving Multi-Step Equations and Inequalities

8. Which equation means *six more than two times a number is forty-five*?

   A. $6 + 2n = 45$ B. $2n - 6 = 45$

   C. $2 + 6n = 45$ D. $6n - 2 = 45$

9. Which word sentence represents the equation $\frac{7n}{14} = 24$?

   A. Seven more than a number divided by fourteen is twenty-four.

   B. Fourteen less than seven times a number is twenty-four.

   C. Twenty-four is seven times a number divided by fourteen.

   D. Seven times a number and fourteen is 24.

Match the equation with the graph of its solution.

10. $9a - 7 = 20$ 11. $6a + 20 = 2$

A.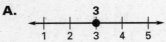

B.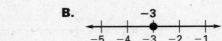

Solve the equation. Graph the solution.

12. $4b - 5b - 12 = -15b + 2$ 13. $3(2b - 4) = 8(b + 2)$

                     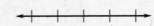

Answers

1. _____
2. _____
3. _____
4. _____
5. _____
6. _____
7. _____
8. _____
9. _____
10. _____
11. _____
12. _____

See graph.

13. _____

See graph.

Name _____   Date _____

| **BOOK 7** | **Test** *continued* |

Fill in the missing symbols, +, −, ×, ÷, for the situation described.

14. Yolanda has a marble collection. She loses 12 marbles in a game with her sister, and her friend gives her 14 marbles. Now, Yolanda has 36 marbles in her collection.

m _____ 12 _____ 14 = 36

15. Hunter donated $\frac{3}{4}$ of his plants to a local park.

$\frac{3}{4}$ _____ p

Match the inequality with the graph of its solution.

16. $5d + 3 > 43$

17. $4d - 34 \geq -2$

A.
   6   7   8   9   10

B.
   6   7   8   9   10

Solve the inequality. Graph the solution.

18. $8y - 11 \leq 6y - 4y + 1$

19. $12(y - 3) < 4(2y - 5)$

Fill in the missing symbols, <, >, ≤, ≥, for the situation described.

20. Logan has at most 15 shirts in his closet.

s _____ 15

21. Jill buys several snack packs at $2 each. She spends under $20.

$2p$ _____ 20

Properties of Exponents

Simplify and rewrite without negative exponents.

22. 8^{-2} **23.** 3^{-4} **24.** 5^0

25. Write the fraction $\frac{1}{27}$ as a power with a negative exponent.

Rewrite the expression without negative exponents.

26. $a^6 \cdot b^{-8}$ **27.** $x^{-4} \cdot y^{-5}$ **28.** $w^{-9} \cdot v^2$

Match the expression with the correct product.

29. $x^2 \cdot y^3 \cdot x^2$ **30.** $y^4 \cdot x^3 \cdot y^2$ **31.** $x^5 \cdot y^4 \cdot x^3$

A. $x^3 \cdot y^6$ **B.** $x^8 \cdot y^4$ **C.** $x^4 \cdot y^3$

Simplify.

32. $c^{-2} \cdot d^{-5} \cdot c^8 \cdot d^7$ **33.** $m^6 \cdot p^{-6} \cdot p^2 \cdot m^{-4}$

Answers

14. See left.

15. See left.

16. _____

17. _____

18. _____

See graph.

19. _____

See graph.

20. See left.

21. See left.

22. _____

23. _____

24. _____

25. _____

26. _____

27. _____

28. _____

29. _____

30. _____

31. _____

32. _____

33. _____

Math Intervention
Teacher's Edition

BOOK 7 **Test** *continued*

Tell whether the equation is true or false.

Answers

34. $(x^{-4})^{-6} = x^{24}$ **35.** $2 \cdot (y^{-3})^2 = \dfrac{2}{y^6}$ **36.** $(z^2)^4 \cdot (z^2)^4 = z^{64}$

34. _____

Evaluate when $a = 2$.

35. _____

37. $5 \cdot (a^{-2})^{-2}$ **38.** $(a^{-2})^3 \cdot (a^4)^2$ **39.** $3a^{13} \cdot (a^2)^{-5}$

36. _____

Match the expression with the correct answer after simplifying.

37. _____

40. $(4bc)^5$ **41.** $(4b^2c^3)^5$ **42.** $4(b^3c^2)^5$

38. _____

A. $4^5 \cdot b^5 \cdot c^5$ **B.** $4 \cdot b^{15} \cdot c^{10}$ **C.** $4^5 \cdot b^{10} \cdot c^{15}$

39. _____

40. _____

Simplify.

43. $(x^4yz)^3$ **44.** $5g \cdot (gh^2k)^6$ **45.** $(2bc)^4$

41. _____

46. Which expression shows $\dfrac{9a^5b^8c^7}{6a^2b^{10}c^3}$ in simplest form?

42. _____

A. $\dfrac{3ab^2c^4}{2a^3bc}$ **B.** $\dfrac{3a^3c^4}{2b^2}$ **C.** $\dfrac{3b^2}{2a^3c^4}$ **D.** $\dfrac{3b^8}{2a^2c^3}$

43. _____

Evaluate.

44. _____

47. $\dfrac{15^3}{15^2}$ **48.** $\dfrac{2^4}{2^9}$ **49.** $\dfrac{3^8}{3^5}$

45. _____

50. Which expression shows $4^3 \cdot \left(\dfrac{d}{4}\right)^2$ in simplest form?

46. _____

A. $\dfrac{8}{d^2}$ **B.** $\dfrac{4}{d^2}$ **C.** $\dfrac{d^2}{4}$ **D.** $4d^2$

47. _____

Tell whether the equation is true or false.

48. _____

51. $81^{\frac{1}{2}} \cdot 4^{\frac{1}{2}} = 16$ **52.** $25^{\frac{1}{2}} \cdot 1^0 = 5$

49. _____

53. Isabella buys a square piece of art board with the area shown. Which numerical expression represents the value of x?

50. _____

51. _____

x in.

52. _____

$A = 64$ in.^{2} x in.

53. _____

A. $64^{\frac{1}{2}}$ **B.** $32^{\frac{1}{2}}$ **C.** $16^{\frac{1}{2}}$ **D.** $8^{\frac{1}{2}}$

54. Simplify the expression $16^{\frac{3}{4}} \cdot 4^{\frac{1}{2}}$.

Problem Solving with Equations and Inequalities

55. Write a word sentence for the equation $\frac{7}{8} = 4 + \frac{x}{5}$.

_____

56. Rory has to scan a total of 135 photos for the yearbook. She has already scanned 27 photos. She plans to scan 9 photos a day. Write and solve an equation to find the number of days it will take for her to finish scanning. Explain your reasoning.

_____

_____

57. A craft warehouse has 1250 spools of yarn. After making 3 equal shipments of yarn, there are 875 spools of yarn left. Ken says there were 125 spools of yarn in each shipment. Write an explanation to check the reasonableness of Ken's claim.

_____

_____

58. Alex spent over $50 at the grocery store. He bought $25 worth of produce and several boxes of cereal at $3 a box. Write and solve an inequality to find the least number of cereal boxes Alex could have bought. Explain your reasoning.

_____

_____

59. Reece reduces a photo to $\frac{3}{5}$ of its original size and then decides to reduce it again to $\frac{3}{5}$ of its new size. Write and simplify an expression to find the total reduction as a power of a quotient. Explain your reasoning.

_____

_____

60. Explain how to simplify $81^{\frac{3}{4}}$ using mental math.

_____

_____

Answers

54. _____

55. See left.

56. See left.

57. See left.

58. See left.

59. See left.

60. See left.

ACADEMIC TERMS

English	Spanish	Chinese	Vietnamese	Cambodian	Laotian
analyze	analizar	分析	Phân tích	វិភាគ	ວິເຄາະ
approximate	aproximar	近似	Xấp xỉ	ប្រហែល	ຄ່າປະມານ
assess	evaluar	評估	Thẩm định	ប្រមាណ	ປະເມີນ
assume	suponer	假定	Giả sử	សន្ទត់	ສົມມຸດ
best answer	la mejor respuesta	最佳答案	Đáp áp tốt nhất	ចម្លើយត្រូវបំផុត	ຄຳຕອບທີ່ຖືກຕ້ອງທີ່ສຸດ
compare	comparar	比較	So sánh	ប្រៀបធៀប	ສົມທຽບ
compute	calcular	計算	Tính toán	គិត	ຄິດໄລ່
conclude	sacar una conclusión	結論	Kết luận	រាប់បញ្ចូល	ສະຫລຸບ
contrast	contrastar	對比	Tương phản	ផ្ទុយគ្នា	ກົງກັນຂ້າມ
criteria	criterios	準則	Điều kiện	លក្ខណៈវិនិច្ឆ័យ	ເງື່ອນໄຂ
data	datos	數據	Dữ liệu	ទិន្នន័យ	ຂໍ້ມູນ
deduce	deducir	演繹	Suy ra	ដក	ອ້າງອີງເຖິງ
define	definir	定義	Định nghĩa	ឲ្យអត្ថន័យ	ກຳນົດຄວາມຫມາຍ
demonstrate	demostrar	證明	Chứng minh	បង្ហាញ	ສາທິດ
derive	derivar	導出	Suy ra từ	កើតចេញពី	ໄດ້ມາຈາກ
describe	describir	描述	Miêu tả	ពិពណ៌នា	ອະທິບາຍ
determine	determinar	決定	Xác định	កំណត់	ກຳນົດອອກ
estimate	estimar	估計	Ước lượng	ស្មាន	ຄາດຄະເນ
evaluate	evaluar	求值	Đánh giá	វាយតម្លៃ	ຕີລາຄາ
exclude	excluir	排除	Loại trừ	មិនរាប់បញ្ចូល	ບໍ່ລວມເຂົ້າ
illustrate	ilustrar	説明	Minh họa	បង្ហាញ	ສະແດງໃຫ້ເຫັນ
imply	significar	隱含	Ngụ ý	បញ្ជាក់	ຫມາຍເຖິງ
interpret	interpretar	詮釋	Diễn giải	បកស្រាយ	ຕີຄວາມຫມາຍຢ່າ
involve	requerir	包含	Bao hàm	ទាក់ទង	ກ່ຽວຂ້ອງ
justify	justificar	證明正確	Ngụy biện	តម្រូវ	ພິສູດ
method	método	方法	Phương pháp	វិធីសាស្ត្រ	ແບບວິທີ
predict	predecir	預測	Tiên đoán	ព្យាករណ៍	ຄາດຄະເນ
principle	principio	原理	Nguyên lý	គោលការណ៍	ຫລັກການ
random	aleatorio/al azar	隨機	Ngẫu nhiên	ចែដន្យ	ສຸ່ມ
relevant	pertinente	相關	Phù hợp	ទាក់ទង	ກ່ຽວຂ້ອງ
represent	representar	代表	Biểu thị	តំណាង	ສະແດງເຖິງ
restrict	restringir	限制	Giới hạn	លិ៍ក្ខខ័ណ្ឌ	ຈຳກັດ
round	redondear	四捨五入	Làm tròn	ធ្វើឲ្យ មូល	ປົ້ນຂໍ້ມ
significant	significativo	有意義的	Đáng kể	សំខាន់	ສຳຄັນ
solve	resolver	解決	Giải	ដោះស្រាយ	ແກ້ໄຂ
specify	especificar	指定	Chỉ định	ជាក់លាក់	ລະບຸແຈ້ງ
survey	encuesta	調査	Khảo cứu	ស្រាវជ្រាវ	ສຳຫລວດ

Nombre _____ Fecha _____

Examen diagnóstico anterior al curso *Para usar antes de los Libros 1 a 7 de Matemáticas: Intervención*

Números naturales

Conceptos de números naturales

1. ¿Qué número falta en esta recta numérica?

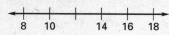

$$8 \quad 10 \quad \quad 14 \quad 16 \quad 18$$

(A) 11   (B) 12   (C) 13   (D) 15

2. ¿Qué tabla de valores posicionales representa el modelo?

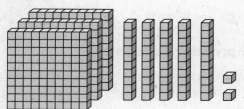

(A)

Centenas	Decenas	Unidades
3	6	2

(B)

Centenas	Decenas	Unidades
5	3	2

(C)

Centenas	Decenas	Unidades
2	5	3

(D)

Centenas	Decenas	Unidades
3	5	2

3. ¿Qué número es 16,372 redondeado a la posición de las centenas?

(A) 16,000   (B) 16,300   (C) 16,400   (D) 17,000

Suma y resta de números naturales

4. ¿Qué operación de resta corresponde a la operación de suma $14 + 3 = 17$?

(A) $17 - 3 = 14$ (B) $14 - 3 = 11$

(C) $17 - 17 = 0$ (D) $17 + 14 = 31$

5. Este mes, Jackson ganó $1500. Gastó $678 en alquiler y $312 en servicios. ¿Cuánto le sobró?

(A) $410   (B) $510

(C) $520   (D) $1134

6. ¿Qué estrategia podrías usar para hallar $15 + 67$? Contar hacia delante…

(A) de 1 en 1 siete veces para ir de 15 a 22. Después contar de 10 en 10 seis veces.

(B) de 5 en 5 dos veces para ir de 15 a 25. Después contar de 10 en 10 seis veces.

(C) de 1 en 1 cinco veces para ir de 15 a 20. Después contar de 10 en 10 seis veces.

(D) de 2 en 2 seis veces para ir de 15 a 21. Después contar de 10 en 10 dos veces.

Multiplicación y división de números naturales

7. Un vendedor vendió 135 CDs a $12 cada uno. ¿Cuánto recaudó el vendedor de estas ventas?

(A) $270   (B) $405   (C) $1485   (D) $1620

8. La maestra Shipman compró 115 regalos para repartir equitativamente entre los 28 estudiantes de su clase. ¿Cuántos regalos recibirá cada estudiante?

(A) 3 regalos cada uno y sobrarán 4 regalos

(B) 3 regalos cada uno y sobrarán 12 regalos

(C) 4 regalos cada uno y sobrarán 3 regalos

(D) 4 regalos cada uno y sobrarán 13 regalos

9. ¿Qué expresión es verdadera?

(A) $6 + 9 \cdot 2^2 - 5 = 55$

(B) $40 \div 8 + 4 \cdot 3^2 = 81$

(C) $(5 + 2) \cdot 4 - 1 = 21$

(D) $12 - 8 \div 2^2 + 7 = 17$

Fracciones y decimales

Conceptos numéricos

10. ¿Cuál es la descomposición en números primos de 252?

(A) $2^2 \times 3^2 \times 7$ (B) $2^2 \times 3^2 \times 7^2$

(C) $2 \times 3^2 \times 7$ (D) $2^2 \times 3 \times 7$

11. Sara tiene 18 cuentas verdes y 42 cuentas rojas. Está dividiendo las cuentas en grupos iguales sin mezclar los colores. ¿Cuántas cuentas hay en cada grupo?

(A) 4   (B) 5

(C) 6   (D) 7

Examen diagnóstico anterior al curso *continúa*

12. ¿Cuál es el mínimo común múltiplo de 8, 16 y 20?

 (A) 20   **(B)** 80   **(C)** 128   **(D)** 2560

Comprender fracciones

13. ¿Qué fracción es equivalente a la fracción representada en el modelo?

 (A) $\frac{10}{12}$ **(B)** $\frac{15}{20}$ **(C)** $\frac{9}{16}$ **(D)** $\frac{4}{8}$

14. ¿Qué comparación es verdadera?

 (A) $\frac{2}{5} < \frac{3}{10}$

 (B) $\frac{4}{7} < \frac{2}{9}$

 (C) $\frac{2}{3} > \frac{9}{11}$

 (D) $\frac{5}{12} > \frac{3}{8}$

15. La tabla muestra las longitudes de cuatro senderos. ¿Qué lista ordena correctamente los senderos de menor a mayor longitud?

Sendero A	$\frac{15}{7}$ millas
Sendero B	$2\frac{3}{7}$ millas
Sendero C	$\frac{25}{14}$ millas
Sendero D	$2\frac{9}{14}$ millas

 (A) Sendero C, Sendero D, Sendero A, Sendero B

 (B) Sendero C, Sendero B, Sendero A, Sendero D

 (C) Sendero D, Sendero B, Sendero C, Sendero A

 (D) Sendero C, Sendero A, Sendero B, Sendero D

Operaciones con fracciones

16. ¿Cuál es la suma de $\frac{7}{9} + \frac{1}{6}$?

 (A) $\frac{8}{15}$ **(B)** $\frac{5}{9}$

 (C) $\frac{17}{18}$ **(D)** $\frac{5}{6}$

17. Lydia tiene $8\frac{1}{3}$ tazas de harina. Utiliza $5\frac{3}{4}$ tazas para hacer galletas. ¿Cuánta harina le sobra?

 (A) $2\frac{1}{4}$ tazas   **(B)** $2\frac{7}{12}$ tazas

 (C) $2\frac{11}{12}$ tazas   **(D)** $3\frac{1}{2}$ tazas

18. ¿Qué enunciado es verdadero?

 (A) $4\frac{1}{2} \div \frac{7}{8} = 5\frac{1}{7}$ **(B)** $4\frac{1}{2} \times \frac{7}{8} = 5\frac{1}{7}$

 (C) $\frac{7}{8} \div 4\frac{1}{2} = 5\frac{1}{7}$ **(D)** $\frac{7}{8} \times 4\frac{1}{2} = 1\frac{3}{4}$

Comprender decimales

19. ¿Cuál de estos números es 14.748 redondeado a la décima más cercana?

 (A) 15   **(B)** 14.8

 (C) 14.75   **(D)** 14.7

20. Mallim tiene una tarjeta que mide 3.875 pulg. de largo. ¿Qué longitud de sobre podría usar para colocar su tarjeta?

 (A) 3.86 pulg.   **(B)** 3.79 pulg.

 (C) 3.9 pulg.   **(D)** 3.871 pulg.

21. ¿Qué recta numérica está rotulada correctamente?

Operaciones con decimales

22. ¿Qué suma es la manera correcta de escribir $4.5215 + 332.3$ en una columna?

 (A)
$$\begin{array}{r} 332.3 \\ +\ 4.5215 \\ \hline \end{array}$$

 (B)
$$\begin{array}{r} 3323 \\ +\ 45215 \\ \hline \end{array}$$

 (C)
$$\begin{array}{r} 332.30 \\ +\ 4.5215 \\ \hline \end{array}$$

 (D)
$$\begin{array}{r} 332.3 \\ +\ \ 4.5215 \\ \hline \end{array}$$

Examen diagnóstico anterior al curso *continúa*

23. ¿Qué número es el producto de 2.9481 × 1000?

- **(A)** 2948.1
- **(B)** 294.81
- **(C)** 29.481
- **(D)** 2.9481

24. Joy pagó $4.83 por 4.2 libras de frutas. ¿Cuánto pagó por libra?

- **(A)** $.12
- **(B)** $.58
- **(C)** $1.15
- **(D)** $11.50

Números enteros y números racionales

Conceptos básicos

25. ¿Qué valor es equivalente a $|-8|$?

- **(A)** 8
- **(B)** el opuesto de 8
- **(C)** 8 al cuadrado
- **(D)** −8

26. ¿Qué número es un número racional?

- **(A)** 1.47526…
- **(B)** 8.01404…
- **(C)** 2.99999…
- **(D)** 4.15158…

27. ¿Qué lista muestra los números en orden de menor a mayor?

- **(A)** $-7.45, -7\frac{7}{9}, -7\frac{1}{9}, 7.01$
- **(B)** $-7\frac{1}{9}, -7\frac{7}{9}, -7.45, 7.01$
- **(C)** $7.01, -7.45, -7\frac{7}{9}, -7\frac{1}{9}$
- **(D)** $-7\frac{7}{9}, -7.45, -7\frac{1}{9}, 7.01$

Operaciones con números enteros y números racionales

28. ¿Qué recta numérica representa a $-2 - (-6)$?

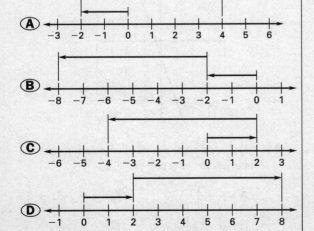

29. ¿Qué tienen en común el producto -12×6 y el cociente $12 \div -6$?

- **(A)** Cuando calculas el valor absoluto de cada resultado, obtienes el mismo número.
- **(B)** Ambos implican usar el opuesto de 12 y el valor absoluto de 6.
- **(C)** El signo que resulta para ambos es positivo.
- **(D)** El signo que resulta para ambos es negativo.

30. Halla la suma de $-2\frac{7}{10} + 0.06$.

- **(A)** −2.76
- **(B)** −2.64
- **(C)** 2.64
- **(D)** 2.76

Razones, tasas, proporciones y porcentajes

Razones, tasas y proporciones

31. La tienda de George tiene 3 cortacéspedes manuales de un total de 24 cortacéspedes. La razón de cortacéspedes manuales a todos los cortacéspedes en la tienda de Arnie es 4 : 40. ¿Qué oración es verdadera?

- **(A)** La fracción de cortacéspedes manuales en la tienda de George es mayor que en la de Arnie.
- **(B)** La fracción de cortacéspedes manuales en la tienda de Arnie es mayor que en la de George.
- **(C)** La razón de cortacéspedes manuales a todos los cortacéspedes es la misma en ambas tiendas.
- **(D)** La razón de cortacéspedes manuales a todos los cortacéspedes en la tienda de George es 1 : 10.

32. Una máquina llena 750 botellas de agua en 3 horas. ¿Cuál es la tasa por hora de la máquina?

- **(A)** 150 botellas de agua por hora
- **(B)** 250 botellas de agua por hora
- **(C)** 750 botellas de agua por hora
- **(D)** 2250 botellas de agua por hora

33. ¿Qué valor de a hace que la proporción $\frac{7}{14} = \frac{9}{a}$ sea verdadera?

- **(A)** 12
- **(B)** 14
- **(C)** 18
- **(D)** 27

Porcentajes, interés y probabilidad

34. ¿Qué fracción es equivalente a 40%?

- **(A)** $\frac{1}{25}$
- **(B)** $\frac{1}{4}$
- **(C)** $\frac{2}{5}$
- **(D)** $\frac{3}{5}$

Examen diagnóstico anterior al curso *continúa*

35. Riley deposita $400 en una cuenta de ahorros que paga 5.2% de interés simple el mismo día que Miguel deposita $400 en una cuenta de ahorros que paga 4.8% de interés compuesto. ¿Qué oración es verdadera?

Ⓐ En 3 años, Riley tendrá más dinero en su cuenta de lo que tendrá Miguel en la suya.

Ⓑ En 3 años, Miguel tendrá más dinero en su cuenta de lo que tendrá Riley en la suya.

Ⓒ En 3 años, Riley y Miguel tendrán la misma cantidad de dineros en sus respectivas cuentas.

Ⓓ En 3 años, la cantidad sumada de ambas cuentas será $924.80.

36. ¿Cuál es la probabilidad de que la flecha giratoria *no* se detenga en un número par?

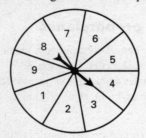

Ⓐ $\frac{1}{3}$ Ⓑ $\frac{2}{3}$

Ⓒ $\frac{4}{9}$ Ⓓ $\frac{5}{9}$

Razonamiento algebraico
Propiedades y conceptos básicos

37. ¿Qué regla describe al patrón 4, 8, 12, 16, 20, . . .?

Ⓐ Comienza con 4. Después multiplica un término por 2 para obtener el próximo término.

Ⓑ Comienza con 4. Después multiplica un término por 3 para obtener el próximo término.

Ⓒ Comienza con 4. Después suma 3 a un término para obtener el próximo término.

Ⓓ Comienza con 4. Después suma 4 a un término para obtener el próximo término.

38. ¿Qué expresión representa a "Doce más que dos veces el número de libros"?

Ⓐ $12b + 2$ Ⓑ $2b + 12$

Ⓒ $2(b + 12)$ Ⓓ $(b + 2) + 12$

39. ¿Cuál es la solución de $n - 9 = -4$?

Ⓐ -13 Ⓑ -5 Ⓒ 5 Ⓓ 13

Relaciones funcionales entre dos cantidades

40. ¿Qué gráfica muestra la recta $y = 3x - 1$?

Ⓐ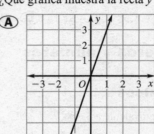

Ⓑ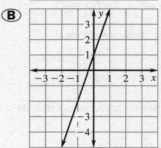

Ⓒ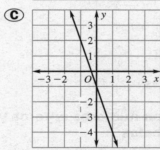

Ⓓ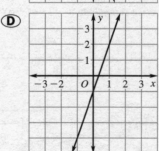

41. ¿Qué recta tiene una pendiente de $\frac{1}{3}$ y una intersección en y de -3?

Ⓐ $y = \frac{1}{3}x - 3$ Ⓑ $y = -3x + \frac{1}{3}$

Ⓒ $y = -\frac{1}{3}x + 3$ Ⓓ $y = -\frac{1}{3}x - 3$

Examen diagnóstico anterior al curso *continúa*

42. ¿Qué relación entre salarios y horas está representada en la gráfica?

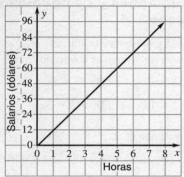

Ⓐ Geneveve gana $6 por cada hora que trabaja.

Ⓑ Geneveve gana $8 por cada hora que trabaja.

Ⓒ Geneveve gana $12 por cada hora que trabaja.

Ⓓ Geneveve gana $24 por cada hora que trabaja.

Análisis de datos y geometría

Análisis de datos

43. ¿Qué lista nombra objetos que son todos productos de papel?

Ⓐ boletín, lápiz, cámara, plato

Ⓑ sobre, boletín, tarjeta profesional, bloc de notas

Ⓒ sobre, cartucho de tinta, pañuelo de papel, sandía

Ⓓ rótulo, botella, papel de construcción, toallas de papel

44. De acuerdo con la lista de tallas de camisetas de las niñas del equipo de baloncesto, ¿cuántas niñas del equipo usan una camiseta de talla mediana (M)?

Tallas de camisetas: S, M, M, M, L, M, L, S, M L, S, M, L, L, L, M, S, S, M, M, S, S, L, L, M

Ⓐ 7   Ⓑ 8   Ⓒ 9   Ⓓ 10

45. La tabla de conteo muestra los resultados de un experimento de probabilidad en el que se lanza una moneda 50 veces. ¿Cuál es la probabilidad experimental de lanzar cruces? *(continúa)*

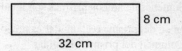

Caras	卌 卌 卌 卌 卌 III
Cruces	卌 卌 卌 卌 II

Ⓐ $\frac{1}{2}$ Ⓑ $\frac{11}{25}$ Ⓒ $\frac{14}{25}$ Ⓓ $\frac{21}{50}$

Longitud y área

46. ¿Cuál es el perímetro del rectángulo?

8 cm

32 cm

Ⓐ 72 cm   Ⓑ 80 cm

Ⓒ 160 cm   Ⓓ 256 cm

47. Se muestran las dimensiones de un triángulo y un paralelogramo. ¿Qué oración es verdadera?

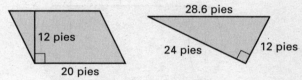

12 pies

20 pies

28.6 pies

24 pies   12 pies

Ⓐ El área del paralelogramo es 120 pies².

Ⓑ El área del triángulo es 288 pies².

Ⓒ El área del paralelogramo es 64 pies².

Ⓓ El área del triángulo es 144 pies².

48. Un círculo tiene un diámetro de 18 metros. ¿Cuál es el área del círculo?

Ⓐ 9π m²   Ⓑ 18π m²

Ⓒ 81π m²   Ⓓ 324π m²

Área de la superficie y volumen

49. ¿Cuál es el área de la superficie del prisma rectangular?

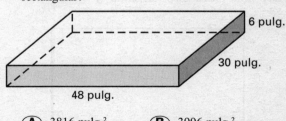

6 pulg.

30 pulg.

48 pulg.

Ⓐ 3816 pulg.²   Ⓑ 3996 pulg.²

Ⓒ 4752 pulg.²   Ⓓ 8640 pulg.²

Examen diagnóstico anterior al curso *continúa*

50. Se muestran las dimensiones de dos prismas. ¿Qué afirmación es verdadera?

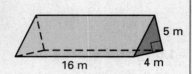

A Los volúmenes de ambos prismas son iguales.

B El volumen del prisma rectangular es menor que el volumen del prisma triangular.

C El volumen del prisma rectangular es mayor que el volumen del prisma triangular.

D El volumen del prisma triangular es 320 m³.

51. ¿Cuál es el volumen del cilindro?

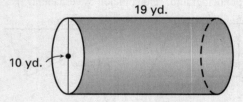

A unas 745.75 yd.³   **B** unas 1491.5 yd.³

C unas 2983 yd.³   **D** unas 5966 yd.³

Otros conceptos de geometría

52. Dos ángulos son suplementarios. Un ángulo mide 46°. ¿Cuál es la medida del otro ángulo?

A 44°   **B** 90°   **C** 104°   **D** 134°

53. ¿Qué valores podrían ser las longitudes, en pulgadas, de los lados de un triángulo rectángulo?

A 7, 24 y 25   **B** 16, 25 y 34

C 8, 15 y 20   **D** 6, 8 y 12

54. ¿Qué líneas son paralelas?

A $\overleftrightarrow{EF}$ y $\overleftrightarrow{FG}$ **B** $\overleftrightarrow{EF}$ y $\overleftrightarrow{EH}$

C $\overleftrightarrow{HG}$ y $\overleftrightarrow{EH}$ **D** $\overleftrightarrow{EH}$ y $\overleftrightarrow{FG}$

Preparación para el álgebra

Resolver ecuaciones y desigualdades de varios pasos

55. ¿Qué ecuación representa a la oración *"Siete menos que cinco veces un número es dieciocho"*?

A $5x - 18 = 7$ **B** $7 - 5x = 18$

C $5x - 7 = 18$ **D** $18 - 5x = 7$

56. ¿Cuál es la solución de $2x + 8 = 14$?

A 3   **B** 6   **C** 7   **D** 8

57. Como una meta de aptitud física, Ned se propone llegar a un total de 1500 flexiones en su rutina de ejercicios realizando 20 flexiones por día. Ya ha acumulado 300 flexiones. ¿Qué ecuación puedes usar para hallar la cantidad de días d que le faltan para alcanzar su meta?

A $300 - 20d = 1500$

B $300 + 20d = 1500$

C $300d - 20 = 1500$

D $300d + 20 = 1500$

Propiedades de los exponentes

58. ¿Cuál es el valor de 5^0?

A 0   **B** 1   **C** 5   **D** 10

59. ¿Qué expresión es equivalente a $(x^4)^8$?

A $x^{(4+8)}$

B $x^8 \cdot x^8 \cdot x^8 \cdot x^8$

C $x^4 \cdot x^4 \cdot x^4 \cdot x^4 \cdot x^4 \cdot x^4 \cdot x^4 \cdot x^4$

D $x^4 + x^{32}$

60. ¿Qué ecuación es verdadera?

A $\dfrac{8a^4b^4}{8a^2b^2} = 8a^2b^2$

B $\dfrac{16a^5b^4}{a^4b^5} = \dfrac{16b}{a}$

C $\dfrac{2ab}{4ab} = \dfrac{ab}{2}$

D $\dfrac{12a^2b^4}{3a^5b} = \dfrac{4b^3}{a^3}$

Teacher's Commentary for Pre-Course Diagnostic Test

The 60 items on the Pre-Course Diagnostic Test shown on pages 47–52 cover the materials across Books 1–7 of the *Math Intervention* program. After you have given a student or group of students the Pre-Course Diagnostic Test, you can use the following chart to determine which mathematical topics are causing the student or students difficulty. If the students miss item 10, for example, on the Pre-Course Test, then you may want the students to complete the materials in Math Intervention Book 2, Lesson 2-1.

You can use this chart to decide which lessons or complete books in the *Math Intervention* program would be most helpful to your students.

Item Analysis

If a student misses the Pre-Course Test item:	then the student has trouble with:	Have the student go to Book:	to work on Lesson(s):
1	identifying and ordering whole numbers	1	1-2, 1-3, and 1-5
2	place value and expanded notation	1	1-4
3	rounding whole numbers	1	1-6
4	addition and subtraction facts	1	1-9
5	adding and subtracting whole numbers	1	1-11 to 1-13 and 1-15 to 1-18
6	mental math strategies for addition	1	1-19
7	multiplying whole numbers	1	1-24 to 1-27 and 1-34
8	dividing whole numbers	1	1-28 to 1-30 and 1-34
9	exponents and/or order of operations	1	1-32 to 1-33
10	prime factorization	2	2-1
11	greatest common factor	2	2-2
12	least common multiple	2	2-3
13	equivalent fractions and/or simplifying fractions	2	2-4 to 2-6
14	comparing and ordering fractions	2	2-7
15	comparing and ordering mixed numbers and improper fractions	2	2-8 to 2-9
16	adding fractions	2	2-10 to 2-12

If a student misses the Pre-Course Test item:	then the student has trouble with:	Have the student go to Book:	to work on Lesson(s):
17	subtracting mixed numbers	2	2-13 and 2-17
18	multiplying and dividing fractions and mixed numbers	2	2-14 to 2-16
19	rounding decimals	2	2-18 to 2-19
20	comparing and ordering decimals	2	2-20
21	converting between decimals and fractions	2	2-21 to 2-22
22	adding decimals	2	2-23
23	multiplying decimals	2	2-24 to 2-26
24	dividing decimals	2	2-27 to 2-28 and 2-30
25	absolute value	3	3-2
26	rational numbers	3	3-4
27	ordering rational numbers	3	3-5
28	adding and subtracting integers	3	3-7 to 3-8
29	multiplying and dividing integers	3	3-9 to 3-10
30	rational number operations	3	3-12
31	ratios	4	4-1
32	unit rates	4	4-2
33	solving proportions	4	4-7
34	percents	4	4-9 to 4-10
35	interest	4	4-14 to 4-15
36	probability	4	4-17
37	patterns	5	5-1 to 5-2
38	writing algebraic expressions	5	5-4
39	solving addition and subtraction equations	5	5-8
40	graphing linear equations	5	5-12 to 5-15
41	slope and y-intercept	5	5-16 and 5-18
42	direct variation	5	5-17
43	sorting objects and data	6	6-1
44	recording and representing data	6	6-2 to 6-3

If a student misses the Pre-Course Test item:	then the student has trouble with:	Have the student go to Book:	to work on Lesson(s):
45	probability experiments	6	6-5
46	finding perimeter	6	6-7
47	finding the area of a parallelogram and a triangle	6	6-9 to 6-10
48	finding the area of a circle	6	6-13
49	finding the surface area of a rectangular prism	6	6-15
50	finding the volume of a rectangular prism and a triangular prism	6	6-16 to 6-17
51	finding the volume of a cylinder	6	6-18
52	complementary and supplementary angles	6	6-21
53	the Pythagorean Theorem	6	6-26 to 6-27
54	parallel and perpendicular lines	6	6-28
55	writing equations	7	7-1
56	solving multi-step equations	7	7-2
57	solving problems with multi-step equations	7	7-3
58	zero and negative exponents	7	7-7
59	finding the power of a power	7	7-9
60	finding the quotient of powers	7	7-11

HOJA DE RESPUESTAS DEL ESTUDIANTE

Hoja de respuestas para el Examen diagnóstico anterior al curso

Marca tu hoja de respuestas cuidadosamente. Tómate un momento para asegurarte que marcas tu respuesta en el lugar correcto. Esto es especialmente importante si no respondes a uno o más problemas. Cuando respondas a exámenes de selección múltiple, asegúrate de rellenar completamente el círculo y, si cambias una respuesta, de borrar todas las huellas de tu marca anterior.

Ejemplo: Ⓐ Ⓑ ● Ⓓ

1. Ⓐ Ⓑ Ⓒ Ⓓ	21. Ⓐ Ⓑ Ⓒ Ⓓ	41. Ⓐ Ⓑ Ⓒ Ⓓ
2. Ⓐ Ⓑ Ⓒ Ⓓ	22. Ⓐ Ⓑ Ⓒ Ⓓ	42. Ⓐ Ⓑ Ⓒ Ⓓ
3. Ⓐ Ⓑ Ⓒ Ⓓ	23. Ⓐ Ⓑ Ⓒ Ⓓ	43. Ⓐ Ⓑ Ⓒ Ⓓ
4. Ⓐ Ⓑ Ⓒ Ⓓ	24. Ⓐ Ⓑ Ⓒ Ⓓ	44. Ⓐ Ⓑ Ⓒ Ⓓ
5. Ⓐ Ⓑ Ⓒ Ⓓ	25. Ⓐ Ⓑ Ⓒ Ⓓ	45. Ⓐ Ⓑ Ⓒ Ⓓ
6. Ⓐ Ⓑ Ⓒ Ⓓ	26. Ⓐ Ⓑ Ⓒ Ⓓ	46. Ⓐ Ⓑ Ⓒ Ⓓ
7. Ⓐ Ⓑ Ⓒ Ⓓ	27. Ⓐ Ⓑ Ⓒ Ⓓ	47. Ⓐ Ⓑ Ⓒ Ⓓ
8. Ⓐ Ⓑ Ⓒ Ⓓ	28. Ⓐ Ⓑ Ⓒ Ⓓ	48. Ⓐ Ⓑ Ⓒ Ⓓ
9. Ⓐ Ⓑ Ⓒ Ⓓ	29. Ⓐ Ⓑ Ⓒ Ⓓ	49. Ⓐ Ⓑ Ⓒ Ⓓ
10. Ⓐ Ⓑ Ⓒ Ⓓ	30. Ⓐ Ⓑ Ⓒ Ⓓ	50. Ⓐ Ⓑ Ⓒ Ⓓ
11. Ⓐ Ⓑ Ⓒ Ⓓ	31. Ⓐ Ⓑ Ⓒ Ⓓ	51. Ⓐ Ⓑ Ⓒ Ⓓ
12. Ⓐ Ⓑ Ⓒ Ⓓ	32. Ⓐ Ⓑ Ⓒ Ⓓ	52. Ⓐ Ⓑ Ⓒ Ⓓ
13. Ⓐ Ⓑ Ⓒ Ⓓ	33. Ⓐ Ⓑ Ⓒ Ⓓ	53. Ⓐ Ⓑ Ⓒ Ⓓ
14. Ⓐ Ⓑ Ⓒ Ⓓ	34. Ⓐ Ⓑ Ⓒ Ⓓ	54. Ⓐ Ⓑ Ⓒ Ⓓ
15. Ⓐ Ⓑ Ⓒ Ⓓ	35. Ⓐ Ⓑ Ⓒ Ⓓ	55. Ⓐ Ⓑ Ⓒ Ⓓ
16. Ⓐ Ⓑ Ⓒ Ⓓ	36. Ⓐ Ⓑ Ⓒ Ⓓ	56. Ⓐ Ⓑ Ⓒ Ⓓ
17. Ⓐ Ⓑ Ⓒ Ⓓ	37. Ⓐ Ⓑ Ⓒ Ⓓ	57. Ⓐ Ⓑ Ⓒ Ⓓ
18. Ⓐ Ⓑ Ⓒ Ⓓ	38. Ⓐ Ⓑ Ⓒ Ⓓ	58. Ⓐ Ⓑ Ⓒ Ⓓ
19. Ⓐ Ⓑ Ⓒ Ⓓ	39. Ⓐ Ⓑ Ⓒ Ⓓ	59. Ⓐ Ⓑ Ⓒ Ⓓ
20. Ⓐ Ⓑ Ⓒ Ⓓ	40. Ⓐ Ⓑ Ⓒ Ⓓ	60. Ⓐ Ⓑ Ⓒ Ⓓ

Matemáticas: Intervención
Libro del maestro
56
Hoja de respuestas del estudiante para el Examen diagnóstico anterior al curso

Nombre _____   Fecha _____

Examen de *Números naturales*

Preguntas de vocabulario

Completa con la(s) palabra(s) que falta(n).

1. El enunciado $5 + 8 = 8 + 5$ muestra la propiedad _____ de la suma.

2. El enunciado $(3 \cdot 9) \cdot 2 = 3 \cdot (9 \cdot 2)$ muestra la propiedad _____ de la multiplicación.

Empareja la palabra con su significado matemático y con su significado cotidiano.

3. contar   **4.** expresión   **5.** dividendo

Significado matemático

A. agregar

B. el número que divides

C. una combinación de números, potencias y símbolos matemáticos

Significado cotidiano

X. dinero pagado a un accionista

Y. palabra o conjunto de palabras

Z. confiar

Respuestas

1. _____

2. _____

3. _____

4. _____

5. _____

6. _____

7. _____

8. _____

9. _____

10. Ver gráfica. _____

11. _____

Conceptos de números naturales

Escribe la forma desarrollada en forma de número.

6. 4 decenas + 8

7. 3 centenas + 6 decenas + 2

Escribe cuántas hay.

8.

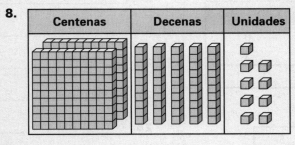

Centenas	Decenas	Unidades

9.

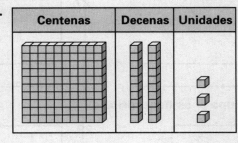

Centenas	Decenas	Unidades

10. Completa la recta numérica con los números que faltan.

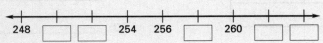

248 ☐ ☐ 254 256 ☐ 260 ☐ ☐

11. ¿Cuál es el valor de 6 monedas de cinco centavos?

A. 25¢   **B.** 30¢   **C.** 35¢   **D.** 40¢

Nombre _____ Fecha _____

 LIBRO 1 **Examen** *continúa*

Escribe el valor en forma desarrollada.

12. 5240   **13.** 306   **14.** 42

Escribe los números en orden de menor a mayor.

15. 435, 431, 433, 432   **16.** 876, 768, 678, 786

Redondea el número al valor posicional del dígito subrayado.

17. 5,633,456   **18.** 31,712   **19.** 428

Suma y resta de números naturales

20. Cuenta saltando para hallar el valor de 7 monedas de diez centavos. Luego resta 5 monedas de diez centavos. ¿Cuál es el nuevo valor?

21. Usa los números 4, 12 y 16 para escribir dos operaciones de suma y dos operaciones de resta.

22. Ejemplifica la familia de operaciones.

$8 + 6 = 14$

$6 + 8 = 14$

$14 - 6 = 8$

$14 - 8 = 6$

Halla la suma o la diferencia.

23. $0 + 95$ **24.** $17 - 0$ **25.** $6 + 2 + 4 + 8$

Escribe la suma.

26.

Decenas	Unidades
8	2
+ 1	6

27.

Decenas	Unidades
3	0
+ 4	3

Suma. Reagrupa si es necesario.

28.

2	8
+ 2	4

29.

1	5
+ 7	5

Halla la suma.

30. $269 + 714$ **31.** $15,040 + 9542$

Respuestas

12. _____

13. _____

14. _____

15. _____

16. _____

17. _____

18. _____

19. _____

20. _____

21. _____

_____

_____

_____

22. Ver izquierda.

23. _____

24. _____

25. _____

26. Ver izquierda.

27. Ver izquierda.

28. Ver izquierda.

29. Ver izquierda.

30. _____

31. _____

Nombre _____ Fecha _____

Resta para hallar cuántos casetes más o cuántos casetes menos hay que cajas.

32.

33.

34. Usa el modelo para hallar $100 - 30$.

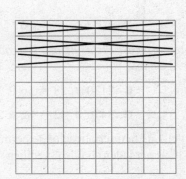

Resta. Reagrupa si es necesario.

35.

Centenas	Decenas	Unidades
3	4	4
−	8	7

36.

Centenas	Decenas	Unidades
7	2	0
−	4	5

¿Cuál de las opciones, A, B, C o D, muestra la diferencia correcta?

37. $62 - 38$

  A. 24   **B.** 26   **C.** 34   **D.** 36

38. $14{,}562 - 1897$

  A. 12,565   **B.** 12,665   **C.** 12,765   **D.** 13,335

Halla la suma o la diferencia.

39. $19 + 64$

40. $80 - 50$

41. $12 + 48 + 7$

42. $17 + 54 + 23$

Multiplicación y división de números naturales

43. Tienes 18 fichas. Das 3 fichas por vez a tus amigos hasta que se te acaban todas tus fichas. ¿Qué enunciado representa esta situación?

  A. $18 - 3 = 15$ **B.** $6 \div 3 = 2$ **C.** $18 \times 3 = 54$ **D.** $18 \div 3 = 6$

Respuestas

32. _____

33. _____

34. _____

35. Ver izquierda.

36. Ver izquierda.

37. _____

38. _____

39. _____

40. _____

41. _____

42. _____

43. _____

LIBRO 1 **Examen** *continúa*

44. Da los 8 primeros múltiplos de 6. Luego halla 7×6.

_____

45. ¿3 veces qué número es 27?

Halla el producto o el cociente.

46. 32×4 **47.** 26×8 **48.** $9,400,000 \div 1000$

49. 157×100 **50.** 24×15 **51.** 341×50

52. 3542×141 **53.** $14,934 \div 6$ **54.** $4000 \div 8$

55. ¿Qué problema de división tiene un dividendo que es un múltiplo exacto del divisor?

  A. $6\overline{)458}$ **B.** $9\overline{)813}$ **C.** $4\overline{)716}$ **D.** $5\overline{)102}$

56. ¿Qué enunciado de división es correcto? *Pista: Estima los cocientes para comprobar si la respuesta es razonable.*

  A. $1520 \div 35 = 63$ R 15   **B.** $2130 \div 28 = 56$ R 12

  C. $2440 \div 48 = 45$ R 40   **D.** $3470 \div 42 = 82$ R 26

57. Sarah dice que la propiedad del 1 de la multiplicación te permite reescribir $4 \cdot (1 \cdot 14)$ como $4 \cdot 1$. ¿Esto es verdadero o falso? Explica.

_____

_____

58. Escribe el producto $3^5 \cdot 3^8$ como una única potencia.

59. ¿Qué debes hacer primero para simplificar $8 \cdot 9 \div 3(2 - 1) + 6^2$?

  A. Halla el valor de $2 - 1$.   **B.** Halla el valor de 6^2.

  C. Halla el valor de $9 \div 3$.   **D.** Halla el valor de $8 \cdot 9$.

60. Hay 12 cajas. Cada caja contiene 16 bolsas de té. ¿Qué operación debes usar para hallar la cantidad total de bolsas de té?

  A. $16 - 12$ **B.** 16×12 **C.** $16 \div 12$ **D.** $16 + 12$

61. Jacklyn tiene 79 botones para coser a unas camisas. Planea coser 3 botones en la parte de arriba de cada camisa. Calcula que $79 \div 3 = 26$ R 1; por lo tanto, puede coser los botones en 26 camisas y le sobrará 1 botón. Muestra cómo puedes comprobar el cociente de Jacklyn escribiendo un problema de suma.

_____

_____

62. Describe 3^6 con palabras. Luego muestra cómo hallar el valor de la potencia.

_____

Respuestas

44. Ver izquierda.

_____

45. _____

46. _____

47. _____

48. _____

49. _____

50. _____

51. _____

52. _____

53. _____

54. _____

55. _____

56. _____

57. Ver izquierda.

58. _____

59. _____

60. _____

61. Ver izquierda.

62. Ver izquierda.

LIBRO 1 **Examen** *continúa*

Resolver problemas con números naturales

Respuestas

63. Una escuela vende tortas heladas con el propósito de recaudar dinero para la Asociación de padres y maestros. La escuela gana $12 por cada torta que se vende. Los estudiantes venden 722 tortas. Explica cómo hallar la cantidad total de dinero que gana la escuela.

_____

_____

64. Cuatro amigos envían tarjetas de Navidad. Sheila manda 37 tarjetas, Helen 42, Catherine 36 y Mel 40. Escribe los nombres de los amigos en orden de menor a mayor cantidad de tarjetas enviadas.

_____

65. Quentin vende 4682 cajas de pasas en junio y 4619 cajas de pasas en julio. Cuando estas cantidades se redondean a la centena más cercana, ¿son iguales? ¿Por qué sí o por qué no?

_____

_____

66. Rhonda compra gomas de borrar. El total que debe pagar en la caja es de 72 centavos. Rhonda tiene varias monedas de un centavo, de 10 centavos, de 5 centavos y de 25 centavos. Haz dibujos para mostrar cuatro maneras diferentes en que Rhonda puede pagar las gomas de borrar, utilizando al menos 1 moneda de 5 centavos.

67. Una cuadrilla de albañiles construye 18 casas nuevas en una comunidad. Un agente inmobiliario vende 7 de estas casas. Explica cómo hallar la cantidad de casas que quedan aún por vender.

_____

_____

68. Eliza pagó $3560 por la construcción de una terraza y $2840 por la instalación de una cerca. Luego gastó $1150 para colocar persianas nuevas en todas sus ventanas. Explica cómo puedes hallar la cantidad total que gastó Eliza en estas tres obras para mejorar su casa.

_____

_____

Respuestas

63. Ver izquierda. _____

64. Ver izquierda. _____

65. Ver izquierda. _____

66. Ver izquierda. _____

67. Ver izquierda. _____

68. Ver izquierda. _____

LIBRO 2 **Examen de *Fracciones y decimales***

Preguntas de vocabulario

Completa con la(s) palabra(s) que faltan.

1. Un número _____ tiene como únicos factores el 1 y él mismo.

2. La _____ de una fracción se refiere a las partes iguales de un conjunto o de un todo.

3. Cuando escribes un número mixto en forma de fracción impropia, conservas el mismo _____ del número mixto. Cuando escribes un número mixto en forma decimal, primero debes escribir el número mixto en forma de _____ _____ y después dividir el _____ por el _____.

Empareja el ítem con su descripción.

4. $7\frac{4}{9}$ **A.** decimal exacto

5. $\frac{5}{2}$ **B.** decimal periódico

6. 0.98   **C.** fracción impropia

7. $0.\overline{5}$ **D.** número mixto

Respuesta

1. _____

2. _____

3. _____

_____

_____

_____

4. _____

5. _____

6. _____

7. _____

8. _____

9. _____

10. _____

11. _____

12. _____

Conceptos numéricos

Escribe la descomposición en factores primos del número.

8. 16   9. 140   10. 515

11. ¿Cuál es el máximo común divisor de 21 y de 45?

  A. 3   **B.** 5   **C.** 7   **D.** 9

12. ¿De qué manera puedes hallar el mínimo común múltiplo de 14 y de 18?

  A. Enumera todos los factores de 14 y de 18 e identifica el mayor de los factores que aparece en ambas listas.

  B. Enumera todos los factores de 14 y de 18 e identifica el menor de los factores que aparece en ambas listas.

  C. Halla la suma de todos los factores primos tanto de 14 como de 18, usando cada factor común sólo una vez.

  D. Halla el producto de todos los factores primos tanto de 14 como de 18, usando cada factor común sólo una vez.

Nombre _____   Fecha _____

LIBRO 2 **Examen** *continúa*

Comprender fracciones

Escribe la fracción representada por el modelo.

13.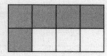

14.

Escribe tres fracciones que sean equivalentes a la fracción.

15. $\dfrac{1}{6}$ **16.** $\dfrac{4}{5}$ **17.** $\dfrac{3}{14}$

Escribe la fracción en su mínima expresión.

18. $\dfrac{10}{18}$ **19.** $\dfrac{9}{9}$ **20.** $\dfrac{24}{32}$

21. ¿Cuál enunciado es verdadero?

   A. $\dfrac{3}{5} > \dfrac{6}{7}$ **B.** $\dfrac{9}{10} > \dfrac{2}{3}$ **C.** $\dfrac{1}{4} < \dfrac{1}{8}$ **D.** $\dfrac{1}{2} < \dfrac{2}{9}$

22. Ordena de menor a mayor las fracciones $\dfrac{5}{12}, \dfrac{4}{17},$ y $\dfrac{3}{8}$.

Usa el modelo para escribir el número mixto en forma de fracción impropia.

23. $1\dfrac{2}{3}$

24. $2\dfrac{1}{5}$

Escribe la fracción impropia en forma de número mixto.

25. $\dfrac{7}{3}$ **26.** $\dfrac{49}{9}$ **27.** $\dfrac{20}{11}$

28. ¿Cuál de las siguientes listas de números está en orden de menor a mayor?

   A. $2\dfrac{4}{7}, \dfrac{14}{5}, 2\dfrac{1}{2}$ **B.** $2\dfrac{1}{2}, 2\dfrac{4}{7}, \dfrac{14}{5}$

   C. $\dfrac{14}{5}, 2\dfrac{4}{7}, 2\dfrac{1}{2}$ **D.** $2\dfrac{1}{2}, \dfrac{14}{5}, 2\dfrac{4}{7}$

29. Escribe un enunciado verdadero usando <, >, o = con los números $6\dfrac{8}{9}$ y $\dfrac{64}{9}$.

Respuestas

13. _____

14. _____

15. _____

16. _____

17. _____

18. _____

19. _____

20. _____

21. _____

22. _____

23. Ver izquierda.

   _____

24. Ver izquierda.

   _____

25. _____

26. _____

27. _____

28. _____

29. _____

EXAMEN DEL LIBRO 2

LIBRO 2 **Examen** *continúa*

Operaciones con fracciones

Halla la suma.

30. $\frac{4}{9} + \frac{1}{9}$

31. $\frac{5}{12} + \frac{7}{12}$

32. $\frac{2}{15} + \frac{8}{15}$

33. ¿Cuánto es la diferencia de $\frac{11}{16} - \frac{9}{16}$?

A. 2 **B.** $\frac{1}{4}$ **C.** $\frac{3}{16}$ **D.** $\frac{1}{8}$

Halla la diferencia.

34. $\frac{5}{6} - \frac{4}{9}$

35. $\frac{7}{8} - \frac{1}{4}$

36. $\frac{2}{3} - \frac{8}{15}$

37. ¿Cuánto es la suma de $\frac{3}{4} + \frac{3}{5}$?

A. $\frac{2}{3}$ **B.** $1\frac{1}{5}$ **C.** $1\frac{3}{10}$ **D.** $1\frac{7}{20}$

Halla la suma.

38. $3\frac{1}{4} + 3\frac{5}{6}$

39. $4\frac{2}{3} + 1\frac{7}{12}$

40. $1\frac{5}{8} + 2\frac{9}{20}$

Halla la diferencia.

41. $3\frac{2}{5} - 1\frac{1}{15}$

42. $5\frac{1}{2} - 3\frac{7}{10}$

43. $8\frac{1}{3} - 5\frac{3}{4}$

44. ¿Qué problema de multiplicación representa este modelo?

A. $\frac{3}{5} \times 10$ **B.** $\frac{3}{5} \times 4$ **C.** $\frac{2}{3} \times 10$ **D.** $\frac{1}{6} \times 4$

Halla el producto.

45. $4 \times \frac{5}{7}$

46. $\frac{2}{3} \times \frac{9}{14}$

47. $\frac{1}{8}$ de $\frac{3}{11}$

48. ¿Cuál es el primer paso para hallar el cociente $\frac{2}{9} \div \frac{2}{3}$?

A. $\frac{2}{9} \div \frac{2}{3} = \frac{4}{27}$

B. $\frac{2}{9} \div \frac{2}{3} = \frac{2}{9} \times \frac{2}{3}$

C. $\frac{2}{9} \div \frac{2}{3} = \frac{9}{2} \times \frac{2}{3}$

D. $\frac{2}{9} \div \frac{2}{3} = \frac{2}{9} \times \frac{3}{2}$

49. ¿Cuál es el primer paso para hallar el producto $1\frac{9}{11} \times \frac{4}{5}$?

A. $1\frac{9}{11} \times \frac{4}{5} = 1\frac{45}{55} \times \frac{44}{55}$

B. $1\frac{9}{11} \times \frac{4}{5} = \frac{20}{11} \times \frac{4}{5}$

C. $1\frac{9}{11} \times \frac{4}{5} = 1\frac{9}{11} \times \frac{5}{4}$

D. $1\frac{9}{11} \times \frac{4}{5} = \frac{4}{5} \times 1\frac{9}{11}$

30. _____
31. _____
32. _____
33. _____
34. _____
35. _____
36. _____
37. _____
38. _____
39. _____
40. _____
41. _____
42. _____
43. _____
44. _____
45. _____
46. _____
47. _____
48. _____
49. _____

LIBRO 2 **Examen** *continúa*

Halla el cociente.

50. $\frac{6}{7} \div \frac{3}{14}$

51. $2\frac{1}{4} \div \frac{5}{16}$

52. $2\frac{8}{9} \div 1\frac{1}{9}$

Comprender decimales

53. En el número 148.723, ¿qué dígito está en la posición de las centésimas?

    A. 1   **B.** 2   **C.** 3   **D.** 4

54. ¿Qué número es el resultado de redondear 34.218 a la posición de las décimas?

    A. 34.2   **B.** 34.3   **C.** 34.21   **D.** 34.22

55. ¿Cuál de los siguientes enunciados es verdadero?

    A. 3.78 < 3.76   **B.** 4.1415 > 4.1425

    C. 0.45 < 0.39   **D.** 72.48 < 72.51

56. Escribe 0.76 en forma de fracción en su mínima expresión.

57. Escribe $2\frac{4}{5}$ en forma decimal.

Operaciones con decimales

58. Usa el espacio dado para escribir 104.25 + 218.04 en una columna. Después halla la suma.

59. ¿Cuánto es la suma de 14.08 + 9.3168?

    A. 23.3968   **B.** 94.576   **C.** 107.248   **D.** 150.1168

60. ¿Cuánto es la diferencia de 5.048 − 2.987?

    A. 2.051   **B.** 2.061   **C.** 2.941   **D.** 3.941

61. Usa el espacio dado para escribir 17.74 − 12.0183 en una columna. Después halla la diferencia.

Halla el producto.

62. 0.04 × 8

63. 1.2 × 0.15

64. 0.09 × 0.76

Halla el cociente.

65. 0.49 ÷ 7

66. 4.2 ÷ 0.14

67. 80 ÷ 0.16

Respuestas

50. _____

51. _____

52. _____

53. _____

54. _____

55. _____

56. _____

57. _____

58. Ver izquierda.
_____

59. _____

60. _____

61. Ver izquierda.
_____
_____

62. _____

63. _____

64. _____

65. _____

66. _____

67. _____

EXAMEN DEL LIBRO 2

LIBRO 2 **Examen** *continúa*

Resolver problemas con fracciones y decimales

Respuestas

68. _____

69. _____

70. _____

71. Ver izquierda.

68. Abres un frasco de almendras y sirves 7 porciones con una cuchara. Cada porción tiene $\frac{1}{4}$ de taza. En el frasco quedan $2\frac{1}{4}$ tazas de almendras. ¿Qué estrategia puedes usar para hallar la cantidad inicial de almendras que había en el frasco?

   A. Multiplica $\frac{1}{4}$ por 7. Después resta $2\frac{1}{4}$.

   B. Multiplica $\frac{1}{4}$ por 7. Después suma $2\frac{1}{4}$.

   C. Divide 7 por $\frac{1}{4}$. Después suma $2\frac{1}{4}$.

   D. Divide 7 por $\frac{1}{4}$. Después resta $2\frac{1}{4}$.

69. Lang dice que $2.97 + 5.341 = 8.311$. ¿Qué método puede usarse para comprobar si la solución de Lang es razonable?

   A. $2 + 5 = 7$; Como 7 no está cerca de 8.311, la respuesta no es razonable.

   B. $3 + 6 = 9$; Como 9 no está cerca de 8.31, la respuesta no es razonable.

   C. $2 + 6 = 8$; Como 8 está cerca de 8.31, la respuesta es razonable.

   D. $3 + 5 = 8$; Como 8 está cerca de 8.31, la respuesta es razonable.

70. Paolo trabajó 5 días la semana pasada y ganó $112.50. Esta semana trabajó 4 días y ganó $142.50. ¿Qué información adicional necesitas para hallar el salario por hora de Paolo?

   A. Paolo trabajó un total de 34 horas en el período de dos semanas.

   B. Paolo trabajó 6 horas el sábado.

   C. Paolo trabajó 3 días más y ganó $75.

   D. No se necesita información adicional.

71. La Escuela de Danza y Técnicas de Ritmo está participando en un desfile. La escuela tiene 18 miembros en el equipo de danza y 78 estudiantes. La maestra Gregg quiere alinear a los participantes en filas iguales de manera que los miembros del equipo y los estudiantes no se mezclen. ¿Cuál es el mayor número de participantes que la maestra Gregg puede asignar a una fila? Explica tu razonamiento.

   _____

   _____

   _____

Examen *continúa*

72. El estante superior de una estantería contiene 16 libros. De ellos, 7 son ediciones de bolsillo. En el segundo estante hay 14 libros en edición de bolsillo. Este estante tiene la misma fracción de libros en edición de bolsillo que el estante superior. ¿Cuántos libros tiene el segundo estante? Explica tu respuesta.

_____

_____

_____

73. Dos tablas de madera miden $5\frac{3}{8}$ pulgadas de largo cada una. Para hallar la longitud total cuando estas tablas se unan por los extremos, Kira multiplica $2 \times 5\frac{3}{8}$ para obtener $10\frac{6}{16}$ y después simplifica para obtener $10\frac{3}{8}$ pulgadas. ¿Está en lo correcto? Explica por qué sí o por qué no.

_____

_____

74. En la tienda de alimentos para mascotas de tu vecindario, el alpiste cuesta $1.15 por libra. Tres sacos de alpiste en un estante pesan 3.46 libras, 3.48 libras y 3.47 libras. Di cómo puedes hallar la *menor* cantidad de dinero que puedes pagar por uno de estos sacos.

_____

_____

75. Estás comprando un cable coaxial para tu televisor. Quieres el cable más largo de dos cables que miden 15.75 pies y $15\frac{5}{8}$ pies. Explica cómo decidir qué cable deberías comprar.

_____

_____

76. Dipa tiene $142.75. Gasta $62.12 en alimentos y después compra 3 camisas a $7.51 cada una. Después deposita la mitad del dinero restante en su cuenta de ahorros. Explica cómo hallar la cantidad de dinero que le queda a Dipa.

_____

_____

_____

Respuestas

72. Ver izquierda.

73. Ver izquierda.

74. Ver izquierda.

75. Ver izquierda.

76. Ver izquierda.

LIBRO 3 · Examen de *Números enteros y números racionales*

Preguntas de vocabulario

Completa con la palabra que falta.

1. Para restar un número entero, puedes sumar su _____ .

2. En una recta numérica, un número entero _____ está a la izquierda del cero.

Empareja la palabra con su significado matemático y con su significado cotidiano.

3. positivo   **4.** base   **5.** operación

Significado matemático

A. describe un número entero mayor que cero

B. suma, resta, multiplicación o división

C. el factor repetido en una potencia

Significado cotidiano

X. apoyo inferior de algo

Y. cierto, verdadero

Z. el proceso que realiza una máquina

Respuestas

1. _____

2. _____

3. _____

4. _____

5. _____

6. Ver gráfica. _____

7. _____

8. _____

9. _____

10. _____

Conceptos básicos

6. Ubica los números enteros 3, -1, -5 y 4 en una recta numérica.

7. ¿Qué números de la lista son números enteros?

$\frac{4}{5}$, -9.6, 2.14, 0, -7, $-\frac{1}{2}$

A. $-\frac{1}{2}$, $\frac{4}{5}$, 0, -7 **B.** 0, -7

C. -9.6, 2.14, 0, -7 **D.** $\frac{4}{5}$, -9.6, 2.14, 0, -7, $-\frac{1}{2}$

8. ¿Qué expresión es equivalente a -45?

A. el opuesto de -45 **B.** el opuesto de 45

C. $|-45|$ **D.** $|45|$

9. Nombra dos números enteros que podrían tener un valor absoluto de 19.

10. Ordena de menor a mayor los números enteros 14, -12, 15 y -16.

Nombre _____ Fecha _____

LIBRO 3 **Examen** *continúa*

11. ¿Qué enunciado es verdadero?

   A. $-25 > -26$ **B.** $32 < -36$ **C.** $-40 < -48$ **D.** $-57 > 53$

12. ¿Qué número es un número racional?

   A. 28.2875…   **B.** 3.1428…   **C.** 1.4444…   **D.** 4.2227…

13. Ubica los números racionales $-3\frac{1}{4}$, -2.65, 0.83 y $2\frac{5}{8}$ en una recta numérica.

14. Ordena los números $-15\frac{2}{9}$, 15.408, $15\frac{4}{5}$, y -15.69 de menor a mayor.

Operaciones con números enteros y números racionales

15. Usa la recta numérica para hallar la suma $-3 + 6$.

Halla la suma usando valores absolutos.

16. $-15 + (-6) + (-14)$ **17.** $-50 + (-70)$

18. Usa la recta numérica para hallar la diferencia de $-12 - (-5)$.

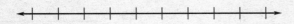

Halla la diferencia usando la regla de la resta.

19. $60 - (-8)$ **20.** $5 - 18$ **21.** $-24 - 14$

22. ¿Qué método usa correctamente la *suma repetida* para hallar el producto $8(-3)$?

   A. Como $8(3)$ es 24, entonces $8(-3) = -24$.

   B. $8 + 8 + 8 = 24$

   C. $-3 + (-3) + (-3) + (-3) + (-3) + (-3) + (-3) + (-3) = -24$

   D. $8 + (-3) = 5$

Halla el producto.

23. $9(-4)$ **24.** $(-12)(-2)$ **25.** $3(-5)(-6)$

Respuestas

11._____

12._____

13. Ver gráfica._____

14._____

15. Ver gráfica._____

_____

16._____

17._____

18. Ver gráfica._____

_____

19._____

20._____

21._____

22._____

23._____

24._____

25._____

LIBRO 3 **Examen** *continúa*

26. ¿Qué problema de multiplicación es igual a $-135 \div (-9)$?

A. $\underline{\ ?\ } \times (-15) = -135$ **B.** $\underline{\ ?\ } \times (-135) = -9$

C. $135 \times (-9) = \underline{\ ?\ }$ **D.** $\underline{\ ?\ } \times (-9) = -135$

Halla el cociente.

27. $64 \div (-4)$ **28.** $-70 \div -14$ **29.** $-36 \div 9$

30. Cada uno de los 18 estudiantes de una clase aporta $3 para los refrescos de una fiesta. ¿Qué método halla la cantidad total aportada por los estudiantes?

A. Sumar 18 y 3 para obtener $21.   **B.** Restar 3 de 18 para obtener $15.

C. Multiplicar 18 por 3 para obtener $54.   **D.** Dividir 18 por 3 para obtener $6.

Identifica la operación sugerida por la frase.

31. una diferencia en dos alturas   **32.** cuarenta y tres puntos más alto

Halla la suma, la diferencia, el producto o el cociente.

33. $12\frac{3}{10} + \left(-8\frac{1}{5}\right)$ **34.** $-14.9 - 7.08$

35. $-10.05 \times (-1.4) \times (-0.2)$ **36.** $-2\frac{4}{9} \div -\frac{11}{15}$

37. ¿Cuál es la *forma desarrollada* de $\left(\frac{2}{5}\right)^4$?

A. $2 \times 2 \times 2 \times 2 + 5 \times 5 \times 5 \times 5$ **B.** $\frac{2}{5} \times \frac{2}{5} \times \frac{2}{5} \times \frac{2}{5}$

C. $\frac{2}{5} + \frac{2}{5} + \frac{2}{5} + \frac{2}{5}$ **D.** $\frac{2}{5} \times 4$

Halla el valor de la potencia.

38. 7^3 **39.** $\left(\frac{2}{3}\right)^5$ **40.** $(4.3)^3$

Resolver problemas con números enteros y números racionales

41. Lindsay anotó 15 canastas durante el partido del jueves y 9 canastas durante el partido del viernes. Explica cómo usar un número entero para representar el cambio en la cantidad de canastas que anotó Lindsay.

_____

_____

Respuestas

26. _____

27. _____

28. _____

29. _____

30. _____

31. _____

32. _____

33. _____

34. _____

35. _____

36. _____

37. _____

38. _____

39. _____

40. _____

41. Ver izquierda. _____

LIBRO 3 **Examen** *continúa*

42. ¿Cómo puedes mostrar que 11 es un número racional? Explica tu respuesta.

_____

_____

43. Bryant intenta colocar una foto en un marco de $3\frac{5}{8}$ pulgadas de ancho, pero el marco es demasiado pequeño. ¿Debería intentar con un marco de $3\frac{4}{9}$ pulgadas de ancho o de 3.65 pulgadas de ancho? Explica tu razonamiento.

_____

_____

44. Camilo y Deanna están en una estación de metro. Camilo encuentra una chaqueta en las escaleras a 15 pies debajo de la superficie y se la lleva a Deanna, que está junto a un torniquete ubicado a 40 pies debajo de la superficie. Di cómo hallar el cambio en la elevación desde el lugar donde Camilo encuentra la chaqueta hasta el torniquete.

_____

_____

45. Henry gasta $4 en peaje cuando va a visitar a su tío. Escribe una expresión de producto para representar cuánto dinero le descuentan a Henry de su abono de peaje después de ir a visitar a su tío 12 veces. Simplifica la expresión y explica qué significa la respuesta.

_____

46. ¿El cociente $-1075 \div 215$ será positivo o negativo? Explica tu respuesta.

_____

_____

47. Hay 15 estudiantes en la clase de la maestra Jerraro. De estos estudiantes, 9 entregan sus trabajos trimestrales a tiempo. Después de que la maestra corrige 7 de esos trabajos, el resto de los estudiantes entrega sus trabajos trimestrales. Explica cómo hallar la cantidad de trabajos trimestrales que la maestra Jerraro aún debe corregir.

_____

_____

48. Janice y Rogelio están enviando por correo paquetes comerciales. El paquete de Janice pesa 14 libras. El paquete de Rogelio pesa $3\frac{1}{8}$ veces el peso del paquete de Janice. Di cómo hallar el peso del paquete de Rogelio.

_____

_____

Respuestas

42. Ver izquierda.

43. Ver izquierda.

44. Ver izquierda.

45. Ver izquierda.

46. Ver izquierda.

47. Ver izquierda.

48. Ver izquierda.

LIBRO 4

Examen de *Razones, tasas, proporciones y porcentajes*

Preguntas de vocabulario

Completa con la(s) palabra(s) que falta(n).

1. Cuando conviertes de centímetros a kilómetros, _____ por una potencia de 10.

2. Para escribir 72% en forma decimal, debes mover el punto decimal dos posiciones a la _____.

3. Puedes usar la multiplicación, o _____ _____, para resolver una proporción.

Empareja la palabra con el ítem que mejor describe.

4. razón   5. tasa unitaria   6. tasa

A. $\dfrac{150 \text{ millas}}{3 \text{ horas}}$ B. $\dfrac{18 \text{ frijoles verdes}}{90 \text{ frijoles totales}}$ C. $\dfrac{6 \text{ páginas}}{1 \text{ minuto}}$

Razones, tasas y proporciones

7. Escribe la razón 14 : 19 de otras dos maneras.

Escribe la tasa en su mínima expresión.

8. 18 libros en 6 meses   9. 630 lámparas en 9 horas

Escribe la expresión o las expresiones necesarias para hacer la conversión.

10. ¿Cuántos miligramos hay en 42 hectogramos?

11. ¿Cuántos metros hay en 1400 centímetros?

12. ¿Cuántos decilitros hay en 250 mililitros?

13. ¿Cuántas horas hay en 540 minutos?

14. ¿Cuántas yardas hay en 8 millas?

15. ¿Cuántas onzas líquidas hay en 3 cuartos?

Compara las unidades.

16. ¿Qué temperatura es más baja, 12ºC o 50ºF?

17. ¿Qué volumen es mayor, 140 pies cúbicos o 3 metros cúbicos?

18. ¿Cuáles son los productos cruzados de $\dfrac{25}{x} = \dfrac{15}{18}$?

   A. 450 y 15x B. 375 y 15x

   C. 375 y 18x D. 270 y 25x

Respuestas

1. _____
2. _____
3. _____
4. _____
5. _____
6. _____
7. _____
8. _____
9. _____
10. _____
11. _____
12. _____
13. _____
14. _____
15. _____
16. _____
17. _____
18. _____

LIBRO 4

Examen *continúa*

19. ¿Cuál es la solución de $\frac{4}{20} = \frac{x}{45}$?

A. 2   **B.** 8   **C.** 9   **D.** 36

20. El puente natural más grande del mundo es el puente Rainbow en Utah. Tiene 290 metros de altura. Amber usó una escala de 1 pulgada : 20 pies para hacer un modelo de este puente. ¿Qué proporción puedes usar para hallar la altura del modelo de Amber?

A. $\frac{1 \text{ pulgada}}{20 \text{ pies}} = \frac{290 \text{ pies}}{x \text{ pulgadas}}$

B. $\frac{x \text{ pulgadas}}{20 \text{ pies}} = \frac{1 \text{ pulgada}}{290 \text{ pies}}$

C. $\frac{1 \text{ pulgada}}{20 \text{ pies}} = \frac{x \text{ pulgadas}}{290 \text{ pies}}$

D. $\frac{1 \text{ pulgada}}{290 \text{ pies}} = \frac{20 \text{ pies}}{x \text{ pulgadas}}$

Porcentajes, interés y probabilidad

21. Escribe una fracción simplificada que sea equivalente a 28%.

22. Escribe un decimal que sea equivalente a 7%.

Escribe el decimal en forma de porcentaje.

23. 0.45   **24.** 0.72   **25.** 0.02

Escribe la fracción en forma de porcentaje.

26. $\frac{17}{20}$ **27.** $\frac{1}{8}$ **28.** $\frac{11}{32}$

Halla el porcentaje del número.

29. 30% de 50   **30.** 48% de 175

Di si el porcentaje de cambio es un *aumento* o una *disminución*. Después halla el porcentaje de cambio.

31. Cantidad original: 65
Cantidad nueva: 26

32. Cantidad original: 40
Cantidad nueva: 54

33. La cuenta por tu comida en un restaurante es $15.40. Dejas una propina de 18%. ¿Qué expresión puedes usar para hallar el costo total de tu comida?

A. $15.40 + 0.18$

B. $\frac{18}{100} = \frac{x}{15.40}$

C. $15.40 - \left(\frac{18}{100} \times 15.40\right)$

D. $15.40 + (0.18)(15.40)$

34. Una tienda de artículos electrónicos está ofreciendo un descuento de 15% en una computadora portátil que originalmente costaba $1260. ¿Cuál es el precio de venta de la computadora?

A. $189   **B.** $1071   **C.** $1197   **D.** $1449

Respuestas

19. _____
20. _____
21. _____
22. _____
23. _____
24. _____
25. _____
26. _____
27. _____
28. _____
29. _____
30. _____
31. _____
_____
32. _____
_____
33. _____
34. _____

Nombre _____ Fecha _____

35. Utoya pagó un precio de venta al por mayor de $12 por cada camisa de manga larga. Planea aumentar el precio en un 60% para venderlas en su tienda. ¿Cuál será el precio de venta al por menor de una de estas camisas?

A. $12.60   **B.** $16.80   **C.** $19.20   **D.** $60.00

Halla el interés simple ganado.

36. Capital: 625
Tasa anual: 6%
Tiempo: 2 años

37. Capital: 4225
Tasa anual: 3.1%
Tiempo: 42 meses

38. John deposita $560 en una cuenta que generará 5.8% de interés compuesto anual. ¿Cuál será el balance en la cuenta dentro de 4 años?

A. $592.48   **B.** $663.20   **C.** $701.67   **D.** $742.36

Usa la siguiente tabla para los Ejercicios 39 y 40. La tabla muestra el contenido de una cesta de calcetines. Un cliente entra y toma un par de calcetines al azar. Halla la probabilidad del evento.

Pares blancos	12
Pares azules	15
Pares negros	14
Pares grises	9

39. escoger un par blanco

40. escoger un par gris

Resolver problemas con razones, tasas, proporciones y porcentajes

41. La tienda de artículos para oficina de Vic vende 75 ítems diferentes, 15 de los cuales son diferentes tipos de sobres. La razón de sobres a la totalidad de los ítems de la tienda de artículos para oficina de Jim es 10 : 25. Di cómo determinar cuál tienda de artículos para oficina tiene una razón mayor de sobres a la cantidad total de ítems.

_____

_____

42. Karlie compra 60 metros de tela roja. Explica cómo hallar la cantidad de milímetros de tela roja que compró.

_____

43. Mae le da a Henao 144 pintas de agua filtrada. Explica cómo hallar la cantidad de agua filtrada en galones que recibió Henao.

_____

Respuestas

35. _____

36. _____

37. _____

38. _____

39. _____

40. _____

41. Ver izquierda.

42. Ver izquierda.

43. Ver izquierda.

Examen *continúa*

44. La razón de niños a niñas en la clase de la maestra Janson es 5 niños : 9 niñas. La clase de la maestra Reid tiene una razón equivalente de niños a niñas. Di cómo escribir y resolver una proporción para hallar la cantidad de niños en la clase de la maestra Reid si hay 27 niñas en la clase.

_____

_____

45. Dee tiene una colección de 415 sellos. Dice que sus amigos contribuyeron con el 60% de su colección. Describe cómo usar una proporción para hallar la cantidad de sellos que le dieron sus amigos.

_____

_____

46. El año pasado, 150 estudiantes se inscribieron en la escuela de artes marciales del maestro Kim. Este año se inscribieron 186 estudiantes. Di si el porcentaje de cambio es un aumento o una disminución. Después determina el porcentaje de cambio. Explica tu respuesta.

_____

_____

47. Nyliam obtiene una comisión del 3% por cada casa que vende. El fin de semana pasado, vendió una casa por $152,500. Di cómo hallar el total de la comisión que ganó.

_____

_____

48. Kirsten pidió prestado $7000 para comprar un carro usado. Devolverá el dinero en 3 años, con un interés simple del 8%. Explica cómo hallar la cantidad de dinero que Kirsten pagará en intereses.

_____

_____

49. Leonard deposita $815 en una cuenta que ganará 3.5% de interés compuesto anual. Di cómo usar la fórmula de interés compuesto para hallar la cantidad de dinero en la cuenta de Leonard dentro de 5 años.

_____

_____

50. Lanzas un cubo con sus 8 lados numerados del 1 al 8. Explica cómo hallar la probabilidad de que *no* salga un número par.

_____

_____

Respuestas

44. Ver izquierda.

45. Ver izquierda.

46. Ver izquierda.

47. Ver izquierda.

48. Ver izquierda.

49. Ver izquierda.

50. Ver izquierda.

EXAMEN DEL LIBRO 4

LIBRO 5 **Examen de *Razonamiento algebraico***

Preguntas de vocabulario

Completa con la palabra que falta.

1. Para resolver la ecuación $4x = 36$, puedes usar la propiedad de igualdad de la _____ para dividir cada lado por 4.

2. Como puedes usar la suma para "deshacer" una resta, la suma se denomina la operación _____ de la resta.

Empareja la palabra con su significado matemático y con su significado cotidiano.

3. regla   **4.** origen   **5.** intersección

Significado matemático

A. el punto donde se intersecan el eje horizontal y el eje vertical

B. un enunciado que describe un patrón

C. el punto donde una recta se interseca con un eje

Significado cotidiano

X. una instrucción que debe obedecerse

Y. conjunto de los elementos que son comunes a dos conjuntos

Z. el comienzo

Respuesta

1. _____
2. _____
3. _____
4. _____
5. _____
6. _____
7. _____
8. _____
9. _____
10. _____
11. _____

Propiedades y conceptos básicos

Escribe los dos números o las dos figuras que siguen en el patrón.

6. 1, 6, 11, 16, . . .

7.

8. ¿Qué regla describe el patrón?

70, 67, 64, 61, . . .

A. Comienza con 70 y resta 2 de cada término.

B. Comienza con 70 y resta 3 de cada término.

C. Comienza con 70 y suma 3 a cada término.

D. Comienza con 70 y suma 7 a cada término.

9. Halla el octavo término del patrón: 12, 16, 20, 24, . . .

Sustituye y usa el orden de las operaciones para hallar el valor de la expresión.

10. $(3a - c) + 4b$ cuando $a = 4$, $b = 1$, y $c = 5$

11. $a^2 - (c + 2b) \cdot 6$ cuando $a = 12$, $b = 10$, y $c = 3$

Nombre _____ Fecha _____

LIBRO 5 **Examen** *continúa*

12. Emilio tiene tres peras menos que cuatro veces la cantidad de peras que hay en una caja. Escribe una expresión algebraica para esta situación.

13. ¿Qué operación usarías en una expresión algebraica para las palabras *disminuyó en*?

   A. suma   **B.** resta   **C.** división   **D.** multiplicación

14. ¿Qué enunciado es un ejemplo de la *propiedad conmutativa de la suma*?

   A. $8 + 6 = 6 + 8$ **B.** $(5 + 3) + 1 = 5 + (3 + 1)$

   C. $14 + 0 = 14$ **D.** $25 + (-25) = 0$

15. ¿Qué enunciado es un ejemplo de la *propiedad de identidad de la multiplicación*?

   A. $9 \cdot 2 = 2 \cdot 9$ **B.** $4(10 \cdot 7) = (4 \cdot 10)7$

   C. $528 \cdot 1 = 528$ **D.** $9 \cdot \frac{1}{9} = 1$

Usa la propiedad distributiva para escribir la expresión de otra manera. Después simplifica la expresión.

16. $12(2 + 4 + 8)$ **17.** $9(14) + 9(5) + 9(11)$

18. ¿Cuál es el coeficiente de x en la expresión $4x^3 + 6x + 5$?

   A. 3   **B.** 4   **C.** 5   **D.** 6

19. Simplifica la expresión $3(x^2 + 8x) + 5x^2 - 2x - 5$.

Resuelve la ecuación.

20. $-1.3 = x + 14.5$ **21.** $y - 27 = -18$

22. $\frac{a}{8} = 4$ **23.** $-6b = 54$

24. Julianne tiene 24 lápices para pintar. Esto es 3 veces la cantidad de lápices para pintar que tiene Braylon. ¿Qué ecuación puedes usar para hallar la cantidad de lápices para pintar p que tiene Braylon?

   A. $24p = 3$ **B.** $\frac{p}{24} = 3$ **C.** $\frac{p}{3} = 24$ **D.** $3p = 24$

25. ¿Qué valor es una solución para $a > -12$?

   A. -15 **B.** -13 **C.** -12 **D.** -10

26. ¿Qué gráfica muestra la solución de $m - 4 \geq 20$?

   A. (recta numérica: 23 24 25 26 27 28 29)

   B. (recta numérica: 20 21 22 23 24 25 26)

   C. (recta numérica: 1 2 3 4 5 6 7)

   D. (recta numérica: -9 -8 -7 -6 -5 -4 -3)

Respuestas

12. _____
13. _____
14. _____
15. _____
16. _____
   _____
17. _____
   _____
18. _____
19. _____
20. _____
21. _____
22. _____
23. _____
24. _____
25. _____
26. _____

LIBRO 5 **Examen** *continúa*

Relaciones funcionales entre dos cantidades

27. Escribe una regla que muestre de qué manera y se relaciona con x.

x	−1	0	1	2
y	3	0	−3	−6

Marca el punto.

28. $A(−1, −2)$

29. $B(2, 3)$

30. $C(4, 1)$

31. $D(−1, 2)$

32. $E(2, −2)$

33. $F(−2, −4)$

34. Completa la tabla de valores para dibujar la gráfica de $y = 2x − 3$.

x	−1	0	1	2
y				

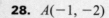

35. Halla la pendiente de la recta.

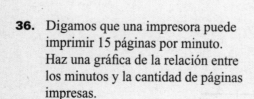

36. Digamos que una impresora puede imprimir 15 páginas por minuto. Haz una gráfica de la relación entre los minutos y la cantidad de páginas impresas.

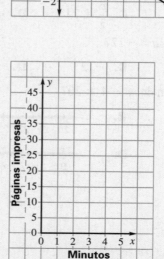

Respuestas

27. _____

28. Ver gráfica. _____

29. Ver gráfica. _____

30. Ver gráfica. _____

31. Ver gráfica. _____

32. Ver gráfica. _____

33. Ver gráfica. _____

34. Ver la tabla. _____
    Ver gráfica. _____

35. _____

36. Ver gráfica. _____

LIBRO 5 **Examen** *continúa*

37. ¿Qué gráfica muestra la recta $y = -\frac{1}{3}x + 1$?

A.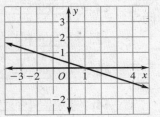

B.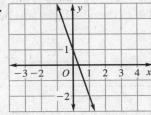

C.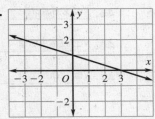

D.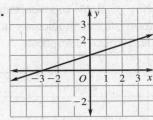

Respuestas

37. _____

38. _____

39. Ver la tabla. _____

   Ver la gráfica. _____

40. Ver izquierda. _____

38. La gráfica muestra la cantidad de dinero que Neill gana cuando trabaja una cierta cantidad de horas. Usa la gráfica para estimar las ganancias de Neill cuando trabaja 6 horas.

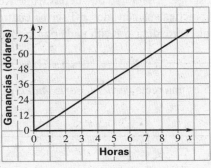

39. Completa la tabla de valores para dibujar la gráfica de $y = \frac{1}{2}x^2$.

x	−2	−1	0	1	2
y					

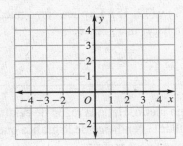

Resolver problemas usando el razonamiento algebraico

40. Kerr está aprendiendo palabras nuevas del diccionario para ampliar su vocabulario. Para el final del primer mes, ha aprendido 6 palabras nuevas. Para el final del segundo mes, ha aprendido un total de 24 palabras, para el final del tercer mes, 96 palabras y para el final del cuarto mes ha aprendido un total de 384 palabras. Si el patrón continúa, explica cómo hallar la cantidad total de palabras que Kerr habrá aprendido para el final del sexto mes.

_____

_____

LIBRO 5 — Examen *continúa*

41. Vladimir vendió 114 corbatas esta semana, es decir, 6 corbatas más que la cantidad que vendió la semana pasada. Escribe y resuelve una ecuación para hallar la cantidad de corbatas que Vladimir vendió la semana pasada. Explica tu razonamiento.

_____

_____

42. Un instructor de karate reparte cupones entre los 15 estudiantes de su clase. Cada estudiante recibe 3 cupones. ¿Cuántos cupones tenía al inicio el instructor de karate? Digamos que resolviste este problema y tu respuesta es 5 cupones. ¿Tu respuesta es razonable? Explica tu respuesta.

_____

_____

43. La ecuación $c = v - 4$ describe la cantidad de vueltas v que Keith nada y la cantidad de veces que practica sus clavados c. Escribe cuatro pares ordenados que hagan la regla verdadera si Keith nada por lo menos 6 vueltas.

_____

44. Di si la gráfica de $y = -15$ es una recta *vertical*, *horizontal* o *diagonal*. Explica tu razonamiento.

_____

_____

45. Una recta pasa por $(-2, 7)$ y $(12, 15)$. Explica cómo puedes hallar la pendiente de esta recta sin hacer una gráfica.

_____

_____

46. Hay 100 centímetros en un metro. Halla la razón de centímetros a metros. Después explica cómo hallar la pendiente de la gráfica que muestra la relación entre los centímetros y los metros.

_____

_____

47. Di si la gráfica de $y = -\frac{3}{4}x^3$ es una *recta*, una *parábola* o una *curva*. Explica tu razonamiento.

_____

_____

Respuestas

41. Ver izquierda. _____

42. Ver izquierda. _____

43. Ver izquierda. _____

44. Ver izquierda. _____

45. Ver izquierda. _____

46. Ver izquierda. _____

47. Ver izquierda. _____

LIBRO 6 **Examen de *Análisis de datos y geometría***

Preguntas de vocabulario

Completa con la(s) palabra(s) que falta(n).

1. Para hallar el/la _____ de un prisma, debes hallar el área total de todas las caras.

2. El número 25 es un/una _____ porque es el cuadrado de un número entero positivo.

Empareja la palabra con su significado matemático y con su significado cotidiano.

3. evento   4. segmento   5. agudo

Significado matemático

A. una parte de una recta con una longitud definida

B. describe un ángulo con una medida menor que 90°

C. algo que puede ocurrir

Significado cotidiano

X. un acontecimiento

Y. una parte en la que algo se separa o se divide

Z. afilado, punzante

Respuestas

1. _____
2. _____
3. _____
4. _____
5. _____
6. _____
7. Ver izquierda.

Análisis de datos

6. ¿Quién ha formado correctamente un grupo con todos los números pares mayores que 15 de la siguiente lista?

10, 15, 14, 18, 16, 19, 20, 21, 4, 48, 7, 12, 33

Maisie: 4, 10, 12, 14, 16, 18, 20, 48

Jerome: 19, 21, 33

Carlo: 16, 18, 20, 48

Laine: 16, 18, 19, 20, 21, 33, 48

A. Maisie   B. Jerome   C. Carlo   D. Laine

7. Registra las frecuencias de los números impares de la lista.

3, 8, 8, 5, 4, 8, 5, 2, 8, 5, 3, 1, 2

_____

_____

LIBRO 6 **Examen** *continúa*

8. Un depósito de una tienda contiene 5 bolsas de nueces, 8 bolsas de pacanas, 11 bolsas de avellanas y 12 bolsas de almendras. Representa los datos en forma de tabla de conteo.

Respuestas

8. Ver la tabla. _____

9. _____

10. _____

11. _____

12. _____

9. Una sala de copiado tiene 15 paquetes de papel blanco, 21 paquetes de papel amarillo y 46 paquetes de papel rosado. Escribe una fracción que muestre la relación entre los paquetes de papel blanco y la cantidad total de paquetes de papel.

10. La gráfica de barras muestra los resultados de lanzar 75 veces un cubo numerado. Usa los resultados para hallar la probabilidad de lanzar un número mayor que 3 en el próximo lanzamiento.

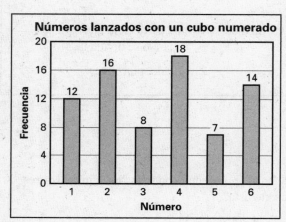

Longitud y área

11. Cada unidad de la cuadrícula de coordenadas representa una pulgada. Calcula la longitud del segmento de recta en pulgadas desde el punto *A* hasta el punto *B*.

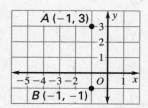

12. Halla el perímetro del rectángulo.

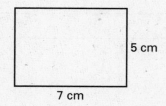

5 cm

7 cm

LIBRO 6   **Examen** *continúa*

13. a. Usando una regla del sistema usual de medidas, dibuja y rotula un rectángulo que tenga 4 pulgadas de largo y 2.5 pulgadas de ancho.

Respuestas

13. a. _Ver izquierda._

 b. _____

14. _____

15. _____

16. a. _____

 b. _____

17. a. _____

 b. _____

 b. Calcula el área en pulgadas cuadradas del rectángulo que dibujaste.

14. Halla el área del paralelogramo.

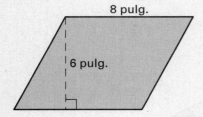

8 pulg.

6 pulg.

15. ¿Cuál es el área de un triángulo que tiene una altura de 10 cm y una base de 12 cm?

16. Halla la circunferencia del círculo. Usa $\pi \approx 3.14$.

a.

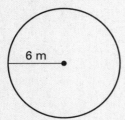

6 m

b.

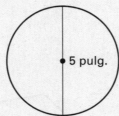

5 pulg.

17. Halla el área del círculo. Usa $\pi \approx 3.14$.

a.

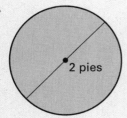

2 pies

b.

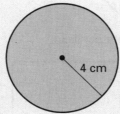

4 cm

LIBRO 6 **Examen** *continúa*

Área de la superficie y volumen

18. Halla el área de la superficie del cubo formado por este patrón.

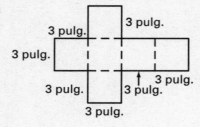

3 pulg.   3 pulg.
3 pulg.
3 pulg.
3 pulg.   3 pulg.
3 pulg.

19.

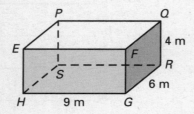

4 m
6 m
9 m

a. Nombra las caras del prisma rectangular.

_____

b. Halla el área de la superficie del prisma.

20. Halla los volúmenes del prisma rectangular y del prisma triangular.

a.

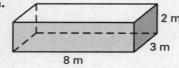

2 m
3 m
8 m

b.

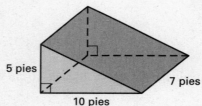

5 pies
7 pies
10 pies

21. ¿Cuál es el volumen de un cilindro de un radio de 8 cm y una altura de 3 cm? Da tu respuesta en términos de π.

Otros conceptos geométricos

22. Mide el ángulo con un transportador.

a.

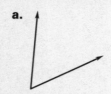

b.

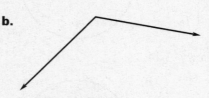

23. Clasifica el ángulo como agudo, recto, obtuso o llano.

a.

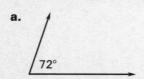

72°

b.

Respuestas

18. _____

19. **a.** Ver izquierda. _____

   b. _____

20. **a.** _____

   b. _____

21. _____

22. **a.** _____

   b. _____

23. **a.** _____

   b. _____

EXAMEN DEL LIBRO 6

LIBRO 6   **Examen** *continúa*

24. Halla las medidas del complemento y del suplemento del ángulo, de ser posible.

   a. $14°$ **b.** $118°$ **c.** $29°$ **d.** $86°$

25. Clasifica el triángulo como acutángulo, rectángulo u obtusángulo.

   a.
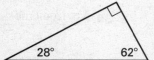
   b.
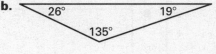

26. Un triángulo tiene lados de longitud 34 centímetros, 15 centímetros y 34 centímetros. ¿Este triángulo es equilátero, isósceles o escaleno?

27. Halla la medida del tercer ángulo del triángulo.

   a. $15°, 34°$ **b.** $102°, 58°$ **c.** $95°, 75°$

28. Halla la medida del cuarto ángulo del cuadrilátero.

   a. $200°, 12°, 56°$ **b.** $94°, 92°, 36°$ **c.** $116°, 124°, 70°$

29. Halla la raíz cuadrada. De ser necesario, redondea tus respuestas a la décima más cercana.

   a. $\sqrt{25}$ **b.** $-\sqrt{63}$ **c.** $-\sqrt{114}$ **d.** $\sqrt{96}$

30. Halla x. Redondea a la décima más cercana de ser necesario.

   a.
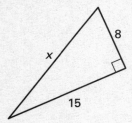
   b.
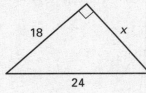

31. Un triángulo tiene lados de 16 pulgadas, 30 pulgadas y 34 pulgadas de largo. Di si el triángulo es un triángulo rectángulo.

32. Di si las rectas son paralelas, perpendiculares o ninguna de las dos.

   a.
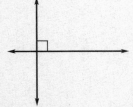
   b.
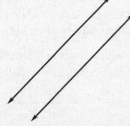

Respuestas

24. a. _____

   b. _____

   c. _____

   d. _____

25. a. _____

   b. _____

26. _____

27. a. _____

   b. _____

   c. _____

28. a. _____

   b. _____

   c. _____

29. a. _____

   b. _____

   c. _____

   d. _____

30. a. _____

   b. _____

31. _____

32. a. _____

   b. _____

LIBRO 6 **Examen** *continúa*

33. ¿Qué figura es congruente con la que se muestra aquí?

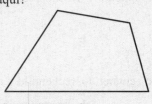

A.
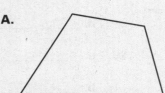

B.
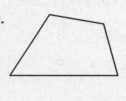

C.

D.

Respuestas

33. _____

34. _____

35. _____

36. Ver izquierda. ____

34. Digamos que $\triangle KLM \cong \triangle EFG$. ¿Qué lista nombra correctamente los pares de ángulos correspondientes?

 A. $\angle M \cong \angle E$, $\angle L \cong \angle F$, $\angle K \cong \angle G$

 B. $\angle K \cong \angle E$, $\angle L \cong \angle F$, $\angle M \cong \angle G$

 C. $\angle K \cong \angle G$, $\angle L \cong \angle E$, $\angle M \cong \angle F$

 D. $\angle M \cong \angle L$, $\angle L \cong \angle K$, $\angle K \cong \angle M$

35. Dado $\triangle ACG \sim \triangle HJP$, ¿cuál es la medida correcta de JP?

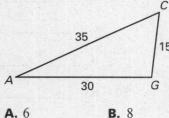

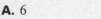

 A. 6   **B.** 8   **C.** 12   **D.** 16

Resolver problemas con análisis de datos y geometría

36. Un almacén vende ropa blanca. La tienda tiene dos vidrieras diferentes que contienen toallas para el rostro, toallas de mano y toallas de baño. La cantidad de cada tipo de toalla se muestra en las listas. Explica cómo puedes hallar la fracción total de toallas de mano que hay en estas vidrieras.

Vidriera 1: 12 toallas para el rostro, 17 toallas de mano y 8 toallas de baño
Vidriera 2: 9 toallas para el rostro, 18 toallas de mano y 6 toallas de baño

_____

_____

Nombre _____ Fecha _____

37. Un sitio de construcción rectangular tiene 24 metros de ancho y 28 metros de largo. ¿Cómo puedes hallar el perímetro y el área de este sitio?

_____

_____

38. Mark dibuja un paralelogramo con una base de 14 centímetros y una altura de 3 centímetros. Holly dibuja un paralelogramo con la misma área. Si la base del paralelogramo de Holly es 7 centímetros, explica cómo hallar la altura del paralelogramo de Holly.

_____

_____

39. Un empleado corta un trozo de queso en forma de prisma triangular. El área de la base del prisma es 14 pulgadas cuadradas. Explica cómo hallar el volumen del queso si la altura del prisma es 8 pulgadas.

_____

_____

40. Sabes que un triángulo tiene dos ángulos agudos. ¿Es información suficiente para que lo clasifiques como un triángulo acutángulo? Usa ejemplos para explicar tu respuesta.

_____

_____

41. ¿Puede un cuadrilátero tener ángulos que midan 90°, 90°, 30° y 140°? ¿Por qué sí o por qué no?

_____

_____

42. Un estacionamiento rectangular tiene 50 pies de largo y 30 pies de ancho. Miriam camina desde una esquina del estacionamiento hasta la esquina opuesta. Describe cómo hallar la distancia que recorre. Redondea la distancia a la décima de pie más cercana, de ser necesario.

_____

_____

43. Los rectángulos son semejantes. Las longitudes de un par de lados correspondientes están rotuladas. Explica cómo hallar la razón de semejanza.

15   18

_____

_____

Respuestas

37. Ver izquierda.

38. Ver izquierda.

39. Ver izquierda.

40. Ver izquierda.

41. Ver izquierda.

42. Ver izquierda.

43. Ver izquierda.

LIBRO 7 — Examen de *Preparación para el álgebra*

Preguntas de vocabulario

Completa con la(s) palabra(s) que falta(n).

1. En la expresión $3^{\frac{1}{2}}$ el $\frac{1}{2}$ se denomina exponente _____.

2. En la expresión $3x - 12 = 15$, el 3 se denomina _____.

3. Un exponente _____ hace que una potencia sea igual a 1.

4. Para hallar el producto $a^3 \cdot a^8$, debes _____ los exponentes.

Empareja la palabra con el ítem que describe.

5. cociente   **6.** desigualdad lineal   **7.** ecuación de varios pasos

A. $8x - 9 = 24$ **B.** $\dfrac{x}{8}$ **C.** $7x > 21$

Resolver ecuaciones y desigualdades de varios pasos

8. ¿Qué ecuación significa *seis más que dos veces un número es cuarenta y cinco*?

A. $6 + 2n = 45$ **B.** $2n - 6 = 45$

C. $2 + 6n = 45$ **D.** $6n - 2 = 45$

9. ¿Qué oración verbal representa la ecuación $\dfrac{7n}{14} = 24$?

A. Siete más que un número dividido por catorce es veinticuatro.

B. Catorce menos que siete veces un número es veinticuatro.

C. Veinticuatro es siete veces un número dividido por catorce.

D. Siete veces un número más catorce es 24.

Empareja la ecuación con la gráfica de su solución.

10. $9a - 7 = 20$ **11.** $6a + 20 = 2$

A.   **B.**
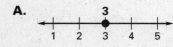   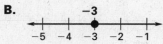

Resuelve la ecuación. Haz una gráfica de la solución.

12. $4b - 5b - 12 = -15b + 2$ **13.** $3(2b - 4) = 8(b + 2)$

Respuestas

1. _____
2. _____
3. _____
4. _____
5. _____
6. _____
7. _____
8. _____
9. _____
10. _____
11. _____
12. _____

Ver gráfica. _____

13. _____

Ver gráfica. _____

Nombre _____ Fecha _____

LIBRO 7 **Examen** *continúa*

EXAMEN DEL LIBRO 7

Completa los símbolos que faltan, +, −, ×, ÷, en la situación descrita.

14. Yolanda tiene una colección de canicas. Pierde 12 canicas en un juego con su hermana y su amiga le da 14 canicas. Ahora Yolanda tiene 36 canicas en su colección.

c _____ 12 _____ 14 = 36

15. Hunter donó $\frac{3}{4}$ de sus plantas a un parque de su vecindario.

$\frac{3}{4}$ _____ p

Empareja la desigualdad con la gráfica de su solución.

16. $5d + 3 > 43$

17. $4d − 34 \geq −2$

A.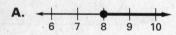
6 7 8 9 10

B.
6 7 8 9 10

Resuelve la desigualdad. Haz una gráfica de la solución.

18. $8y − 11 \leq 6y − 4y + 1$

19. $12(y − 3) < 4(2y − 5)$

Completa los símbolos que faltan, <, >, ≤, ≥, en la situación descrita.

20. Logan tiene como máximo 15 camisas en su ropero.

c _____ 15

21. Jill compra varios paquetes de bocadillos a \$2 cada uno. Gasta menos de \$20.

$2p$ _____ 20

Propiedades de los exponentes

Simplifica y reescribe sin exponentes negativos.

22. 8^{-2} **23.** 3^{-4} **24.** 5^0

25. Escribe la fracción $\frac{1}{27}$ en forma de potencia con un exponente negativo.

Reescribe la expresión sin exponentes negativos.

26. $a^6 \cdot b^{-8}$ **27.** $x^{-4} \cdot y^{-5}$ **28.** $w^{-9} \cdot v^2$

Empareja la expresión con el producto correcto.

29. $x^2 \cdot y^3 \cdot x^2$ **30.** $y^4 \cdot x^3 \cdot y^2$ **31.** $x^5 \cdot y^4 \cdot x^3$

  A. $x^3 \cdot y^6$ **B.** $x^8 \cdot y^4$ **C.** $x^4 \cdot y^3$

Simplifica.

32. $c^{-2} \cdot d^{-5} \cdot c^8 \cdot d^7$ **33.** $m^6 \cdot p^{-6} \cdot p^2 \cdot m^{-4}$

Respuestas

14. Ver izquierda.

15. Ver izquierda.

16. _____

17. _____

18. _____

    Ver gráfica.

19. _____

    Ver gráfica.

20. Ver izquierda.

21. Ver izquierda.

22. _____

23. _____

24. _____

25. _____

26. _____

27. _____

28. _____

29. _____

30. _____

31. _____

32. _____

33. _____

LIBRO 7 **Examen** *continúa*

Di si la ecuación es verdadera o falsa.

34. $(x^{-4})^{-6} = x^{24}$ **35.** $2 \cdot (y^{-3})^2 = \dfrac{2}{y^6}$ **36.** $(z^2)^4 \cdot (z^2)^4 = z^{64}$

Halla el valor cuando $a = 2$.

37. $5 \cdot (a^{-2})^{-2}$ **38.** $(a^{-2})^3 \cdot (a^4)^2$ **39.** $3a^{13} \cdot (a^2)^{-5}$

Empareja la expresión con la respuesta correcta después de simplificar.

40. $(4bc)^5$ **41.** $(4b^2c^3)^5$ **42.** $4(b^3c^2)^5$

A. $4^5 \cdot b^5 \cdot c^5$ **B.** $4 \cdot b^{15} \cdot c^{10}$ **C.** $4^5 \cdot b^{10} \cdot c^{15}$

Simplifica.

43. $(x^4yz)^3$ **44.** $5g \cdot (gh^2k)^6$ **45.** $(2bc)^4$

46. ¿Qué expresión muestra a $\dfrac{9a^5b^8c^7}{6a^2b^{10}c^3}$ en su mínima expresión?

A. $\dfrac{3ab^2c^4}{2a^3bc}$ **B.** $\dfrac{3a^3c^4}{2b^2}$ **C.** $\dfrac{3b^2}{2a^3c^4}$ **D.** $\dfrac{3b^8}{2a^2c^3}$

Halla el valor.

47. $\dfrac{15^3}{15^2}$ **48.** $\dfrac{2^4}{2^9}$ **49.** $\dfrac{3^8}{3^5}$

50. ¿Qué expresión muestra a $4^3 \cdot \left(\dfrac{d}{4}\right)^2$ en su mínima expresión?

A. $\dfrac{8}{d^2}$ **B.** $\dfrac{4}{d^2}$ **C.** $\dfrac{d^2}{4}$ **D.** $4d^2$

Di si la ecuación es verdadera o falsa.

51. $81^{\frac{1}{2}} \cdot 4^{\frac{1}{2}} = 16$ **52.** $25^{\frac{1}{2}} \cdot 1^0 = 5$

53. Isabella compra un pedazo cuadrado de lienzo que tiene el área que se muestra. ¿Qué expresión numérica representa el valor de x?

x pulg.

$A = 64$ pulg.^{2} x pulg.

A. $64^{\frac{1}{2}}$ **B.** $32^{\frac{1}{2}}$ **C.** $16^{\frac{1}{2}}$ **D.** $8^{\frac{1}{2}}$

Respuestas

34. _____
35. _____
36. _____
37. _____
38. _____
39. _____
40. _____
41. _____
42. _____
43. _____
44. _____
45. _____
46. _____
47. _____
48. _____
49. _____
50. _____
51. _____
52. _____
53. _____

54. Simplifica la expresión $16^{\frac{3}{4}} \cdot 4^{\frac{1}{2}}$.

Resolver problemas con ecuaciones y desigualdades

55. Escribe una oración para la ecuación $\frac{7}{8} = 4 + \frac{x}{5}$.

_____

56. Rory tiene que escanear un total de 135 fotos para el anuario. Ya ha escaneado 27 fotos. Planea escanear 9 fotos por día. Escribe y resuelve una ecuación para hallar la cantidad de días que le tomará terminar de escanear las fotos. Explica tu razonamiento.

_____

_____

57. Una mercería tiene 1250 carretes de hilo. Después de despachar 3 envíos iguales de hilo, quedan 875 carretes de hilo. Ken dice que había 125 carretes de hilo en cada envío. Escribe una explicación para comprobar si la afirmación de Ken es razonable.

_____

_____

58. Alex gastó más de $50 en el supermercado. Compró frutas y verduras por un valor de $25 y varias cajas de cereal a $3 la caja. Escribe y resuelve una desigualdad para hallar la menor cantidad de cajas de cereales que Alex pudo haber comprado. Explica tu razonamiento.

_____

_____

59. Romualdo reduce una foto a $\frac{3}{5}$ de su tamaño original y después decide reducirla nuevamente a $\frac{3}{5}$ de su nuevo tamaño. Escribe y simplifica una expresión para hallar la reducción total en forma de potencia de un cociente. Explica tu razonamiento.

_____

_____

60. Explica cómo simplificar $81^{\frac{3}{4}}$ usando el cálculo mental.

_____

_____

Respuestas

54. _____

55. Ver izquierda. _____

56. Ver izquierda. _____

57. Ver izquierda. _____

58. Ver izquierda. _____

59. Ver izquierda. _____

60. Ver izquierda. _____

Activity Master for Activity 1-7

Number Squares

5	6	7	8	9	10
11	12	13	15	16	17
18	19	20	21	22	23
24	25	30	50	60	70
80	90	95	100	120	130

Activity Master for Activity 2-10

Addition Expressions

$$\frac{1}{3} + \frac{1}{3} \qquad \frac{5}{9} + \frac{2}{9} \qquad \frac{1}{10} + \frac{2}{10}$$

$$\frac{3}{12} + \frac{4}{12} \qquad \frac{1}{5} + \frac{1}{5} \qquad \frac{2}{6} + \frac{3}{6}$$

$$\frac{2}{4} + \frac{1}{4} \qquad \frac{2}{5} + \frac{2}{5} \qquad \frac{3}{8} + \frac{2}{8}$$

$$\frac{2}{5} + \frac{1}{5} \qquad \frac{1}{7} + \frac{4}{7} \qquad \frac{9}{12} + \frac{2}{12}$$

$$\frac{3}{9} + \frac{1}{9} \qquad \frac{4}{8} + \frac{2}{8} \qquad \frac{4}{12} + \frac{1}{12}$$

$$\frac{2}{8} + \frac{1}{8} \qquad \frac{4}{9} + \frac{4}{9} \qquad \frac{3}{10} + \frac{6}{10}$$

$$\frac{1}{6} + \frac{3}{6} \qquad \frac{4}{9} + \frac{1}{9} \qquad \frac{2}{7} + \frac{1}{7}$$

$$\frac{5}{10} + \frac{2}{10} \qquad \frac{1}{4} + \frac{1}{4} \qquad \frac{1}{6} + \frac{2}{6}$$

Activity Master for Activity 2-10

Game Cards

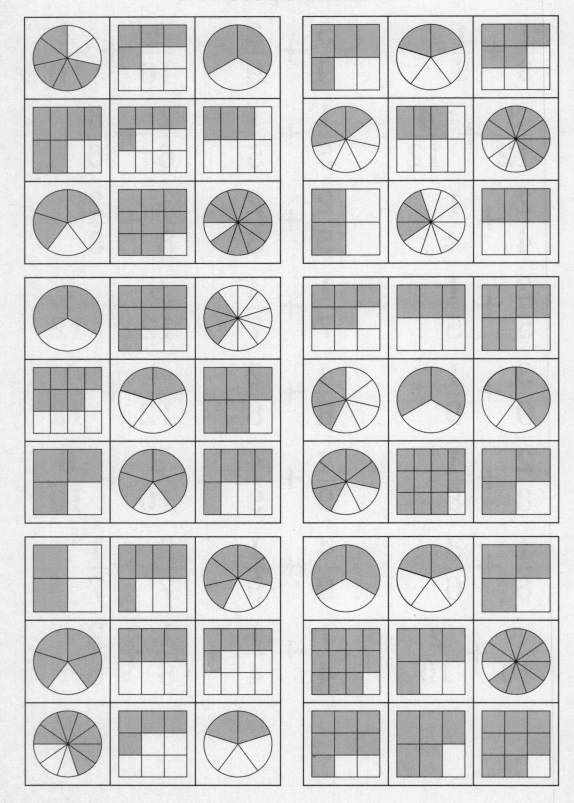

Activity Master for Activity 2-25

10×10 Blank Grids

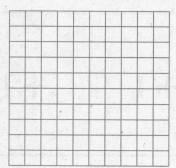

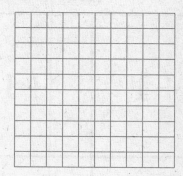

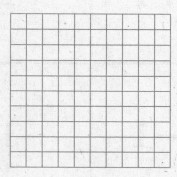

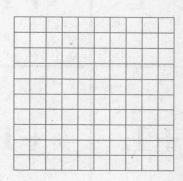

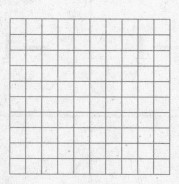

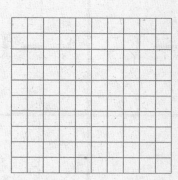

Activity Master for Activity 3-6

+1 and −1 Cards

+1	+1	+1	+1
+1	+1	+1	+1
+1	+1	−1	−1
−1	−1	−1	−1
−1	−1	−1	−1

Activity Master for Activity 5-14
Graph Paper

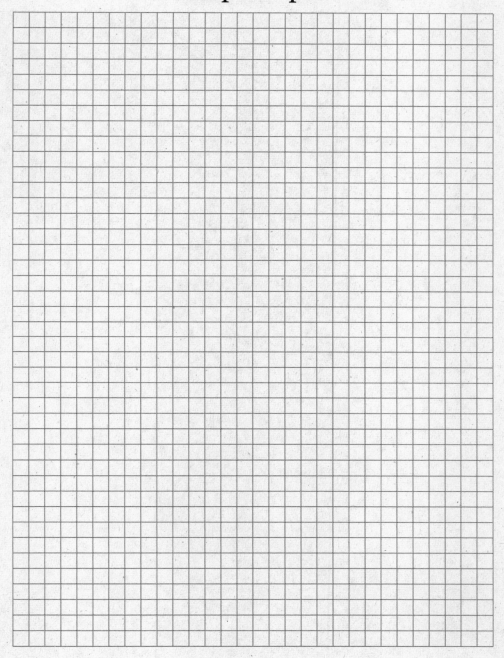

Activity Master for Activity 6-14
Pattern for 2 in. × 2 in. × 2 in. Cube

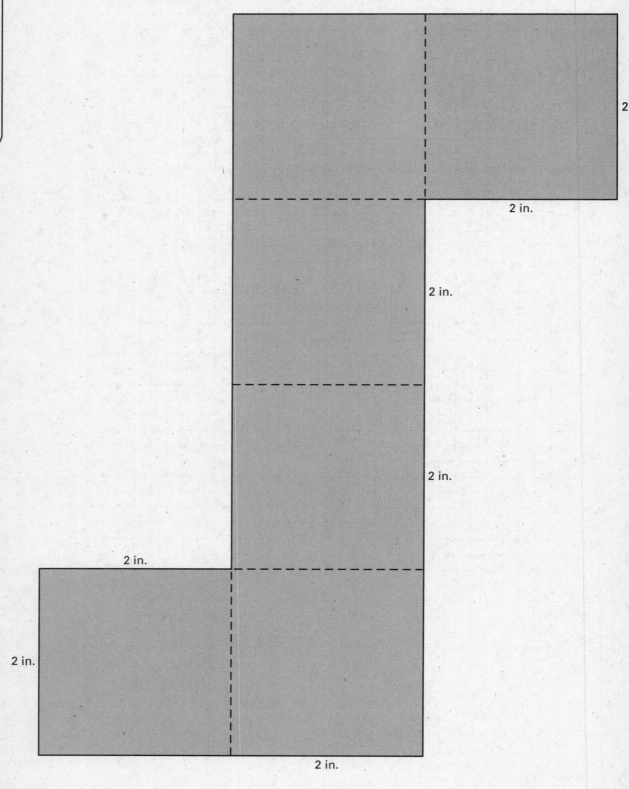

Math Intervention
Teacher's Edition

Activity Masters

Activity Master for Activity 6-14

Pattern for 4 in. × 2 in. × 1 in. Box

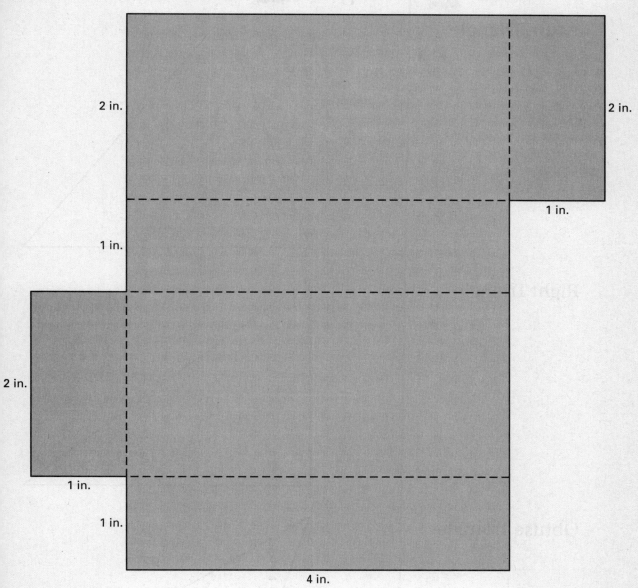

Activity Master for Activity 6-23
Triangle Patterns

Acute Triangle

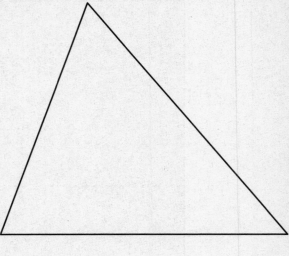

Right Triangle

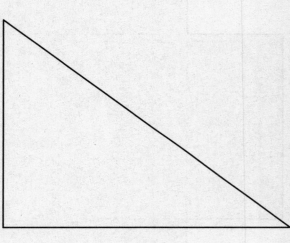

Obtuse Triangle

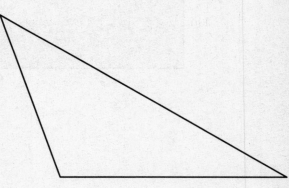

Powers of 4 Cards

4^4	4^3	4^2	4^1	4^0
4^{-1}	4^{-2}	4^{-3}	4^{-4}	
256	64	16	4	1
$\dfrac{1}{4}$	$\dfrac{1}{16}$	$\dfrac{1}{64}$	$\dfrac{1}{256}$	

Answers

Answers to Pre-Course Diagnostic Test

1. B **2.** D **3.** C **4.** A **5.** B **6.** A **7.** D **8.** C
9. D **10.** A **11.** C **12.** B **13.** B **14.** D **15.** D
16. C **17.** B **18.** A **19.** D **20.** C **21.** B **22.** D
23. A **24.** C **25.** A **26.** C **27.** D **28.** A **29.** D
30. B **31.** A **32.** B **33.** C **34.** C **35.** A **36.** D
37. D **38.** B **39.** C **40.** D **41.** A **42.** C **43.** B
44. D **45.** B **46.** B **47.** D **48.** C **49.** A **50.** C
51. B **52.** D **53.** A **54.** D **55.** C **56.** A **57.** B
58. B **59.** C **60.** D

Answers to Book 1 Test

1. commutative **2.** associative **3.** A, Z
4. C, Y **5.** B, X **6.** 48 **7.** 362 **8.** 259 **9.** 123
10.

248 250 252 254 256 258 260 262 264

11. B **12.** $5000 + 200 + 40$ **13.** $300 + 6$
14. $40 + 2$ **15.** 431, 432, 433, 435 **16.** 678,
768, 786, 876 **17.** 6,000,000 **18.** 32,000
19. 400 **20.** 20¢ **21.** $4 + 12 = 16$; $12 + 4 = 16$; $16 - 12 = 4$; $16 - 4 = 12$

22. *Sample answer:*

23. 95 **24.** 17 **25.** 20 **26.** 98 **27.** 73
28. 52 **29.** 90 **30.** 983 **31.** 24,582 **32.** 5 more
tapes **33.** 1 more tape **34.** 70 **35.** 257 **36.** 675
37. A **38.** B **39.** 83 **40.** 30 **41.** 67 **42.** 94
43. D **44.** 6, 12, 18, 24, 30, 36, 42, 48; 42
45. 9 **46.** 128 **47.** 208 **48.** 9400 **49.** 15,700
50. 360 **51.** 17,050 **52.** 499,422 **53.** 2489
54. 500 **55.** C **56.** D **57.** false; *Sample
answer:* $1 \cdot 14 = 14$, not 1 **58.** 3^{13} **59.** A **60.** B
61. *Sample answer:* Add 26 three times and
then add 1 to see if the total is 79. $26 + 26 + 26 + 1 = 79$, so the quotient checks.
62. *Sample answer:* 3^6 is three to the sixth power.
It means that 3 is multiplied by itself 6 times.
To evaluate, multiply $3 \cdot 3 \cdot 3 \cdot 3 \cdot 3 \cdot 3 = 729$.
63. *Sample answer:* The school earns $12 for
each cake, and there are 722 cakes, so multiply
722×12 to get 8664. The school earns a total
of $8664. **64.** Catherine, Sheila, Mel, Helen
65. no; *Sample answer:* 4682 rounds up to 4700
because the 8 in the tens' place is greater than or
equal to 5. 4619 rounds down to 4600 because the
1 in the tens' place is less than 5.

66. *Sample answer:*

67. *Sample answer:* To find the houses left to sell,
subtract $18 - 7$ to get 11. There are 11 houses
left to sell. **68.** *Sample answer:* You can write
the numbers in columns and then add the ones,
then the tens, and then the hundreds, regrouping
as necessary. So, $3560 + 2840 + 1150 = 7550$.
The total amount Eliza spent was $7550.

Answers to Book 2 Test

1. prime **2.** numerator **3.** denominator;
improper fraction; numerator; denominator
4. D **5.** C **6.** A **7.** B **8.** 2^4 **9.** $2^2 \cdot 5 \cdot 7$
10. $5 \cdot 103$ **11.** A **12.** D **13.** $\frac{5}{8}$ **14.** $\frac{2}{9}$
15. *Sample answer:* $\frac{2}{12}, \frac{3}{18}, \frac{4}{24}$ **16.** *Sample
answer:* $\frac{8}{10}, \frac{12}{15}, \frac{16}{20}$ **17.** *Sample answer:* $\frac{6}{28}, \frac{9}{42},$
$\frac{12}{56}$ **18.** $\frac{5}{9}$ **19.** 1 **20.** $\frac{3}{4}$ **21.** B **22.** $\frac{4}{17}, \frac{3}{8}, \frac{5}{12}$
23. $\frac{5}{3}$

24. $\frac{11}{5}$

25. $2\frac{1}{3}$ **26.** $5\frac{4}{9}$ **27.** $1\frac{9}{11}$ **28.** B **29.** $6\frac{8}{9} < \frac{64}{9}$ or
$\frac{64}{9} > 6\frac{8}{9}$ **30.** $\frac{5}{9}$ **31.** 1 **32.** $\frac{2}{3}$ **33.** D **34.** $\frac{7}{18}$ **35.** $\frac{5}{8}$
36. $\frac{2}{15}$ **37.** D **38.** $7\frac{1}{12}$ **39.** $6\frac{1}{4}$ **40.** $4\frac{3}{40}$ **41.** $2\frac{1}{3}$
42. $1\frac{4}{5}$ **43.** $2\frac{7}{12}$ **44.** A **45.** $2\frac{6}{7}$ **46.** $\frac{3}{7}$ **47.** $\frac{3}{88}$
48. D **49.** B **50.** 4 **51.** $7\frac{1}{5}$ **52.** $2\frac{3}{5}$ **53.** B **54.** A
55. D **56.** $\frac{19}{25}$ **57.** 2.8 **58.** $\begin{array}{r} 104.25 \\ 218.04 \\ \hline \end{array}$; 322.29
59. A **60.** B **61.** $\begin{array}{r} 17.74 \\ -12.0183 \\ \hline \end{array}$; 5.7217 **62.** 0.32
63. 0.18 **64.** 0.0684 **65.** 0.07 **66.** 30 **67.** 500

Answers continued

68. B **69.** D **70.** A **71.** 6 participants; *Sample answer:* The greatest common factor of 18 and 78 is 6. This is the largest number of participants Mrs. Gregg can arrange in equal rows without mixing team members and students. **72.** 32 books; *Sample answer:* The fraction of paperback books on the top shelf is $\frac{7}{16}$. To find the total number of books on the second shelf, I completed the equivalent fraction $\frac{7}{16} = \frac{14}{?}$ to get 32 books. **73.** no; *Sample answer:* Kirk multiplies 2 by the whole number, numerator, and denominator and then simplifies the fraction. He should have written $5\frac{3}{8}$ as $\frac{43}{8}$, then multiplied $\frac{43}{8} \times 2$ to get $\frac{86}{8} = \frac{43}{4} = 10\frac{3}{4}$.

74. *Sample answer:* Compare the decimals, 3.46, 3.48, and 3.47 to find that 3.46 is the least amount. Multiply 1.15 by 3.46 to get 3.979 and round to the nearest hundredth to get $3.98. **75.** *Sample answer:* Write $15\frac{5}{8}$ as 15.625 and compare the decimals. Since $15.75 > 15.625$, you should get the cable that measures 15.75 feet. **76.** *Sample answer:* Subtract $142.75 - 62.12$ to get 80.63. Multiply 7.51×3 to get 22.53. Subtract $80.63 - 22.53$ to get 58.10. Divide $58.10 \div 2$ to get 29.05. She puts $29.05 in the bank and has $29.05 left.

Answers to Book 3 Test

1. opposite **2.** negative **3.** A, Y **4.** C, X **5.** B, Z

6.

7. B **8.** B **9.** -19 and 19 **10.** $-16, -12, 14, 15$ **11.** A **12.** C

13.

14. $-15.69, -15\frac{2}{9}, 15.408, 15\frac{4}{5}$ **15.** Check students' drawings; 3 **16.** -35 **17.** -120 **18.** Check students' drawings; -7 **19.** 68 **20.** -13 **21.** -38 **22.** C **23.** -36 **24.** 24 **25.** 90 **26.** D **27.** -16 **28.** 5 **29.** -4 **30.** C **31.** subtraction **32.** addition **33.** $4\frac{1}{10}$ **34.** -21.98 **35.** -2.814 **36.** $3\frac{1}{3}$ **37.** B **38.** 343 **39.** $\frac{32}{243}$ **40.** 79.507 **41.** *Sample answer:* The change

in the number of baskets Lindsay scored is $15 - 9 = 6$ baskets. Since the number of baskets decreased, the sign of the integer should be negative, so the change can be represented by -6 baskets. **42.** *Sample answer:* I can show that 11 is a rational number by writing it as the quotient of two integers. Since $\frac{11}{1} = 11$, then 11 is a rational number. **43.** 3.65 inches wide; *Sample answer:* She needs to use a frame that is wider than $3\frac{5}{8}$ inches. Since $3\frac{5}{8} = 3.625$ and $3.625 < 3.65$, she should use the frame that is 3.65 inches wide. The other frame at $3\frac{4}{9}$ inches wide is even smaller because $3\frac{4}{9} = 3.\overline{4}$ and $3.625 > 3.\overline{4}$, so $3\frac{5}{8} > 3\frac{4}{9}$. **44.** *Sample answer:* Subtract -15 from -40. $-40 - (-15) = -25$, so the change in elevation is -25 feet. **45.** $12(-4) = -48$; *Sample answer:* Henry deducts $48 from his toll account after making 12 trips to visit his uncle. **46.** negative; *Sample answer:* The quotient will be negative because the integers in the expression have different signs. **47.** *Sample answer:* Subtract $9 - 7$ to get 2 term papers to grade from the first ones turned in. Subtract $15 - 9$ to get 6 additional term papers. Add $6 + 2$ to get 8 term papers she has yet to grade. **48.** *Sample answer:* Multiply 14 by $3\frac{1}{8}$ to get $43\frac{3}{4}$ pounds for the weight of Ron's package.

Answers to Book 4 Test

1. divide **2.** left **3.** cross products **4.** B **5.** C **6.** A **7.** *Sample answer:* 14 to 19; $\frac{14}{19}$ **8.** 3 books per month **9.** 70 lamps per hour **10.** 42 hg $\times$ 100, 4200 g $\div$ 0.001 **11.** 1400 cm $\times$ 0.01 **12.** 250 mL $\times$ 0.001, 0.25 L $\div$ 0.1 **13.** 540 min $\div$ 60 **14.** 8 mi $\times$ 1760 **15.** 3 qt $\times$ 2, 6 pt $\times$ 2, 12 c $\times$ 8 **16.** 50°F **17.** 140 cubic feet **18.** A **19.** C **20.** C **21.** $\frac{7}{25}$ **22.** 0.07 **23.** 45% **24.** 72% **25.** 2% **26.** 85% **27.** 12.5% **28.** 34.375% **29.** 15 **30.** 84 **31.** decrease; 60% **32.** increase; 35% **33.** D **34.** B **35.** C **36.** $75 **37.** $458.41 **38.** C **39.** $\frac{6}{25}$ **40.** $\frac{9}{50}$

41. *Sample answer:* The ratio at Van's is $\frac{15}{75}$, and the ratio at Jim's is $\frac{10}{25} = \frac{30}{75}$. Since $\frac{30}{75} > \frac{15}{75}$, the ratio is greater at Jim's Office Supply.

42. *Sample answer:* Divide 60 by 0.001 to get 60,000. Karlie has 60,000 mm of red material.
43. *Sample answer:* Divide 144 by 2 to get 72 quarts. Divide 72 by 4 to get 18. Henao has 18 gallons of filtered water. **44.** *Sample answer:* Write the fraction $\frac{5 \text{ boys}}{9 \text{ girls}}$ to represent the ratio in Mr. Janson's class. Set this equal to $\frac{x \text{ boys}}{27 \text{ girls}}$ to represent the ratio in Mrs. Reid's class, keeping like parts of the ratio across from each other to write the proportion $\frac{5 \text{ boys}}{9 \text{ girls}} = \frac{x \text{ boys}}{27 \text{ girls}}$. Find cross products to solve the proportion. So, $135 = 9x$ and $x = 135 \div 9$, or 15. There are 15 boys in Mrs. Reid's class. **45.** *Sample answer:* Let x represent the number of stamps that were given to Dee by friends. Write the fraction $\frac{60}{100}$ to represent 60%. Set up the proportion $\frac{60}{100} = \frac{x}{415}$ and solve to find that $x = 249$. This means that 249 stamps in Dee's collection came from friends. **46.** increase; 24%; *Sample answer:* Since $186 > 150$, the percent of change is an increase. To find the percent of change I wrote and simplified the expression $\frac{186 - 150}{150}$ to get 0.24. Then I wrote 0.24 as 24%. **47.** *Sample answer:* Multiply 0.03 by 152,500 to get 4575. She earned a commission of $4575. **48.** *Sample answer:* Use the formula $I = Prt$. Substitute 7000 for P, 0.08 for r, and 3 for t. Evaluate $I = (7000)(0.08)(3)$ to get $I = 1680$. Kirsten will pay $1680 in interest. **49.** *Sample answer:* Use the formula $A = P(1 + r)^t$. Substitute 815 for P, 0.035 for r, and 5 for t. Evaluate $A = 815(1 + 0.035)^5$ to get about 967.96433. There will be about $967.96 in Leonard's account after 5 years. **50.** *Sample answer:* There are 4 numbers on the cube that are not even numbers and 8 total numbers on the cube. The probability of not rolling an even number is $\frac{4}{8}$ or $\frac{1}{2}$.

Answers to Book 5 Test

1. division **2.** inverse **3.** B, X **4.** A, Z **5.** C, Y
6. 21, 26

7.

8. B **9.** 40 **10.** 11 **11.** 6
12. *Sample answer:* $4n - 3$ **13.** B **14.** A
15. C **16.** $12(2) + 12(4) + 12(8)$; 168

17. $9(14 + 5 + 11)$; 270 **18.** D
19. $8x^2 + 22x - 5$ **20.** $x = -15.8$ **21.** $y = 9$
22. $a = 32$ **23.** $b = -9$ **24.** D **25.** D **26.** A
27. $y = -3x$

28–33.

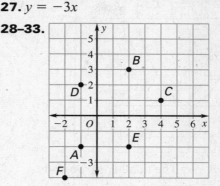

34.

x	−1	0	1	2
y	−5	−3	−1	1

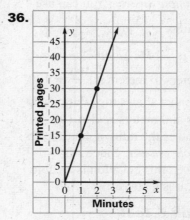

35. $-\frac{2}{3}$

36.

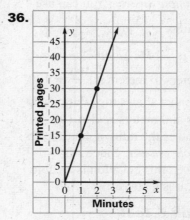

37. C **38.** $48

39.

x	−2	−1	0	1	2
y	2	$\frac{1}{2}$	0	$\frac{1}{2}$	2

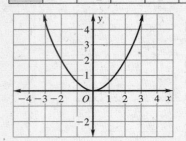

40. *Sample answer:* The number of words is being multiplied by 4 each month, so after the fifth month, Kerr will have learned 384 × 4, or 1536 words, and by end of the sixth month, she will have learned 1536 × 4, or 6144 words.

41. *Sample answer:* Let w represent the number of ties Vladimir sold last week. Then $w + 6 = 114$ because 114 ties is 6 more than he sold last week. To solve the equation $w + 6 = 114$, subtract 6 from each side to get $w = 108$. So, Vladimir sold 108 ties last week. **42.** no; *Sample answer:* Each of 15 students got a coupon, so the instructor had to have started with at least 15 coupons. Since 5 is less than 15, your answer is not reasonable. **43.** *Sample answer:* (6, 2), (7, 3), (8, 4), (9, 5) **44.** *Sample answer:* The y-values are the same for each x-value, so the line is horizontal. **45.** *Sample answer:* You can use the formula $\frac{y_2 - y_1}{x_2 - x_1}$. Since $\frac{15 - 7}{12 - (-2)} = \frac{8}{14} = \frac{4}{7}$, the slope of the line is $\frac{4}{7}$. **46.** *Sample answer:* The ratio of centimeters to meters is $\frac{100}{1}$ or 100. The slope of the line that shows the relationship between centimeters and meters is also 100 because it is the same as the ratio of centimeters to meters. **47.** *Sample answer:* Since x is raised to the 3rd power, this equation is a cubic equation. Therefore, it is a curve.

Answers to Book 6 Test

1. surface area **2.** perfect square **3.** C, X **4.** A, Y **5.** B, Z **6.** C **7.** 1 occurs 1 time, 3 occurs 2 times, and 5 occurs 3 times

8.

walnuts	‖‖‖
pecans	‖‖‖ ‖‖
hazelnuts	‖‖‖ ‖‖‖ ‖
almonds	‖‖‖ ‖‖‖ ‖‖

9. $\frac{15}{82}$ **10.** $\frac{13}{25}$ or 0.52 **11.** 4 in. **12.** 24 cm
13. a. Check students' drawings. **b.** 10 in.² **14.** 48 in.² **15.** 60 cm² **16. a.** 37.68 m **b.** 15.7 in. **17. a.** 3.14 ft² **b.** 50.24 cm² **18.** 54 in.² **19. a.** *Sample answer*: EPQF, FQRG, SRGH, EPSH, PQRS, EFGH **b.** 228 m² **20. a.** 48 m³ **b.** 175 ft³ **21.** 192π cm³ **22. a.** 60° **b.** 125° **23. a.** acute **b.** right **24. a.** 76°; 166° **b.** no complement; 62° **c.** 61°; 151° **d.** 4°; 94° **25. a.** right **b.** obtuse **26.** isosceles **27. a.** 131° **b.** 20° **c.** 10° **28. a.** 92° **b.** 138° **c.** 50° **29. a.** 5 **b.** −7.9 **c.** −10.7 **d.** 9.8 **30. a.** 17 **b.** 15.9 **31.** yes **32. a.** perpendicular **b.** parallel **33.** A **34.** B **35.** A **36.** *Sample answer:* First find the total number of items by adding them all together. Then add to find the total number of hand towels. Finally divide the total number of hand towels by the total number of items. There are 70 total items and 35 hand towels. $\frac{35}{70} = \frac{1}{2}$ **37.** *Sample answer:* To find the perimeter, add 24 + 24 + 28 + 28 to get 104 m. To find the area, multiply the width (24) by the length (28) to get 672 m². **38.** *Sample answer:* Find the area of Mark's parallelogram: 14 × 3 = 42 cm². Divide this area by the base of Holly's parallelogram (42 ÷ 7) to get a height of 6 cm. **39.** *Sample answer:* Multiply the area of the base (14) by the height of the prism (8) to get 112 in.³. **40.** no; *Sample answer*: The triangle could be acute if the third angle is also acute, such as 75°, 65°, and 40°. The triangle could be right if the third angle is 90°, such as 45°, 45°, 90°. The triangle could be obtuse if the third angle is obtuse, such as 15°, 16°, and 149°. **41.** no; *Sample answer:* The sum of the measures of the given angles is 350°, and the sum of the measures of the angles of a quadrilateral must be 360°. **42.** *Sample answer:* Let x represent the distance Miriam walks. Use the Pythagorean Theorem to write $50^2 + 30^2 = x^2$ and simplify to solve for x. In this case, x is approximately 58.3, so Miriam walks about 58.3 feet. **43.** *Sample answer:* Write and simplify a fraction that compares the pair of corresponding sides in the two rectangles. The ratio of similarity is $\frac{15}{18}$ or $\frac{5}{6}$.

Answers to Book 7 Test

1. fractional **2.** coefficient **3.** zero **4.** add **5.** B **6.** C **7.** A **8.** A **9.** C **10.** A **11.** B

12. $b = 1$;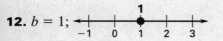

13. $b = -14$;

14. $-$; $+$ **15.** $\times$ **16.** B **17.** A

18. $y \le 2$;

19. $y < 4$;

20. $\le$ **21.** $<$ **22.** $\frac{1}{64}$ **23.** $\frac{1}{81}$ **24.** 1 **25.** 3^{-3}

26. $\frac{a^6}{b^8}$ **27.** $\frac{1}{x^4 y^5}$ **28.** $\frac{v^2}{w^9}$ **29.** C **30.** A **31.** B

32. $c^6 d^2$ **33.** $\frac{m^2}{p^4}$ **34.** true **35.** true **36.** false

37. 80 **38.** 4 **39.** 24 **40.** A **41.** C **42.** B

43. $x^{12} y^3 z^3$ **44.** $5g^7 h^{12} k^6$ **45.** $16 b^4 c^4$ **46.** B

47. 15 **48.** $\frac{1}{32}$ **49.** 27 **50.** D **51.** false

52. true **53.** A **54.** 16 **55.** *Sample answer*: Seven-eighths is equal to four more than a number divided by five. **56.** $9p + 27 = 135$; $p = 12$; *Sample answer:* Let p represent the number of days it will take for Rory to finish scanning. So the term $9p$ represents scanning 9 photos a day. Add 27 to represent the photos she has already scanned. Set this equal to the total number of photos she has to scan, or 135. To solve the equation $9p + 27 = 135$, subtract 27 from each side and then divide by 9.
57. *Sample answer*: You start with 1250 spools of yarn. If you make 3 equal shipments of 125 spools of yarn, then you must subtract 3×125, or 375 spools of yarn from the original 1250. Since $1250 - 375$ leaves 875 spools of yarn, Ken's claim is reasonable. **58.** $25 + 3b > 50$; $b > 8\frac{1}{3}$; *Sample answer:* Let b represent the boxes of cereal. So the term $3b$ represents what Alex spends on cereal. Add this to the \$25 he spends on produce. The sum $25 + 3b$ is greater than 50 because he spends over \$50, so the linear inequality is $25 + 3b > 50$. Alex bought 9 or more boxes of cereal. **59.** $\left(\frac{3}{5}\right)^2 = \frac{9}{25}$; *Sample answer:* She reduces the original photo to $\frac{3}{5}$ its original size and reduces the first

reduction to $\frac{3}{5}$ its size, so you multiply $\frac{3}{5} \cdot \frac{3}{5}$, which is $\left(\frac{3}{5}\right)^2$. **60.** *Sample answer:* $(81)^{\frac{3}{4}}$ is the same as $\left(\sqrt[4]{81}\right)^3$. Take the fourth root of 81, which is 3. Then cube 3 to get 27.

Answers *continued*

ANSWERS

Answers to Book 1 Whole Numbers

Activity 1-1, pp. 2–3
Example 2: Step 1. 4; 5
Example 3: Step 1. 100; 10; 2
Practice: 1. 41 **2.** 33 **3.** 50

4.
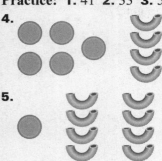

5.

6.
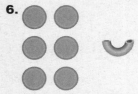

7. 245 is two hundreds, four tens, and five ones;

8. 67 **9.** 89 **10.** 90 **11.** 709 **12.** 592

Lesson 1-2, pp. 4–7
Try this: 1. 432 **2.** 307 **3.** 625, 626, 629, 630, 631 **4.** 993, 996, 997, 999, 1000 **5.** odd **6.** even **7.** even **8.** odd
Practice: 1. 160 **2.** 347 **3.** 405 **4.** 234 **5.** 100, 103, 105, 106 **6.** 397, 398, 400, 401, 402 **7.** 753, 754, 756, 758, 759 **8.** odd **9.** even **10.** even **11.** odd **12.** odd **13.** even **14.** odd **15.** even **16.** 1030, 1032 **17.** six **18.** 101; odd; 99; odd **19.** hundreds; tens; ones **20.** 996, 997, 998, 999, 1000 **21.** no; *Sample answer:* You look only at the ones' place to tell if a number is odd or even.

Lesson 1-3, pp. 8–11
Try this: 1. 36, 42, 44, 48 **2.** 259, 263, 265, 269 **3.** 4, 10, 12, 16 **4.** 12, 18, 20, 24 **5.** 60¢ **6.** 80¢ **7.** 35¢ **8.** 45¢
Practice: 1. 10, 25, 30 **2.** 60, 62, 66, 68 **3.** 500, 520, 550, 560, 580 **4.** 613, 617, 619, 625, 627 **5.** 125, 145, 155, 175 **6.** 22, 37, 42, 52 **7.** 50¢ **8.** 20¢ **9.** 35¢ **10.** no; *Sample answer:* The next winner will have ticket number 707.

11.

| 5¢ | 10¢ | 15¢ | 20¢ | 25¢ |

5 nickels **12.** 21 miles **13.** 120; 130 **14.** even; *Sample answer:* Odds and evens alternate. Therefore, if you skip count every other number, you will skip over all the odd numbers.
15. Check students' work.

Lesson 1-4, pp. 12–15
Try this: 1.

Hundreds	Tens	Ones
4	2	3

2.

Hundreds	Tens	Ones
1	4	6

3.

Thousands	Hundreds	Tens	Ones
2	4	0	5

4. 3000 + 700 + 8 **5.** 9000 + 100 + 40 + 5
Practice:

1.

Hundreds	Tens	Ones
4	4	7

2.

Thousands	Hundreds	Tens	Ones
3	0	0	5

3.

Thousands	Hundreds	Tens	Ones
1	1	6	0

4. 100 + 50 + 9 **5.** 200 + 60 + 4 **6.** 300 + 80 + 7 **7.** 100 + 7 **8.** 300 + 30 **9.** 600 + 90 **10.** 1000 + 1 **11.** 4000 + 800 + 90 **12.** 4000 + 900 + 6 **13.** 7000 + 20 **14.** 8000 + 40 + 4 **15.** 9000 + 700 + 10 + 9 **16.** *Sample answer:* 80 is 8 tens, so 8 guides meet the students.

17.

Thousands	Hundreds	Tens	Ones
1	4	6	6

1000 + 400 + 60 + 6 **18.** 4 $100 bills, 7 $10 bills, and 2 $1 bills **19.** hundreds; ones **20.** In 1520, the 5 represents 500. In 1250, the 5 represents 50. **21.** *Sample answers:* 342, 1345, 2340

Lesson 1-5, pp. 16–19
Try this: 1. 5 **2.** 9 **3.** 7 **4.** 11 **5.** 541 > 218 **6.** 743 < 748 **7.**

```
              205 215
   ●    ●   ●    ●   ●
  180  190  200  210  220  230
```

Answers continued

8.
360 370 380 390 400 410

Practice: 1. < **2.** > **3.** = **4.** > **5.** < **6.** < **7.** <
8. = **9.** < **10.** > **11.** > **12.** = **13.** > **14.** > **15.** <
16.
98 101
85 90 95 100 105 110 115

17.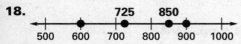
531 533
520 525 530 535

18.
725 850
500 600 700 800 900 1000

19. 18, 19, 23, 33 **20.** 41, 48, 50, 55 **21.** 95, 99, 100, 101 **22.** 115, 118, 119, 120 **23.** 195, 196, 198, 201 **24.** 380, 381, 383, 384 **25.** 135, 242, 280, 530 **26.** 168, 618, 681, 861 **27.** Beth, Camille, Donna, Andre **28.** length of Louise < length of Topaz **29.** 7 P.M., 1 P.M., 10 A.M., 4 P.M. **30.** tens, ones **31.** The greater number is on the right. *Sample answer:* On a number line, the numbers increase in value as you move to the right. **32.** 13 < 18; *Sample answer:* Use the symbol that points to the lesser number.

Lesson 1-6, pp. 20–23
Try this: 1. 729,000 **2.** 43,000 **3.** 800,000 **4.** 4,000,000 **5.** 18,700 **6.** 38,800 **7.** 750,000 **8.** 90,000
Practice: 1. tens **2.** hundreds **3.** thousands **4.** ten thousands **5.** hundreds'; up; less than; 6; 3; 0; 43,000 **6.** 1100 **7.** 26,000 **8.** 3,900,000 **9.** 107,000 **10.** 32,300 **11.** 700,000 **12.** 101,000 **13.** 200,000 **14.** 40,000 **15.** 7020 **16.** 80,000 **17.** 2,330,000 **18.** 1600 **19.** 20,060 **20.** 20,000 **21.** 11,000 **22.** 23,530 **23.** 6,980,000 **24.** 1100 **25.** 480,000 **26.** 800,000 **27.** 27,000 **28.** 22,000 **29.** $48,400 **30.** tens'; greater; up **31.** *Sample answer:* When you round 6972 to the nearest hundred, you round up because the tens' digit is greater than or equal to 5. If you add 1 to the hundreds' column, you get 10. This means you rename 69 hundreds as 70 hundreds, or 7000. **32.** *Sample answer:* 6805, 6849, 6800

Mixed Practice for Lessons 1-2 to 1-6, pp. 24–25
1. B, X **2.** A, Y **3.** addition **4.** 6 **5.** 207 **6.** 433 **7.** even **8.** even **9.** odd **10.** odd
11.
20 30 40 50 60 70 80 90 100 110

12.
52 62 72 82 92 102 112 122 132 142

13.
10 30 50 70 90 110 130 150 170 190

14.
200 400 600 800 1000 1200 1400 1600 1800 2000

15. 60 **16.** 350 **17.** 7000 + 400 + 3 **18.** 600 + 80 + 8 **19.** 2000 + 1 **20.** 100 + 9 **21.** 190, 202, 212, 240 **22.** 270, 310, 340, 380 **23.** < **24.** > **25.** > **26.** < **27.** > **28.** > **29.** 50 **30.** 2000 **31.** 80,000 **32.** 3,458,000 **33.** 1039, 1041; *Sample answer:* Each number is 2 apart, so add 2 two times. **34.** no; *Sample answer:* Since the numbers are 100 apart, if you add 100 to 28,952, you get 29,052. **35.** yes; *Sample answer:* The 4 in 1042 is worth 40, while the 4 in 1402 is worth 400.

Activity 1-7, pp. 26–27
Example: Step 1. 14 **Step 2.** 14 **Step 3.** 8 **Step 4.** 8 **Step 5.** 21, 9
Make It a Game: Check students' work; *Sample answers:* 7 + 6 = 13, 13 − 6 = 7; 7 + 12 = 19, 19 − 7 = 12; 5 + 15 = 20, 20 − 15 = 5; 20 + 50 = 70, 70 − 20 = 50
Practice: 1. *Sample answers:* 12 + 7 = 19; 7 + 12 = 19; 19 − 7 = 12; 19 − 12 = 7 **2.** 57 − 18 = 39; 57 − 39 = 18 **3.** 60 cents **4.** 20 cents **5.** *Sample answer:* Since 48 + 18 = 66, the result of 66 − 48 − 18 is 0; It checks. **6.** 60; 60 **7.** 22; 22

Lesson 1-8, pp. 28–31
Try this: 1. *Sample answers:* 4 + 6 = 10, 6 + 4 = 10, 10 − 4 = 6, 10 − 6 = 4 **2.** *Sample answers:* 1 + 9 = 10, 9 + 1 = 10, 10 − 1 = 9, 10 − 9 = 1 **3.** 80 + 20 = 100; Check students' drawings. **4.** 50 + 50 = 100; Check students' drawings. **5.** Check students' work; *Sample answer:* 11 + 9, 11 + 2 + 7, 11 + 3 + 6, 11 + 4 + 5, 11 + 3 + 3 + 3, 11 + 2 + 2 + 5, 11 + 5 + 2 + 2, 11 + 3 + 3 + 1 + 2
Practice: 1. 2 + 8 = 10, 8 + 2 = 10, 10 − 2 = 8, 10 − 8 = 2 **2.** 5 + 15 = 20, 15 + 5 = 20, 20 − 5 = 15, 20 − 15 = 5 **3.** 40 + 60 = 100, 60 + 40 = 100, 100 − 40 = 60, 100 − 60 = 40 **4.** 30 + 20 = 50; Check students' drawings. **5.** 10 + 50 = 60; Check students' drawings. **6.** Check students' work; *Sample answer:* 13 + 7, 13 + 2 + 5, 13 + 3 + 4, 13 + 4 + 3, 13 + 3 + 3 + 1, 13 + 2 + 2 + 3, 13 + 5 + 2,

Answers continued

13 + 3 + 1 + 2 + 1 **7.** add; Check students' drawings; *Sample answer:* one $10 bill, three $5 bills, and three $1 bills; two $10 bills, one $5 bill, and three $1 bills; one $10 bill, two $5 bills, and eight $1 bills **8.** add; Check students' drawings; *Sample answer:* three 5-cent stamps, three 2-cent stamps, and one 1-cent stamp; two 5-cent stamps, five 2-cent stamps, and two 1-cent stamps; one 5-cent stamp, seven 2-cent stamps, and three 1-cent stamps **9.** add; minus
10. Check students' work; *Sample answer:*
5 + 3, 2 + 6, 9 − 1 **11.** *Sample answer:* In a game, John earned 10 points for landing on red and 90 points for giving a correct answer. How many total points did John earn on his turn? 10 represents points for landing on red. 90 represents points for giving a correct answer. To find the solution add 10 + 90 = 100. The 100 represents the total points John earned on his turn.

Lesson 1-9, pp. 32–35
Try this: 1. Check students' drawings.
2. Check students' drawings. **3.** F **4.** G **5.** C
6. E **7.** A **8.** H **9.** D **10.** I **11.** B **12.** R **13.** Q
14. N **15.** L **16.** J **17.** P **18.** O **19.** M **20.** K
Practice: 1. Check students' drawings.
2. Check students' drawings. **3.** *Sample answer:*
20 − 20 = 0 **4.** *Sample answer:* 12 − 7 = 5
5. *Sample answer:* 16 − 2 = 14 **6.** *Sample answer:* 14 − 8 = 6 **7.** *Sample answer:*
17 − 1 = 16 **8.** *Sample answer:* 20 − 9 = 11
9. *Sample answer:* 12 + 0 = 12 **10.** *Sample answer:* 4 + 3 = 7 **11.** *Sample answer:*
18 + 2 = 20 **12.** *Sample answer:* 8 + 8 = 16
13. *Sample answer:* 8 + 1 = 9 **14.** *Sample answer:* 14 + 5 = 19 **15.** subtract, 15 − 9 = 6;
Check students' drawings. **16.** subtract,
19 − 8 = 11; Check students' drawings.
17. addition, fact family **18.** *Sample answer:*
16 is the sum because it is the greatest number.

Lesson 1-10, pp. 36–39
Try this: 1. 37 **2.** 42 **3.** 20 **4.** 20 **5.** 22 **6.** 21
7. 23 **8.** 30
Practice: 1. identity **2.** commutative
3. associative **4.** 27 **5.** 15 **6.** 33 **7.** 0 **8.** 2; 4;
2; 10; 10; 20 **9.** 20 **10.** 10 **11.** 20 **12.** 10
13. 20 **14.** 19 **15.** They each have $13. Yes, they can each buy a ticket. **16.** They each have $18. **17.** 9 purple martins **18.** the number, the number **19.** Check students' drawings.

Lesson 1-11, pp. 40–43
Try this: 1. 63 **2.** 27 **3.** 70 **4.** 70 **5.** 65
6. 28 **7.** 79 **8.** 59
Practice: 1. B **2.** D **3.** A **4.** C **5.** 38 **6.** 89
7. 77 **8.** 36 **9.** 98 **10.** 85 **11.** 97 **12.** 68
13. 69 **14.** 82 **15.** 67 **16.** 97 people **17.** 86
text messages **18.** 99 pages **19.** tens', ones'
20. *Sample answer:* Doug wrote the 5 in the tens' place instead of the ones' place. **21.** 48;
Check students' drawings.

Lesson 1-12, pp. 44–47
Try this: 1. 2 tens and 2 ones; 22 **2.** 3 tens and 1 one; 31 **3.** 4 tens and 5 ones; 45 **4.** 7 tens and 8 ones; 78 **5.** 71 **6.** 31 **7.** 45
Practice: 1. yes; 51 **2.** yes; 32 **3.** no; 79
4. 80 **5.** 92 **6.** 80 **7.** 71 **8.** 87 **9.** 80 **10.** 44
11. 67 **12.** 89 **13.** 70 **14.** 31 **15.** 97 **16.** 62
girl scouts **17.** 31 miles **18.** 54 pounds **19.** $91
20. 0 tens and 35 ones, 1 ten and 25 ones, 2 tens and 15 ones **21.** no; *Sample answer:* If the sum of the ones is less than 10, you do not need to regroup. For example, 33 + 12 = 45, and no regrouping is needed.

Lesson 1-13, pp. 48–51
Try this: 1. 952 **2.** 4705 **3.** 543 **4.** 5126
5. 7202 **6.** 34,872
Practice: 1. Check students' work; 399
2. Check students' work; 616 **3.** Check students' work; 612 **4.** Check students' work; 900
5. Check students' work; 850 **6.** Check students' work; 460 **7.** 5700 **8.** 4246 **9.** 12,198
10. 89,112 **11.** 39,917 **12.** 92,976 **13.** 405
14. 1314 **15.** 7049 **16.** 8132 **17.** 19,115
18. 67,276 **19.** 37,757 + 9450; 47,207 miles
20. 2500 + 1550; $4050 **21.** *Sample answer:*
Two numbers with hundreds that have a sum greater than 10 will result in a 4-digit sum, such as 500 + 500 = 1000. **22.** no; *Sample answer:*
The greatest 3-digit number is 999, and even 999 + 999 has a 4-digit sum.

Lesson 1-14, pp. 52–55
Try this: 1. 10; −; 6; 4 **2.** 19; −; 10; 9
Practice: 1. 5; 2; 3 **2.** 6; 4; 2 **3.** 4; 1; 3
4. 7; 5; 2 **5.** 3; Check students' drawings **6.** 1;
Check students' drawings **7.** 6; −; 2; 4 more shirts **8.** 7; −; 4; 3 fewer shirts **9.** 9 − 7 = 2;
2 balls **10.** 10 − 4 = 6, 6 kilometers **11.** *Sample answer:* Abby has 8 tangerines. She does not eat any of them. How many tangerines are left?

Answers *continued*

12. Check students' drawings. *Sample answer:* $7 + 1$ is one more flower than before. $7 - 1$ is one less flower than before.

Lesson 1-15, pp. 56–59

Try this: 1. 6 **2.** 2 **3.** 52 **4.** 38 **5.** 30 **6.** 60
Practice: 1. B **2.** D **3.** A **4.** C **5.** 31 **6.** 13
7. 51 **8.** Check students' work; 12 **9.** Check students' work; 13 **10.** Check students' work; 60 **11.** 14 **12.** 34 **13.** 4 **14.** 31 **15.** 12 **16.** 11 **17.** 22 **18.** 10 **19.** $12 - 9 = 3$; 3 posters **20.** $27 - 14 = 13$; 13 kittens **21.** $59 - 13 = 46$; 46 episodes **22.** Subtract 6 from 9; *Sample answer:* Since 6 and 9 are both in the ones' place, you would subtract 6 ones from 9 ones. **23.** 90; Check students' models.

Lesson 1-16, pp. 60–63

Try this: 1. 36 **2.** 52 **3.** 32 **4.** 90
Practice: 1. A **2.** C **3.** 80 **4.** 115 **5.** 208 **6.** 390 **7.** 336 **8.** 543 **9.** $40 - 12 = 28$; 28 years old **10.** $210 - 170 = 40$; 40 pounds **11.** $90 - 15 = 75$; 75 degrees Fahrenheit **12.** 21; Check students' models. **13.** yes; *Sample answer:* You have to regroup 1 hundred as 10 tens for a subtraction such as $100 - 50$, and as 9 tens 10 ones to find $100 - 32$.

Lesson 1-17, pp. 64–67

Try this: 1. 34 **2.** 22 **3.** 37 **4.** 69
Practice: 1. A **2.** B **3.** C **4.** 14 **5.** 39 **6.** 27 **7.** B **8.** A **9.** $52 - 14 = 38$; \$38 **10.** $91 - 55 = 36$; 36 pages **11.** $62 - 8 = 54$; 54 inches **12.** 6; 10 **13.** *Sample answer:* Kevin is wrong in saying that you always replace the number of ones with 10 ones. You add ten to the number of ones. If you start with 0 ones, you have 10 ones after renaming, which is why Kevin's example of $50 - 19$ is correct.

Lesson 1-18, pp. 68–71

Try this: 1. 364 **2.** 643 **3.** 845 **4.** 771
Practice: 1. 494 **2.** 212 **3.** 324 **4.** 2820 **5.** 6110 **6.** 23,500 **7.** 23,041 **8.** 9937 **9.** 44,919 **10.** B **11.** A **12.** $510 - 147 = 363$; \$363 **13.** $230 - 65 = 165$; 165 miles **14.** $1000 - 99 = 901$; 901 employees **15.** tens; 9; 10 **16.** Check students' examples and explanations. *Sample answer:* Regrouping is necessary any time the digit you are subtracting has a greater value than the digit you are subtracting from.

Lesson 1-19, pp. 72–75

Try this: 1. 70 **2.** 80 **3.** 10 **4.** 40 **5.** 79 **6.** 42
Practice: 1. 80 **2.** 73 **3.** 62 **4.** 86 **5.** 60 **6.** 20 **7.** 56 **8.** 51 **9.** A **10.** C **11.** B **12.** A **13.** B **14.** B **15.** C **16.** add; \$80 **17.** subtract; 26 miles **18.** subtract; 1983 **19.** *Sample answer:* It is the same because of the commutative property of addition. The order in which you add addends does not matter. **20.** *Sample answer:* You know Dianne made a mistake because any positive number you add to 30 should have a sum greater than 30. Dianne's error was counting on by ones three times. She should have counted on by tens three times to get 47.

Lesson 1-20, pp. 76–79

Try this: 1. 9 **2.** 14 **3.** 49 **4.** 67 **5.** 66 **6.** 129 **7.** 704 **8.** 754
Practice: 1. 99 **2.** 97 **3.** 79 **4.** 87 **5.** 75 **6.** 98 **7.** 156 **8.** 208 **9.** 324 **10.** 710 **11.** 471 **12.** 995 **13.** A **14.** B **15.** C **16.** 18 inches **17.** \$69 **18.** 610 miles **19.** *Sample answer:* It is easier to add multiples of ten to other numbers. **20.** *Sample answer:* Ezekiel added $45 + 11$ to get 56 and then stopped. He forgot to add 21 to the total to get 77.

Mixed Practice for Lessons 1-8 to 1-20, pp. 80–81

1. A, Y **2.** B, X **3.** $12 - 4 = 8$; $12 - 8 = 4$ **4.** *Sample answer:* $9 + 7 = 16$ **5.** *Sample answer:* $4 + 16 = 20$, $20 - 16 = 4$; $20 - 4 = 16$ **6.** *Sample answer:* $30 + 70 = 100$; $100 - 30 = 70$; $100 - 70 = 30$ **7.** C **8.** B **9.** D **10.** A **11.** 20 **12.** 18 **13.** 16 **14.** 20 **15.** 20 **16.** 20 **17.** 20 **18.** 20 **19.** 14 **20.** *Sample answer:* $8 + 7$; $8 + 6 + 1$; $8 + 5 + 2$; $8 + 4 + 3$; $8 + 5 + 1 + 1$; $8 + 3 + 3 + 1$ **21.** 50 **22.** 60 **23.** 48 **24.** 59 **25.** 22,112 **26.** 914 **27.** 6081 **28.** 329 **29.** 508 **30.** 486 **31.** 108 **32.** 99 **33.** 1098 **34.** 2944 **35.** 5700 **36.** 16,878 **37.** 93,748 **38.** 81,100 **39.** 909,529 **40.** 724,089 **41.** 939 **42.** 493 **43.** 82; 3; 20; 20; 20; 20; 60; 82; 60; 142 **44.** 2 ft; *Sample answer:* $14 - 1 - 3 - 8 = 13 - 3 - 8 = 10 - 8 = 2$ **45.** 1414 mi; *Sample answer:* $33,108 - 32,561 = 547$; $33,975 - 33,108 = 867$; $547 + 867 = 1414$

Lesson 1-21, pp. 82–83

Example 1: Step 2. 15 **Step 3.** 3; 15
Step 4. 2; 8

Answers *continued*

Example 2: **Step 1.** 3 **Step 2.** 3; 12
Step 3. 24; 4
Example 3: 22; 5
Practice: 1. 3; 4; 12 **2.** 12; 6; 2 **3.** 8 **4.** 24
5. 30 **6.** 25 **7.** 5 **8.** 5 **9.** 6 + R3 **10.** 2 +
R4 **11.** 100 × 5 = 500; 100 ÷ 5 = 20; *Sample conjecture:* When you multiply, the result is the total number in the 5 groups. When you divide, the result is the number in one of 5 equal groups.

Lesson 1-22, pp. 84–87
Try this: 1. 5; 5; 10; 10; 15; 100 **2.** 32nd;
2 × 32 = 64 **3.** 60; 60; 40; 4; none; 4; 0
Practice: 1. 5, 10, 15, 20, 25, 30, 35, 40, 45,
50; 40 **2.** 0 + 6 = 6; 6 + 6 = 12; 12 + 6 = 18;
18 + 6 = 24; 24 + 6 = 30; 30 + 6 = 36; 36 +
6 = 42 **3.** 0 + 9 = 9; 9 + 9 = 18; 18 + 9 = 27;
27 + 9 = 36; 36 + 9 = 45; 45 + 9 = 54; 54 +
9 = 63; 63 + 9 = 72 **4.** 0 + 11 = 11; 11 +
11 = 22; 22 + 11 = 33; 33 + 11 = 44; 44 + 11 =
55 **5.** 0 + 15 = 15; 15 + 15 = 30; 30 + 15 =
45; 45 + 15 = 60; 60 + 15 = 75 **6.** B **7.** A
8. C **9.** 15th; 5 × 15 = 75 or 15 × 5 = 75 **10.** 1,
2, 3, 4, 6, 8, 12, 24 **11.** 1, 2, 5, 10 **12.** 1, 2, 3,
5, 6, 10, 15, 30 **13.** 1, 7, 49 **14.** 1, 2, 4, 5, 10,
20; *Sample answer:* 20 ÷ 10 = 2; 20 ÷ 1 = 20;
20 ÷ 5 = 4 **15.** 28 − 7 = 21; 21 − 7 = 14;
14 − 7 = 7; 7 − 7 = 0; 4 **16.** 40 − 10 = 30;
30 − 10 = 20; 20 − 10 = 10; 10 − 10 = 0; 4
17. 32 − 5 = 27; 27 − 5 = 22; 22 − 5 = 17;
17 − 5 = 12; 12 − 5 = 7; 7 − 5 = 2; 6 R2
18. 50 − 8 = 42; 42 − 8 = 34; 34 − 8 = 26;
26 − 8 = 18; 18 − 8 = 10; 10 − 8 = 2; 6 R2
19. 5 **20.** 2 **21.** 13 **22.** 7 **23.** 6 **24.** 14 R1
25. 20 R3 **26.** 6 **27.** $15 because 5 × 3 = 15
28. 4 months because 800 ÷ 200 = 4
29. 11 months because 26 − 4 = 22 and
22 ÷ 2 = 11 **30.** 15; 3 **31.** *Sample answer:* You earned $6 babysitting for 3 weeks in a row. How much did you earn? $18 **32.** *Sample answer:*
Yes, your friend is correct because 32 ÷ 8 = 4.

Lesson 1-23, pp. 88–91
Try this: 1. 2 × 1 = 2; 2 × 2 = 4; 2 × 3 = 6;
2 × 4 = 8; 2 × 5 = 10; 2 × 6 = 12; 2 × 7 = 14;
2 × 8 = 16; 2 × 9 = 18; 2 × 10 = 20
2. 4 × 1 = 4; 4 × 2 = 8; 4 × 3 = 12; 4 × 4 = 16;
4 × 5 = 20; 4 × 6 = 24; 4 × 7 = 28; 4 × 8 =
32; 4 × 9 = 36; 4 × 10 = 40 **3. a.** ×; 3 **b.** ÷; 3
4. 1, 3, 7, and 21
Practice: 1. 1 × 1 = 1; 1 × 2 = 2; 1 × 3 = 3;

1 × 4 = 4; 1 × 5 = 5; 1 × 6 = 6; 1 × 7 = 7;
1 × 8 = 8; 1 × 9 = 9; 1 × 10 = 10 **2.** 2 ×
1 = 2; 2 × 2 = 4; 2 × 3 = 6; 2 × 4 = 8; 2 ×
5 = 10; 2 × 6 = 12; 2 × 7 = 14; 2 × 8 = 16;
2 × 9 = 18; 2 × 10 = 20 **3.** 3 × 1 = 3; 3 ×
2 = 6; 3 × 3 = 9; 3 × 4 = 12; 3 × 5 = 15; 3 ×
6 = 18; 3 × 7 = 21; 3 × 8 = 24; 3 × 9 = 27;
3 × 10 = 30 **4.** 4 × 1 = 4; 4 × 2 = 8; 4 × 3 =
12; 4 × 4 = 16; 4 × 5 = 20; 4 × 6 = 24; 4 ×
7 = 28; 4 × 8 = 32; 4 × 9 = 36; 4 × 10 = 40
5. 5 × 1 = 5; 5 × 2 = 10; 5 × 3 = 15; 5 × 4 =
20; 5 × 5 = 25; 5 × 6 = 30; 5 × 7 = 35; 5 × 8 =
40; 5 × 9 = 45; 5 × 10 = 50 **6.** 6 × 1 = 6;
6 × 2 = 12; 6 × 3 = 18; 6 × 4 = 24; 6 × 5 = 30;
6 × 6 = 36; 6 × 7 = 42; 6 × 8 = 48; 6 × 9 =
54; 6 × 10 = 60 **7.** 7 × 1 = 7; 7 × 2 = 14;
7 × 3 = 21; 7 × 4 = 28; 7 × 5 = 35; 7 × 6 = 42;
7 × 7 = 49; 7 × 8 = 56; 7 × 9 = 63; 7 × 10 =
70 **8.** 8 × 1 = 8; 8 × 2 = 16; 8 × 3 = 24; 8 ×
4 = 32; 8 × 5 = 40; 8 × 6 = 48; 8 × 7 = 56;
8 × 8 = 64; 8 × 9 = 72; 8 × 10 = 80 **9.** 9 × 1 =
9; 9 × 2 = 18; 9 × 3 = 27; 9 × 4 = 36; 9 × 5 =
45; 9 × 6 = 54; 9 × 7 = 63; 9 × 8 = 72;
9 × 9 = 81; 9 × 10 = 90 **10.** 10 × 1 = 10;
10 × 2 = 20; 10 × 3 = 30; 10 × 4 = 40;
10 × 5 = 50; 10 × 6 = 60; 10 × 7 = 70; 10 ×
8 = 80; 10 × 9 = 90; 10 × 10 = 100
11. Check students' answers. **12.** 1, 2, 3, 6
13. 1, 2, 4, 8 **14.** 1, 3, 5, 15 **15.** 1, 2, 4, 8,
16 **16.** 1, 2, 13, 26 **17.** 1, 2, 3, 4, 6, 9, 12, 18,
36 **18.** 1, 2, 4, 13, 26, 52 **19.** 1, 2, 4, 5, 8, 10,
16, 20, 40, 80 **20.** 1, 7 **21.** 1, 23 **22.** 1, 31
23. 1, 53 **24.** *Sample answer:* They have no other factors besides 1 and themselves. A prime number is a number that has only 1 and itself as factors. **25.** 6 **26.** 9 **27.** 1 **28.** 3 **29.** multiple;
$40; *Sample answer:* Since your allowance adds up, you multiply $8 × 5 = $40. **30.** factor: 10;
Sample answer: Since you divide up the amount you have to save by how much per week, you find $250 ÷ $25 = 10. **31.** *Sample answer:* 12,
20, 40 **32.** 7 teams; *Sample answer:* 28 ÷ 4 = 7

Lesson 1-24, pp. 92–95
Try this: 1. 39 **2.** 82 **3.** 60 **4.** 87 **5.** Check students' work. The product is 265. **6.** Check students' work. The product is 288.
Practice: 1. 96 **2.** 48 **3.** 48 **4.** 54 **5.** 54 **6.** 76
7. 280 **8.** 203 **9.** 340 **10.** 300 **11.** B **12.** B
13. $108 **14.** $94 **15.** 486 mi **16.** Check students' work. The product is 148. **17.** *Sample*

Answers *continued*

answer: When Joelene multiplied 4×3, she should have regrouped the product 12 as 1 ten and 2 ones, then added 1 ten to the product of 8 and 3. The correct answer is 252.

Lesson 1-25, pp. 96–99
Try this: **1.** 2300 **2.** 42,810 **3.** 65,370
4. 1000 **5.** 571,400 **6.** 7321
Practice: **1.** 320 **2.** 280 **3.** 550 **4.** 18,200
5. 1,297,000 **6.** 5130 **7.** 78,700 **8.** 481,000
9. 9300 **10.** 840 **11.** 93,200 **12.** 82 **13.** 7605
14. 17,350 **15.** 934 **16.** C **17.** C **18.** divide;
Sample answer: $22 because $220 \div 10 = $22
19. multiply; *Sample answer:* $130 because
$13 \times $10 = $130 **20.** multiply; *Sample answer:*
$5200 because there are 52 weeks in the year and
$100 \times 52 = $5200 **21.** multiply; 2 **22.** 4000 ×
100; *Sample answer:* Multiplying 4000×100
adds two zeros to 4000 to get 400,000. Dividing
$4000 \div 100$ subtracts two zeros from 4000 to get
40. 400,000 > 40. **23.** *Sample answer:* If you
multiply by 10, you make the number 10 times as
large. If you divide by 10, you make the number
$\frac{1}{10}$ the size. So multiplying by 10 and dividing by
10 are inverse operations.

Lesson 1-26, pp. 100–103
Try this: **1.** 416 **2.** 264 **3.** 2369 **4.** 4720
5. 4085 **6.** 17,484
Practice: **1.** 492 **2.** 1001 **3.** 294 **4.** 308
5. 1426 **6.** 4158 **7.** 4851 **8.** 625 **9.** 24,156
10. 76,908 **11.** 2989 **12.** 12,012 **13.** C
14. C **15.** 98×40: Find $98 \times 10 = 980$. Add
$980 + 980 + 980 + 980 = 3920$. **16.** 90×82:
Find $82 \times 10 = 820$. Add $820 + 820 + 820 +$
$820 + 820 + 820 + 820 + 820 + 820 = 7380$.
17. 124×40: Find $124 \times 10 = 1240$. Add
$1240 + 1240 + 1240 + 1240 = 4960$. **18.** $8850
19. *Sample answer:* Since $17 \times 19 = 323$,
Scott does not have enough money to buy all
the DVDs. $323 - $200 = $123. He is $123
short. **20.** $12,180 **21.** *Sample answer:* A good
estimate would be 150×100 or 15,000. The
actual answer is 14,504, so the estimate is close.
22. *Sample answer:* When Juan multiplied
4×3, he should have regrouped the product
12 as 1 ten and 2 ones, then added 1 ten to the
product of 8 and 3. The correct answer is 1092.
23. *Sample answer:* Pauline could look at 750
as 75×10. Then she could multiply 250×75
to get 18,750. Then she could use a pattern to
multiply $18,750 \times 10$, or 187,500.

Lesson 1-27, pp. 104–107
Try this: **1.** Check students' grids; 132,160
2. Check students' grids; 35,893 **3.** Check
students' grids; 95,604 **4.** Check students' grids;
607,110 **5.** Check students' grids; 2,060,493
6. Check students' grids; 1,714,528
Practice: **1.** 49,200 **2.** 100,011 **3.** 37,023
4. 53,671 **5.** 85,070 **6.** 19,558 **7.** 28,798
8. 734,105 **9.** 884,754 **10.** 6,980,880
11. 299,390 **12.** 18,161 **13.** C **14.** C
15. 150×400: $150 \times 100 = 15,000$. Since
$400 = 4 \times 100$, add $15,000 + 15,000 + 15,000 +$
$15,000 = 60,000$. **16.** 900×700: $900 \times 100 =$
90,000. Since $700 = 7 \times 100$, add $90,000 +$
$90,000 + 90,000 + 90,000 + 90,000 + 90,000 +$
$90,000 = 630,000$. **17.** 1240×300: $1240 \times$
$100 = 124,000$. Since $300 = 3 \times 100$, add
$124,000 + 124,000 + 124,000 = 372,000$.
18. $7,412,400 **19.** $100,000 **20.** $40,800
21. $2552 \times 978 \rightarrow 2500 \times 1000 = 2,500,000$.
The actual product is 2,495,856, so the estimate
is good. **22.** *Sample answer:* Marina can
eliminate the 3-digit choice since the 3 digits
are too small for this product. The smallest
3-digit number is 100. If you multiply
100×100, you get 10,000, which has 5 digits.
Since both of these numbers are over 100,
Marina can also eliminate the 4-digit choice.
The answer is 5 or 6 digits. The actual answer is
582,400, which is 6 digits. **23.** *Sample answer:*
If she multiplies 25×2, she will get 50. Use a
pattern to add 4 zeros. The product is 500,000.

Lesson 1-28, pp. 108–111
Question after Example 1. 8; 8
Question after Example 2. A quotient may
include a zero if there is a zero in the dividend.
Try this: **1.** 243 **2.** 56 **3.** 5261 **4.** 720
Practice: **1.** divisor: 8, dividend: 96; quotient:
12 **2.** divisor: 7, dividend: 588; quotient: 84
3. divisor: 6, dividend: 3126; quotient: 521
4. 4228 **5.** 550 **6.** 800 **7.** 900 **8.** 5631 **9.** 8854
10. 632 **11.** 5743 **12.** 63,000 **13.** B **14.** B
15. $32 \div 8$: $32 - 8 = 24$, $24 - 8 = 16$,
$16 - 8 = 8$, $8 - 8 = 0$; $32 \div 8 = 4$ **16.** $25 \div 5$:
$25 - 5 = 20$, $20 - 5 = 15$, $15 - 5 = 10$,
$10 - 5 = 5$, $5 - 5 = 0$; $25 \div 5 = 5$ **17.** $45 \div 9$:
$45 - 9 = 36$, $36 - 9 = 27$, $27 - 9 = 18$,
$18 - 9 = 9$, $9 - 9 = 0$; $45 \div 9 = 5$ **18.** $9
19. 25; $200 \div 8 = 25$; 25 CDs **20.** $200;
$1200 \div 2 = 600$; $600 \div 3 = 200$ **21.** *Sample answer:*
A good estimate would be $2700 \div 3 = 900$.

Answers *continued*

The actual answer is 890, so the estimate is close. **22.** *Sample answer:* Jackie forgot to subtract $30 - 28$ when she divided the hundreds. The correct answer is 760. **23.** *Sample answer:* Marcus could find $25 \div 5 = 5$ and use a pattern that adds the other zeros. The answer is 50,000.

Lesson 1-29, pp. 112–115
Try this: 1. 187 R3; $(187 \times 4) + 3 = 748 + 3 = 751$ **2.** 587 R3; $(587 \times 6) + 3 = 3522 + 3 = 3525$ **3.** 20,666 R2 **4.** 5214 R1
Practice: 1. 10 R6 **2.** 13 R6 **3.** 4217 R1 **4.** 618 R5 **5.** 781 R5 **6.** 1600 R2 **7.** 900 R2 **8.** 4345 R2 **9.** 8687 R1 **10.** 66 R4 **11.** 4290 R3 **12.** 120 R2 **13.** C **14.** A **15.** $39 - 8 = 31$, $31 - 8 = 23$, $23 - 8 = 15$, $15 - 8 = 7$. The quotient is 4 R7. **16.** $86 - 16 = 70$, $70 - 16 = 54$, $54 - 16 = 38$, $38 - 16 = 22$, $22 - 16 = 6$. The quotient is 5 R6. **17.** $58 - 6 = 52$, $52 - 6 = 46$, $46 - 6 = 40$, $40 - 6 = 34$, $34 - 6 = 28$, $28 - 6 = 22$, $22 - 6 = 16$, $16 - 6 = 10$, $10 - 6 = 4$. The quotient is 9 R4. **18.** 86 batches; 4 shirts **19.** 15 games; 3 students **20.** *Sample answer:* Sam divides $2550 in 4 ways. He gives equal amounts to four employees and puts the remaining amount in a benefits account. How much does each employee get? How much does Sam put in the benefits account? Answer: Since $2550 \div 4 = 637$ R2, each employee gets $637, and Sam puts $2 in the benefits account. **21.** *Sample answer:* Multiply 762×4 to get 3048. Add the remainder 2 to get 3050. The division is correct. **22.** *Sample answer:* Find the sum of $221 + 221 + 221 + 221 + 3$. Since $221 + 221 + 221 + 221 + 3 = 887$, the division is correct.

Lesson 1-30, pp. 116–119
Try this: 1. 50 R15; $(50 \times 36) + 15 = 1800 + 15 = 1815$ **2.** 112 R16; $(112 \times 22) + 16 = 2464 + 16 = 2480$ **3.** 1900; $1900 \times 32 = 60,800$ **4.** 4800; $4800 \times 18 = 86,400$
Practice: 1. 10 R60 **2.** 115 **3.** 201 R38 **4.** 231 R4 **5.** 4133 R5 **6.** 32 **7.** 320 **8.** 281 **9.** 623 **10.** 5200 **11.** 1076 R8 **12.** 1428 R48 **13.–18.** Check students' estimates. **13.** 8 **14.** 270 **15.** 1200 **16.** 10,101 **17.** 5000 **18.** 6006 **19.** $20; *Sample answer:* To find the price of each shirt, divide $960 \div 48$ to get 20. **20.** 4 buses **21.** $4250 **22.** estimate, subtract, quotient, remainder **23.** 1560; $(25 \times 62) + 10 = 1550 + 10 = 1560$ **24.** no;

Sample answer: She did not bring down the digits correctly. When she had a 0 difference, she should have written 0 as the next digit in the quotient. The correct answer is 2202.

Lesson 1-31, pp. 120–123
Try this: 1. 24 **2.** 9 **3.** $2(9 \cdot 5) = 2(5 \cdot 9) = (2 \cdot 5) \cdot 9 = 10 \cdot 9 = 90$ **4.** $(8 \cdot 3) \cdot 3 = 8 \cdot (3 \cdot 3) = 8 \cdot 9 = 72$ **5.** $0 \cdot (6 \cdot 9) + 4 \cdot 1 = 0 + 4 \cdot 1 = 4$ **6.** $(30 \div 1) + (10 \cdot 1) = 30 + (10 \cdot 1) = 30 + 10 = 40$
Practice: 1. 86 **2.** 2340 **3.** 0 **4.** 0 **5.** 4 **6.** 24 **7.** 36 **8.** 21 **9.** 160 **10.** 8 **11.** 24 **12.** 10 **13.** 18; division property of 1 **14.** 0; multiplication property of 0 **15.** 6; division property of 1 and commutative property of multiplication **16.** 3; multiplication property of 1 **17.** 3; associative property of multiplication **18.** 32; multiplication property of 0 and division property of 1 **19.** associative property of multiplication **20.** multiplication property of 0 **21.** multiplication property of 1 **22.** commutative property of multiplication **23.** *Sample answer:* Distance = Average speed $\times$ Number of hours per day $\times$ Number of days = $11 \cdot 6 \cdot 5 = 11 \cdot (6 \cdot 5) = 11 \cdot 30 = 330$ miles **24.** *Sample answer:* Division by 0 is undefined; $18 \div 1 = 18$ **25.** zero; the factors; order **26.** $15 \div 1 = 15$ **27.** *Sample answer:* Use the multiplication property of 0 to say that $8(3)(0)(2) = 0$.

Lesson 1-32, pp. 124–127
Try this: 1. 1^3 **2.** 12^3 **3.** m^5 **4. a.** two to the sixth power. **b.** six squared or six to the second power; *Sample answer:* Two to the sixth power means to multiply 2 by itself 6 times: $2 \times 2 \times 2 \times 2 \times 2 \times 2 = 64$. Six to the second power means to multiply 6 by itself two times: $6 \times 6 = 36$. **5.** 3; 3; 3; 27 **6.** 4; 4; 4; 4; 256 **7.** 3^7 **8.** 5^7 **9.** 2^{10}
Practice: 1. B **2.** A **3.** C **4.** True **5.** False **6.** False **7.** 8^3 **8.** 6^4 **9.** 20^2 **10.** 11^5 **11.** 7^5 **12.** 15^3 **13.** ten cubed or ten to the third power **14.** x to the fortieth power **15.** three to the fourth power **16.** seven to the sixty-sixth power **17.** z squared or z to the second power **18.** three to the tenth power **19.** 125 **20.** 1296 **21.** 64 **22.** 3^5 **23.** 4^5 **24.** 2^{13} **25.** 10^6 **26.** 8^6 **27.** 5^8 **28.** 8^3; 512 cm³ **29.** $16 \cdot 4^2 + 8 \cdot 5^2 + 24 \cdot 3^2$; 672 in.² **30.** fourth, eighth

31. *Sample answer:* $(2^4)^2 = 2^4 \times 2^4 = (2 \times 2 \times 2 \times 2) \times (2 \times 2 \times 2 \times 2) = 2 \times 2 \times 2 \times 2 \times 2 \times 2 \times 2 \times 2 = 2^8 = 256$ **32.** no; *Sample answer:* $3^1 + 3^2 + 3^3 = 3 + 9 + 27 = 39$, while $3^6 = 3 \cdot 3 \cdot 3 \cdot 3 \cdot 3 \cdot 3 = 729$.

Lesson 1-33, pp. 128–131

Try this: 1. 19 **2.** 26 **3.** 23 **4.** 6 **5.** 16
6. 52 **7.** 22 **8.** 42 **9.** 49 **10.** 19
Practice: 1. C **2.** A **3.** B **4.** True **5.** False
6. False **7.** 18 **8.** 36 **9.** 24 **10.** 6 **11.** 128
12. 2 **13.** 3 **14.** 1 **15.** 3 **16.** 23 **17.** 14 **18.** 3
19. 2 **20.** 20 **21.** 8 **22.** $5 \cdot (2 + 4) - 6 = 24$
23. $30 \div (2 + 4) - 2 = 3$ **24.** $(8 + 2) \cdot (3 + 4) = 70$ **25.** $22; *Sample answer:* To find the total cost write $(3 \times 4) + (5 \times 2)$ and simplify to get 22. **26.** $111; *Sample answer:* To find the cost write $(4 \times 36) - (3 \times 11)$ and simplify to get 111. **27.** $1820; *Sample answer:* To find the money that the school will contribute write $52(75 - 40)$ and simplify to get 1820. **28.** parentheses; exponents; multiply and divide from left to right; add and subtract from left to right **29.** $4 \cdot 36 + 3 \cdot 24 = 216$; 216 cookies **30.** no; *Sample answer:* The order of operations would not be to add $3 + 2$ first to get a product of 40. The correct answer is 19.

Lesson 1-34, pp. 132–135

Try this: 1. divide; $\div$; 80; $80; $1755 **2.** yes; *Sample answer:* $6192 + (15 \times 102) = 6192 + 1500 = 7692$, and since $7776 > 7692$, she still has enough fabric.
Practice: 1. $\div$ **2.** $-$ **3.** $\cdot$ **4.** $+$ **5.** subtraction **6.** division **7.** addition **8.** add; $+$; 7332; 7332 **9.** divide; 12; $\div$; 500; 500 **10.** division; 109 groups; 6 cards; $1314 \div 12 = 109$ R6 **11.** multiplication, addition, subtraction; $3; $30 - [4(3) + 12 + 3(1)] = 3$ **12.** addition, subtraction, multiplication; $388; $750 - [12(23) + 9(14)] - 5(8) + 8(10) = 388$ **13.** *Sample answer:* Jared earns $18 per week for 4 weeks delivering newspapers. How much does he earn?; $18 \times 4 = 72$; Multiplication is used to find the total of 4 groups of 18. **14.** yes; 24 more; $600 - [48(8) + 32(6)] = 600 - [384 + 192] = 600 - 576 = 24$

Mixed Practice for Lessons 1-22 to 1-34, pp. 136–137

1. B, X **2.** A, Y **3.** itself **4.** power; base **5.** $3 + 3 + 3 + 3 + 3 + 3 + 3 = 21$ **6.** $9 + 9 +$

$9 + 9 = 45$ **7.** $12 + 12 + 12 + 12 = 48$ **8.** $10 + 10 + 10 + 10 + 10 + 10 = 60$ **9.** 1, 2, 4, 8 16
10. 1, 2, 4; 8, 16, 32 **11.** 1, 2, 4, 5, 8, 10, 20, 40
12. 1, 3, 9, 27, 81 **13.** 125 **14.** 729 **15.** 512
16. 2^5 **17.** 9^4 **18.** 4^7 **19.** 19,200
20. 1,387,000 **21.** 51,300 **22.** 9 **23.** 20
24. 78 **25.** 12; Multiplication property of one
26. 4; Associative property of multiplication
27. 0; Multiplication property of zero **28.** 7; Commutative property of multiplication
29. 96 **30.** 1008 **31.** 544 **32.** 869 **33.** 2210
34. 14,721 **35.** 71,060 **36.** 256,998 **37.** 6
38. 16 **39.** 20 **40.** 120 **41.** 15 **42.** 35 **43.** 160
44. 1600 **45.** 1,089,672 **46.** 562 **47.** 325,318
48. 420 **49.** 28 **50.** 32 **51.** 9 **52.** 2 **53.** 20
54. 8 **55.** $372 **56.** $109 **57.** $15,520

Answers to Book 2 Fractions and Decimals

Lesson 2-1, pp. 2–5

Try this: 1. 1, 2, 3, 6, 9, 18 **2.** 1, 5, 7, 35
3. prime **4.** composite **5.** $2 \times 2 \times 2 \times 5 \times 5 = 2^3 \times 5^2$ **6.** 3×5
Practice: 1. 1, 2 **2.** 1, 2, 4, 8 **3.** 1, 17 **4.** 1, 5, 25
5. 1, 2, 3, 4, 6, 9, 12, 18, 36 **6.** 1, 7, 49 **7.** 1, 2, 3, 4, 5, 6, 10, 12, 15, 20, 30, 60 **8.** 1, 73 **9.** 1, 3, 9, 11, 33, 99 **10.** 1, 2, 3, 4, 6, 9, 12, 18, 27, 36, 54, 108 **11.** 1, 11, 121 **12.** 1, 2, 4, 5, 8, 10, 20, 25, 40, 50, 100, 200 **13.** composite **14.** prime
15. composite **16.** composite **17.** prime
18. composite **19.** composite **20.** composite
21. prime **22.** composite **23.** composite
24. composite **25.** C **26.** D **27.** B **28.** A
29. 7×1 **30.** $2^2 \times 3$ **31.** $2^2 \times 5$ **32.** $2^2 \times 3^2$
33. 43×1 **34.** 2×29 **35.** 2^6 **36.** $2^2 \times 23$
37. 5^3 **38.** 2×67 **39.** 157×1 **40.** $2 \times 5 \times 17$ **41.** $2^2 \times 5 \times 11$ **42.** $5^2 \times 13$ **43.** $2^3 \times 43$
44. $3 \times 11 \times 17$ **45.** *Sample answer:* find factors; I can use factors to make equal rows. The factors of 30 are 1, 2, 3, 5, 6, 10, 15, and 30. I want more than 1 row and more than 1 plant in each row, so 1 row of 30 and 30 rows of 1 are not reasonable options. The possibilities are 2 rows of 15 plants, 15 rows of 2 plants, 3 rows of 10 plants, 10 rows of 3 plants, 5 rows of 6 plants, or 6 rows of 5 plants. **46.** *Sample answer:* write a prime factorization; To write 240 as a product of prime numbers, I can write the prime factorization of 240. The prime factorization of 240 is $2^4 \times 3 \times 5$. There are four 2's, one 3, and one 5, a total of six digits. **47.** *Sample answer:* identify prime

Answers *continued*

and composite numbers; A number divisible only by 1 and itself is prime. All the birthdays are composite except June 13, which is prime.
48. factors **49.** no; *Sample answer:* The factors of 90 are 1, 2, 3, 5, 6, 9, 10, 15, 18, 30, 45, and 90. The factors 6, 9, 10, 15, 18, 30, 45, and 90 are composite, not prime.

Lesson 2-2, pp. 6–9
Try this: 1. Factors of 14: 1, 2, 7, 14; Factors of 34: 1, 2, 17, 34; Common factors: 1 and 2
2. Factors of 28: 1, 2, 4, 7, 14, 28; Factors of 72: 1, 2, 3, 4, 6, 8, 9, 12, 18, 24, 36, 72; Common factors: 1, 2, and 4 **3.** 8 **4.** 9
5. GCF: 4;

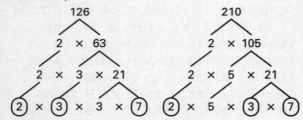

6. GCF: 42;

Practice: 1. Factors of 6: 1, 2, 3, 6; Factors of 8: 1, 2, 4, 8; Common factors: 1 and 2 **2.** Factors of 9: 1, 3, 9; Factors of 18: 1, 2, 3, 6, 9, 18; Common factors: 1, 3, and 9 **3.** 1 and 2 **4.** 1, 3, 5, and 15 **5.** Factors of 4: 1, 2, 4; Factors of 74: 1, 2, 37, 74; GCF: 2 **6.** Factors of 21: 1, 3, 7, 21; Factors of 49: 1, 7, 49; GCF: 7 **7.** 8 **8.** 15
9. 8 **10.** 30 **11.** 15 **12.** 20 **13.** *Sample answer:* greatest common factor; Ms. Randolf wants to divide each class into the largest possible equal-sized groups. The greatest common factor is 7. **14.** *Sample answer:* common factors; Finding the common factors of 30 and 40 gives possible group sizes if you divide 30 apples and 40 pears into equal-sized groups without mixing apples and pears. The common factors are 1, 2, 5, and 10. Since there must be more than 1 piece

of fruit in each group, the possible group sizes are 2, 5, and 10. **15.** *Sample answer:* greatest common factor; The greatest common factor of 220 and 400 is 20. This is the largest number of photos that you can arrange in equal groups on each poster without mixing the types of photos.
16. product **17.** *Sample answer:* 6 and 12

Lesson 2-3, pp. 10–13
Try this: 1. 1; 20; 2; 40; 3; 60; 4; 80; 5; 100
2. 1; 16; 2; 32; 3; 48; 4; 64; 5; 80; 6; 96 **3.** 40
4. 12 **5.** 96 **6.** 360
Practice: 1. 14; 21; 28; 35; 42; 49; 56; 63; 70
2. 6; 12; 24; 30; 36; 42; 48; 54; 60; 66; 72; 78
3. 12 **4.** 15 **5.** 45 **6.** 40 **7.** 240 **8.** 21 **9.** 108
10. 144 **11.** 20 **12.** 120 **13.** 156 **14.** 308
15. *Sample answer:* The least common multiple of 8 and 12 gives the number of each item that you will have so you can pair each pouch with a drink. The LCM is 24. **16.** *Sample answer:* The least common multiple of 4, 6, and 14 is 84. That is the first day Katy will lift weights, swim laps, and take a yoga class. **17.** *Sample answer:* The least common multiple of 36 and 48 is the number of the helmet that will have both defects. The LCM is 144. **18.** smallest; multiples **19.** *Sample answers:* 5, 10, 15, 20, 30, 60, 90, or 180

Mixed Practice for Lessons 2-1 to 2-3, pp. 14–15
1. C **2.** A **3.** B **4.** least common multiple
5. greatest or largest **6.** GCF: 4, LCM: 36,000;

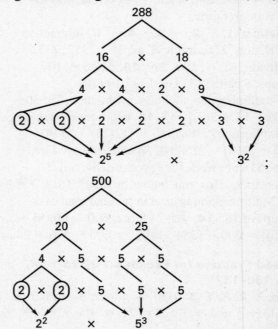

Answers continued

7. 9 **8.** 5 **9.** 6 **10.** 4 **11.** 4 **12.** 3 **13.** 43
14. 20 **15.** 15 **16.** 25 **17.** 9 **18.** 6 **19.** least
common multiple (LCM); 8, 16, 24, 32, 40, …;
6, 12, 18, 24, 30, …; 24 **20.** 60 **21.** 6 **22.** 70
23. 80 **24.** 56 **25.** 45 **26.** 21 **27.** 175 **28.** 42
29. 22 **30.** 72 **31.** 680 **32.** *Sample answer:* To
find the number of shirts in each group, find the
GCF of 50 and 20, which is 10. Since 50 shirts
divided into stacks of 10 will make 5 groups and
20 shirts divided into stacks of 10 will make 2
groups, there is a total of $5 + 2 = 7$ groups of
shirts. **33.** *Sample answer:* To find the number
of months from now, find the LCM of 3 and 4,
which is 12.

Lesson 2-4, pp. 16–19

Try this: 1. three fifths **2.** $\frac{1}{12}$

3. *Sample answer:*

4. *Sample answer:*

5. $\frac{2}{7}$ **6.** $\frac{1}{4}$

Practice: 1. five eighths **2.** four fifths **3.** nine
tenths **4.** three sevenths **5.** eight elevenths
6. five sixths **7.** sixteen hundredths **8.** nine
twelfths **9.** seven ninths **10.** $\frac{2}{3}$ **11.** $\frac{3}{4}$ **12.** $\frac{1}{6}$
13. $\frac{4}{7}$ **14.** $\frac{2}{9}$ **15.** $\frac{6}{11}$

16. *Sample answer:*

17. *Sample answer:*

18. *Sample answer:*

19. *Sample answer:*

20. *Sample answer:*

21. *Sample answer:*

22. *Sample answer:*

23. *Sample answer:*

24. $\frac{3}{5}$ **25.** $\frac{1}{8}$ **26.** $\frac{8}{11}$ **27.** $\frac{5}{6}$ **28.** numerator: 3,
denominator: 11: $\frac{3}{11}$; *Sample answer:* Three
students are selected from a set of 11 students.
29. numerator: 5, denominator: 12: $\frac{5}{12}$;
Sample answer: Five apartments are shaded in a
set of 12 apartments. **30.** numerator: 4,
denominator: 7: $\frac{4}{7}$; *Sample answer:* Four
afternoons are selected from a set of 7 days.
31. numerator; denominator

32. *Sample answer:*

Lesson 2-5, pp. 20–23

Try this: 1. $\frac{2}{24}, \frac{3}{36}, \frac{4}{48}$ **2.** $\frac{6}{14}, \frac{9}{21}, \frac{12}{28}$ **3.** 12 **4.** 7
5. The models represent equivalent fractions.

Practice: 1. $\frac{6}{8}, \frac{9}{12}, \frac{12}{16}$ **2.** $\frac{14}{20}, \frac{21}{30}, \frac{28}{40}$ **3.** $\frac{2}{12}, \frac{3}{18},$
$\frac{4}{24}$ **4.** $\frac{4}{18}, \frac{6}{27}, \frac{8}{36}$ **5.** $\frac{8}{14}, \frac{12}{21}, \frac{16}{28}$ **6.** $\frac{22}{24}, \frac{33}{36}, \frac{44}{48}$
7. 70 **8.** 63 **9.** 10 **10.** 40 **11.** 6 **12.** 21
13. The models do not represent equivalent
fractions. **14.** The models represent equivalent
fractions. **15.** The models do not represent
equivalent fractions. **16.** The models represent
equivalent fractions. **17.** identify; *Sample
answer:* Fraction of blue marbles in your
collection: $\frac{4}{7}$, fraction of blue marbles in your
friend's collection: $\frac{8}{14}$. Since 4 and 7 are each
multiplied by 2 to get 8 and 14, the fractions $\frac{4}{7}$
and $\frac{8}{14}$ are equivalent. **18.** complete; *Sample
answer:* Fraction of baseball players in the math
club: $\frac{5}{12}$, fraction of baseball players in the drama
club: $\frac{?}{36}$. Since the fraction of baseball players in
each club is the same, I completed the equivalent
fraction $\frac{5}{12} = \frac{?}{36}$ to get 15 baseball players in the
drama club. **19.** write; *Sample answer:* I
multiplied 3 and 8 by three nonzero whole
numbers to write three equivalent fractions for
the fraction of ham and cheese sandwiches:
$\frac{6}{16}, \frac{9}{24}, \frac{12}{32}$. **20.** Equivalent fractions

Answers _continued_

ANSWERS

21. _Sample answer:_ 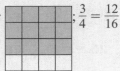 $\frac{3}{4} = \frac{12}{16}$

Lesson 2-6, pp. 24–27
Try this: 1. no **2.** yes **3.** $\frac{7}{13}$ **4.** 1 **5.** B
Practice: 1. yes **2.** no **3.** no **4.** yes **5.** yes
6. yes **7.** no **8.** no **9.** yes **10.** no **11.** $\frac{1}{3}$ **12.** $\frac{4}{9}$
13. $\frac{2}{5}$ **14.** $\frac{3}{7}$ **15.** $\frac{3}{4}$ **16.** $\frac{2}{3}$ **17.** $\frac{2}{7}$ **18.** $\frac{1}{10}$ **19.** $\frac{9}{20}$
20. $\frac{5}{18}$ **21.** $\frac{11}{13}$ **22.** $\frac{1}{2}$ **23.** B **24.** C **25.** A
26. $\frac{20}{30}; \frac{2}{3}$ **27.** $\frac{18}{24}; \frac{3}{4}$ **28.** $\frac{10}{25}; \frac{2}{5}$
29. simplest form **30.** _Sample answer:_

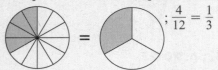 $; \frac{4}{12} = \frac{1}{3}$

31. yes; _Sample answer:_ I have read 15 of 20
pages, or $\frac{15}{20}$. The fraction $\frac{15}{20}$ in simplest form
is $\frac{3}{4}$, so I am $\frac{3}{4}$ of the way through the story.

Lesson 2-7, pp. 28–31
Try this: 1. 9 **2.** 10 **3.** < **4.** < **5.** $\frac{1}{12}, \frac{1}{9}, \frac{1}{4}$
6. $\frac{1}{6}, \frac{2}{3}, \frac{7}{8}$
Practice: 1. 14 **2.** 18 **3.** 35 **4.** 24 **5.** 60
6. 30 **7.** 28 **8.** 80 **9.** 30 **10.** < **11.** < **12.** >
13. < **14.** = **15.** > **16.** > **17.** < **18.** >
19. $\frac{1}{12}, \frac{1}{9}, \frac{1}{3}$ **20.** $\frac{4}{7}, \frac{5}{8}, \frac{3}{4}$ **21.** $\frac{5}{12}, \frac{5}{6}, \frac{9}{10}$ **22.** $\frac{5}{18},$
$\frac{7}{9}, \frac{5}{6}$ **23.** $\frac{3}{20}, \frac{7}{10}, \frac{4}{5}$ **24.** $\frac{3}{8}, \frac{13}{32}, \frac{11}{16}$ **25.** $\frac{1}{4}, \frac{4}{15}, \frac{5}{16}$
26. $\frac{5}{12}, \frac{9}{20}, \frac{3}{5}$ **27.** $\frac{3}{4}, \frac{7}{9}, \frac{6}{7}$ **28.** _Sample answer:_ I
finished $\frac{3}{10}$ of the books, and my friend finished $\frac{2}{5}$
of the books. The fraction $\frac{4}{10}$ is equivalent to $\frac{2}{5}$.
Since 4 > 3, then $\frac{4}{10} > \frac{3}{10}$, and $\frac{2}{5} > \frac{3}{10}$. So, my
friend has read more books. **29.** _Sample answer:_
The LCD of the fractions is 36. After writing
the equivalent fractions $\frac{7}{9} = \frac{28}{36}, \frac{3}{4} = \frac{27}{36}$, and $\frac{5}{6}$
$= \frac{30}{36}$, I can see that 27 < 28 < 30. The lengths
in order from least to greatest are $\frac{3}{4}$ yard, $\frac{7}{9}$ yard,
and $\frac{5}{6}$ yard. **30.** _Sample answer:_ The LCD
of $\frac{7}{12}, \frac{9}{16}$, and $\frac{5}{8}$ is 48. The first piece I attached

measured $\frac{7}{12}$ or $\frac{28}{48}$ inch. $\frac{9}{16} = \frac{27}{48}$ and $\frac{5}{8} = \frac{30}{48}$.
Since 27 < 30, then $\frac{27}{48} < \frac{30}{48}$, or $\frac{9}{16} < \frac{5}{8}$. The piece
that measures $\frac{9}{16}$ inch is slightly shorter
than the piece that measures $\frac{5}{8}$ inch. **31.** least
common denominator **32.** _Sample answer:_

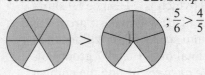 $; \frac{5}{6} > \frac{4}{5}$

Lesson 2-8, pp. 32–35
Try this: 1. $3\frac{1}{2}$ **2.** $1\frac{7}{9}$ **3.** $\frac{(3 \times 6) + 1}{6} = \frac{18 + 1}{6} = \frac{19}{6}$
4. $\frac{(1 \times 7) + 4}{7} = \frac{7 + 4}{7} = \frac{11}{7}$
5. $\frac{9}{4};$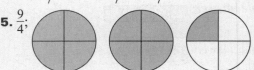
Practice: 1. $1\frac{5}{7}$ **2.** $2\frac{4}{5}$ **3.** $7\frac{1}{2}$ **4.** $2\frac{2}{3}$ **5.** $1\frac{3}{4}$
6. $2\frac{5}{6}$ **7.** $2\frac{1}{10}$ **8.** $2\frac{7}{9}$ **9.** $\frac{23}{8}$ **10.** $\frac{21}{4}$ **11.** $\frac{11}{3}$
12. $\frac{13}{9}$ **13.** $\frac{31}{7}$ **14.** $\frac{17}{5}$ **15.** $\frac{51}{10}$ **16.** $\frac{77}{12}$
17. $\frac{12}{5};$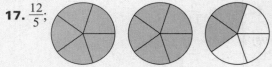
18. $\frac{10}{9};$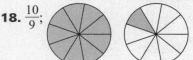
19. $\frac{23}{10};$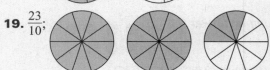
20. $\frac{11}{6};$
21. $\frac{23}{16};$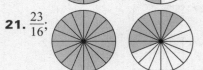
22. $\frac{21}{8};$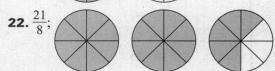

Math Intervention
Teacher's Edition

118

Answers

Answers continued

23. $2 \times 2 + 1 = 5; \frac{5}{2}$ **24.** $11 \div 2 = 5$ R $1; 5\frac{1}{2}$

25. $2\frac{5}{8}$ **26.** mixed number; improper fraction

27. Stacy should have multiplied the whole number by the denominator of the fraction, not the numerator. Then she should have added the numerator to the product: $5 \times 9 + 4 = 49$. The correct answer is $\frac{49}{9}$. **28.** $\frac{9}{2}$;

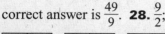

1 inch

Lesson 2-9, pp. 36–39

Try this: 1. < **2.** > **3.** < **4.** > **5.** $\frac{41}{24}, 2\frac{1}{6}, 2\frac{7}{12}$

6. $\frac{33}{10}, \frac{67}{20}, 3\frac{4}{5}$

Practice: 1. > **2.** > **3.** < **4.** < **5.** < **6.** > **7.** <

8. > **9.** > **10.** $\frac{25}{14}$ **11.** $\frac{9}{2}$ **12.** $9\frac{2}{5}$ **13.** $1\frac{5}{8}$

14. $2\frac{1}{8}$ **15.** $\frac{35}{6}$ **16.** $\frac{9}{4}, \frac{41}{16}, 3\frac{1}{16}$ **17.** $\frac{17}{12}, 1\frac{7}{12},$

$\frac{13}{8}$ **18.** $\frac{8}{3}, 2\frac{5}{6}, \frac{26}{9}$ **19.** $2\frac{1}{2}, \frac{18}{7}, \frac{8}{3}$ **20.** $\frac{49}{12}, \frac{41}{10}, 4\frac{2}{15}$

21. $\frac{16}{3}, \frac{43}{8}, 5\frac{7}{12}$ **22.** *Sample answer:* Use the LCD to compare the mixed numbers. Writing $3\frac{3}{4}$ and $3\frac{7}{16}$ as improper fractions with a common denominator, I can see that $\frac{60}{16} > \frac{55}{16}$. Since $3\frac{3}{4} > 3\frac{7}{16}$, you use more flour to bake bread than to bake the cake. **23.** *Sample answer:* Since $3\frac{1}{2} < 3\frac{5}{8}$ and $3\frac{5}{8} < \frac{11}{3}$, the widths from least to greatest are $3\frac{1}{2}$ cm, $3\frac{5}{8}$ cm, and $\frac{11}{3}$ cm. The letters from narrowest to widest are B, D, and G. **24.** *Sample answer:* Since $\frac{11}{9} < \frac{8}{3}$, Sam walked farther.

25. mixed number; improper fraction; LCD
26. yes; *Sample answer:* The lengths from least to greatest are $8\frac{5}{12}$ in., $8\frac{2}{3}$ in., and $\frac{35}{4}$ in. Since $8\frac{2}{3}$ falls between $8\frac{5}{12}$ and $\frac{35}{4}$, the canvas should fit in the frame.

Mixed Practice for Lessons 2-4 to 2-9, pp. 40–41

1. B, Z **2.** A, Y **3.** C, X **4.** equivalent
5. denominator **6.** numerator: 5, denominator: 8;

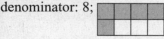

7. numerator: 2, denominator: 9;

8. numerator: 1, denominator: 5;

9. $\frac{5}{4}$;

10. $\frac{17}{6}$;

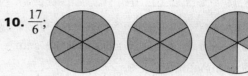

11. $\frac{9}{7}$;

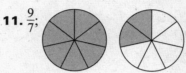

12. 9 **13.** 4 **14.** 15 **15.** 21 **16.** $\frac{3}{8}, \frac{3}{7}, \frac{4}{9}$ **17.** $3\frac{2}{3},$

$3\frac{5}{6}, \frac{25}{6}$ **18.** $\frac{21}{8}, \frac{11}{4}, 2\frac{7}{8}$ **19.** greater; >, <; $\frac{2}{9}$ **20.** $\frac{2}{5}$

21. $\frac{1}{4}$ **22.** $\frac{2}{7}$ **23.** $\frac{2}{5}$ **24.** $2\frac{8}{9}$ **25.** $4\frac{1}{8}$ **26.** $4\frac{2}{3}$

27. $5\frac{5}{12}$ **28.** < **29.** < **30.** > **31.** > **32.** > **33.** <

34. > **35.** < **36.** *Sample answer:* The windows are lined up in order from shortest to tallest, so I need to order the heights from least to greatest and then label the windows. The heights in order are $\frac{41}{20}$ ft, $3\frac{7}{10}$ ft, and $3\frac{4}{5}$ ft, so this is the order they are labeled on the windows. **37.** *Sample answer:* To find out who is farther along, compare $\frac{3}{8}$ to $\frac{5}{12}$. Since $\frac{5}{12} > \frac{3}{8}$, Alexandra is farther along.

Activity 2-10, pp. 42–43
Practice:

1. $\frac{7}{9}$;

2. $\frac{2}{5}$;

3. $\frac{3}{4}$;

4. $\frac{2}{3}$;

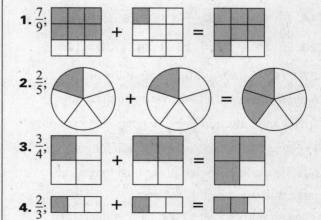

Math Intervention
Teacher's Edition **119**

Answers *continued*

5. $\frac{7}{10}$;

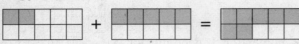

6. $\frac{11}{12}$;

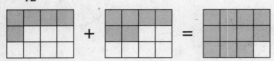

7. *Sample answer:* For fractions with the same denominator, add the numerators. Write this sum over the denominator. **8.** $\frac{4}{5}$ **9.** $\frac{5}{9}$

Lesson 2-11, pp. 44–47

Try this: 1. $\frac{4}{7}$;

2. $\frac{5}{6}$;

3. $\frac{3+5}{8} = \frac{8}{8} = 1$ **4.** $\frac{8+11}{16} = \frac{19}{16} = 1\frac{3}{16}$
5. $\frac{6-2}{7} = \frac{4}{7}$ **6.** $\frac{7-3}{8} = \frac{4}{8} = \frac{1}{2}$

Practice: 1. B **2.** C **3.** A

4. $\frac{4}{5}$;

5. $\frac{4}{4} = 1$;

6. $\frac{5}{11}$ **7.** $\frac{6}{7}$ **8.** $\frac{2}{3}$ **9.** 1 **10.** $\frac{2}{3}$ **11.** $\frac{4}{5}$ **12.** 1 **13.** $\frac{3}{5}$
14. $1\frac{3}{5}$ **15.** $1\frac{1}{2}$ **16.** $\frac{10}{11}$ **17.** $\frac{2}{3}$ **18.** $\frac{7}{9}$ **19.** $\frac{3}{5}$
20. $\frac{11}{17}$ **21.** $\frac{1}{3}$ **22.** $\frac{1}{2}$ **23.** 0 **24.** $\frac{1}{3}$ **25.** $\frac{1}{7}$ **26.** $\frac{1}{5}$
27. $\frac{5}{8}$ **28.** $\frac{1}{3}$ **29.** $\frac{1}{2}$ **30.** add; $\frac{1}{2}$ of the pizza;
Sample answer: To find how much pizza my friend and I ate, add $\frac{1}{8} + \frac{3}{8}$ to get $\frac{4}{8}$. Then simplify to get $\frac{1}{2}$. **31.** subtract; about $\frac{3}{8}$ inch longer;
Sample answer: To find how much longer the large milkweed bug is, subtract $\frac{9}{16} - \frac{3}{16}$ to get $\frac{6}{16}$. Then simplify to get $\frac{3}{8}$. **32.** sum; numerators; denominator **33.** difference; numerators;

denominator **34. a.** *Sample answer:*
$\frac{1}{5} + \frac{3}{5} = \frac{4}{5}$;

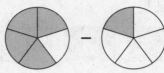

b. *Sample answer:* $\frac{4}{5} - \frac{1}{5} = \frac{3}{5}$;

35. no; *Sample answer:* She should have written the sum of the numerators over the denominator. Instead she wrote the sum of the numerators over the sum of the denominators. The answer should be $\frac{2}{6}$, which simplifies to $\frac{1}{3}$.

Lesson 2-12, pp. 48–51

Try this: 1. 2; $\frac{3}{4}$;

2. 4; $\frac{5}{6}$;

3. $\frac{7}{9}$ **4.** $1\frac{7}{12}$ **5.** $\frac{24}{35}$ **6.** $1\frac{1}{6}$ **7.** $\frac{1}{8}$ **8.** $\frac{7}{15}$ **9.** $\frac{1}{18}$ **10.** $\frac{2}{3}$

Practice: 1. $\frac{5}{9}$;

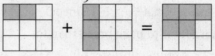

2. $\frac{7}{10}$;

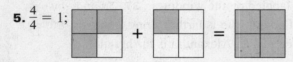

3. $\frac{11}{12}$;

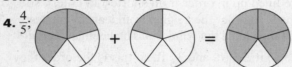

4. $\frac{7}{8}$;

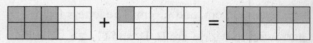

5. $1\frac{3}{8}$ **6.** $1\frac{1}{4}$ **7.** $1\frac{5}{14}$ **8.** $\frac{5}{12}$ **9.** $\frac{1}{2}$ **10.** $1\frac{1}{8}$ **11.** $\frac{19}{20}$
12. $\frac{7}{8}$ **13.** $\frac{5}{12}$ **14.** $\frac{2}{9}$ **15.** $\frac{1}{2}$ **16.** $\frac{11}{24}$ **17.** $\frac{9}{20}$
18. $\frac{1}{3}$ **19.** $\frac{1}{3}$ **20.** $\frac{5}{18}$ **21.** add; *Sample answer:*
To find how much of the quilt they sewed, add $\frac{1}{6}$ and $\frac{3}{8}$. Change $\frac{1}{6}$ to $\frac{4}{24}$ and $\frac{3}{8}$ to $\frac{9}{24}$. Then add $\frac{4}{24}$

Answers *continued*

and $\frac{9}{24}$ to get $\frac{13}{24}$ of the quilt. **22.** add; *Sample answer:* To find how much of the measuring cup is full, add $\frac{1}{3}$ and $\frac{1}{4}$. Change $\frac{1}{3}$ to $\frac{4}{12}$ and $\frac{1}{4}$ to $\frac{3}{12}$. Then add $\frac{4}{12} + \frac{3}{12}$ to get $\frac{7}{12}$ cup.

23. subtract; *Sample answer:* To find how much farther from my house the post office is than the library, subtract $\frac{2}{3}$ from $\frac{8}{9}$. Change $\frac{2}{3}$ to $\frac{6}{9}$. Subtract $\frac{8}{9} - \frac{6}{9}$ to get $\frac{2}{9}$ mi. **24.** LCD; equivalent fractions; sum; numerators; denominator **25.** no; *Sample answer:* My friend wrote the difference of the numerators over the difference of the denominators. He should have used the LCD to write equivalent fractions. Then he should have written the difference of the numerators over the denominator. $\frac{7}{8} - \frac{1}{4} = \frac{7}{8} - \frac{2}{8} = \frac{5}{8}$

Lesson 2-13, pp. 52–55

Try this: 1. $\frac{23}{8} = 2\frac{7}{8}$;

2. $\frac{22}{6} = 3\frac{2}{3}$;

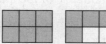

3. $7\frac{1}{8}$ **4.** $4\frac{1}{3}$ **5.** $4\frac{11}{18}$ **6.** $2\frac{7}{10}$ **7.** $3\frac{3}{14}$ **8.** $\frac{7}{20}$ **9.** $1\frac{4}{15}$ **10.** $3\frac{1}{6}$

Practice: 1. C; $2\frac{1}{2}$ **2.** A; 3 **3.** B; $2\frac{5}{7}$ **4.** $3\frac{14}{15}$ **5.** $3\frac{7}{9}$ **6.** $5\frac{1}{4}$ **7.** $5\frac{5}{12}$ **8.** $7\frac{1}{8}$ **9.** $4\frac{1}{18}$ **10.** $6\frac{5}{18}$ **11.** $4\frac{7}{20}$ **12.** $3\frac{5}{9}$ **13.** $1\frac{1}{3}$ **14.** $1\frac{3}{7}$ **15.** $2\frac{19}{20}$ **16.** $1\frac{7}{16}$ **17.** $1\frac{2}{5}$ **18.** $1\frac{7}{12}$ **19.** $\frac{3}{14}$ **20.** $\frac{3}{4}$ **21.** $2\frac{11}{20}$

22. add; *Sample answer:* To find the amount of material your mom buys in all, add $2\frac{1}{2}$ and $1\frac{3}{4}$ to get $4\frac{1}{4}$ yd. **23.** subtract; *Sample answer:* To find how much the plant has grown, subtract $2\frac{11}{18} - 2\frac{1}{3}$ to get $\frac{5}{18}$ in. **24.** subtract; *Sample answer:* To find how thick the blue pad is, subtract

$2\frac{5}{6} - 1\frac{1}{4}$ to get $1\frac{7}{12}$ cm. **25.** mixed numbers; mixed numbers; improper fractions; difference; numerators; denominator **26.** *Sample answer:* I can write $4\frac{1}{5}$ as $\frac{21}{5}$ and then as $\frac{42}{10}$. Then I can write $2\frac{7}{10}$ as $\frac{27}{10}$.

Lesson 2-14, pp. 56–59

Try this: 1. 3;

2. 4;

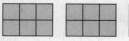

3. $\frac{15 \times 3}{5} = \frac{45}{5} = 9$

4. $\frac{5 \times 12}{6} = \frac{60}{6} = 10$ **5.** 6 **6.** $1\frac{1}{9}$ **7.** $\frac{3 \times 2}{4 \times 5} = \frac{6}{20} = \frac{3}{10}$ **8.** $\frac{1 \times 3}{6 \times 5} = \frac{3}{30} = \frac{1}{10}$ **9.** $\frac{5}{18}$ **10.** $\frac{1}{14}$

Practice: 1. B **2.** C **3.** A **4.** $\frac{2}{3} \times 12$ **5.** $\frac{1}{2} \times 6$ **6.** $\frac{1}{7} \times 7$ **7.** 16 **8.** 10 **9.** 12 **10.** $4\frac{2}{3}$ **11.** 2 **12.** $8\frac{1}{3}$ **13.** $2\frac{1}{2}$ **14.** $9\frac{1}{3}$ **15.** $1\frac{1}{2}$ **16.** $\frac{1}{3}$ **17.** $\frac{1}{5}$ **18.** $\frac{3}{20}$ **19.** $\frac{5}{21}$ **20.** $\frac{4}{11}$ **21.** $\frac{1}{5}$ **22.** $\frac{2}{11}$ **23.** $\frac{5}{14}$ **24.** $\frac{1}{4}$ **25.** 14 students; *Sample answer:* To find $\frac{2}{3}$ of 21, multiply $\frac{2}{3} \times 21$ to get 14. **26.** $3\frac{3}{4}$ miles; *Sample answer:* To find the total distance that I walked, multiply $5 \times \frac{3}{4}$ to get $3\frac{3}{4}$. **27.** $\frac{1}{8}$ hour; *Sample answer:* To find $\frac{1}{4}$ of $\frac{1}{2}$, multiply $\frac{1}{4} \times \frac{1}{2}$ to get $\frac{1}{8}$. **28.** product; numerators; product; denominators **29.** *Sample answer:* $\frac{2}{4} \times 16 = \frac{1}{2} \times 16 = \frac{1 \times 16}{2} = \frac{16}{2} = 8$;

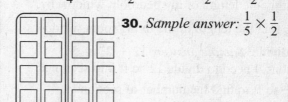

30. *Sample answer:* $\frac{1}{5} \times \frac{1}{2}$

Lesson 2-15, pp. 60–63

Try this: 1. $\frac{11}{7}$ or $1\frac{4}{7}$ **2.** 15 **3.** $\frac{1}{3}$ **4.** 2 **5.** $\frac{9}{16}$ **6.** $\frac{6}{7}$ **7.** $\frac{2}{11}$ **8.** $\frac{1}{8}$ **9.** 12

Practice: 1. $\frac{7}{2}$ or $3\frac{1}{2}$ **2.** $\frac{4}{3}$ or $1\frac{1}{3}$ **3.** $\frac{12}{5}$ or $2\frac{2}{5}$

Answers continued

4. 11 **5.** 2 **6.** $\frac{1}{9}$ **7.** $\frac{1}{15}$ **8.** $\frac{1}{3}$ **9.** C **10.** A **11.** D
12. B **13.** $\frac{3}{4}$ **14.** $1\frac{2}{3}$ **15.** $\frac{11}{20}$ **16.** $\frac{4}{15}$ **17.** $\frac{7}{24}$
18. $\frac{1}{12}$ **19.** $6\frac{2}{3}$ **20.** 30 **21.** $10\frac{1}{2}$ **22.** $1\frac{5}{16}$ **23.** $\frac{2}{25}$
24. $6\frac{2}{5}$ **25.** 12 batches; *Sample answer:* To find
how many batches, divide: $8 \div \frac{2}{3} = 12$.
26. 6 servings; *Sample answer:* To find how
many servings, divide: $\frac{3}{4} \div \frac{1}{8} = 6$. **27.** $\frac{1}{12}$ yard;
Sample answer: To find how far apart to place
the marks, divide: $\frac{5}{6} \div 10 = \frac{1}{12}$.
28. denominator; numerator **29.** no; *Sample
answer:* Malik multiplied by the divisor instead
of by the reciprocal of the divisor. He should have
multiplied $\frac{8}{15} \times \frac{6}{5}$ to get $\frac{48}{75}$ or $\frac{16}{25}$. **30.** $\frac{4}{5} \div 4$

Lesson 2-16, pp. 64–67

Try this: 1. $\frac{13}{18}$ **2.** $1\frac{2}{5}$ **3.** $3\frac{1}{6}$ **4.** $7\frac{7}{8}$ **5.** $3\frac{5}{9}$ **6.** $\frac{3}{11}$
7. $3\frac{1}{2}$ **8.** $\frac{5}{8}$

Practice: 1. A **2.** C **3.** D **4.** B **5.** $\frac{11}{28}$ **6.** $3\frac{2}{5}$
7. $\frac{4}{7}$ **8.** $1\frac{1}{2}$ **9.** $7\frac{1}{3}$ **10.** $7\frac{1}{4}$ **11.** $8\frac{3}{4}$ **12.** $7\frac{3}{4}$ **13.** $1\frac{1}{2}$
14. $9\frac{2}{5}$ **15.** $13\frac{1}{3}$ **16.** 1 **17.** $4\frac{3}{4}$ **18.** $8\frac{1}{2}$ **19.** $\frac{7}{20}$
20. $\frac{2}{15}$ **21.** $1\frac{3}{5}$ **22.** $1\frac{1}{9}$ **23.** $4\frac{2}{7}$ **24.** $1\frac{7}{20}$ **25.** $5\frac{5}{6}$
26. $2\frac{1}{2}$ **27.** $\frac{2}{5}$ **28.** $1\frac{5}{9}$ **29.** multiply; *Sample
answer:* $5 \times 1\frac{1}{4} = 6\frac{1}{4}$ quarts. I know that I
need $1\frac{1}{4}$ qt for 1 birdhouse, so I multiply $1\frac{1}{4}$ by
5 to find how much paint I need for 5 birdhouses.
30. multiply; *Sample answer:* $\frac{5}{9} \times 2\frac{3}{5} = 1\frac{4}{9}$
yards. Since the living room window is $2\frac{3}{5}$
times as long as my bedroom window, I can
multiply the length of my bedroom window by
$2\frac{3}{5}$ to find the length of the living room window.
31. divide; *Sample answer:* $12 \div 2\frac{2}{5} = 5$
sections. I need to divide 12 sq ft into sections
of $2\frac{2}{5}$ sq ft to find the number of sections.
32. mixed number; improper fraction **33.** no;
Sample answer: Becca wrote the product of the
dividend and the divisor rather than the product
of the dividend and the reciprocal of the divisor.
The problem should be written as $\frac{7}{1} \times \frac{7}{9}$.

Lesson 2-17, pp. 68–71

Try this: 1. Step 1. subtract; **Step 2.** $-$; $\frac{3}{4}$;
Step 3. 0; 0; 1; close to 1; **Step 4.** $\frac{3}{4}$ **2.** To find
out how much paper you will use to make 12
art projects, multiply $1\frac{1}{3}$ by 12 to get 16. Then
subtract 16 from 30 to find out how much paper
you will have left on the roll: $30 - 16 = 14$ ft.
Practice: 1. $\times$ **2.** $+$ **3.** $\div$ **4.** $-$ **5.** subtraction
6. addition **7.** multiplication **8.** 2, 1 **9.** 1, 2
10. multiplication; \$512; *Sample answer:* To find
how much Mario saved, multiply $\frac{1}{5}$ by 2560 to
get 512. **11.** subtraction and multiplication; 45
min; *Sample answer:* To find how many minutes
you have left to wait, first subtract $1\frac{1}{2} - \frac{3}{4}$ to
get $\frac{3}{4}$ hour. To find $\frac{3}{4}$ of 60 minutes, multiply
$\frac{3}{4} \times 60$ to get 45. **12.** addition and subtraction;
Sample answer: $\frac{67}{80}$ of the hard drive space is
left; To find how much of the hard drive space
is taken up by applications and all other files,
add $\frac{9}{80} + \frac{1}{20}$ to get $\frac{13}{80}$. Then subtract $1 - \frac{13}{80}$ to
find the space that is left. **13.** *Sample answer:*
About $\frac{1}{4}$ of the students at your school belong
to a club. Another $\frac{3}{8}$ of the students are in the
band. What fraction of students at your school
are either in a club or in the band?; To find
the answer, add $\frac{3}{8}$ and $\frac{1}{4}$.; $\frac{3}{8} + \frac{1}{4} = \frac{5}{8}$; $\frac{5}{8}$ of the
students at my school are in a club or in the band.
14. no; *Sample answer:* To find how many
$1\frac{5}{6}$-foot shelves the carpenter can make from
7 feet of board, you need to divide $7 \div \frac{15}{6} = 2\frac{4}{5}$.
It does not make sense to make part of a shelf,
so 2 is a reasonable answer. The carpenter cannot
make 4 shelves because $2\frac{4}{5} < 4$.

Mixed Practice for Lessons 2-11 to 2-17, pp. 72–73

1. B **2.** C **3.** A **4.** reasonableness **5.** least
common denominator

6. $\frac{1}{7}$; **7.** $\frac{5}{6}$; **8.** $\frac{3}{4}$;

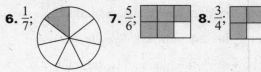

Answers *continued*

9. $2\frac{1}{3}$;

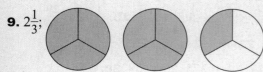

10. $\frac{5}{7}$ **11.** $\frac{2}{27}$ **12.** $\frac{9}{32}$ **13.** $\frac{5}{8}$ **14.** $\frac{5}{42}$ **15.** $5\frac{1}{9}$

16. 5 **17.** $1\frac{1}{2}$ **18.** $3\frac{2}{5}$ **19.** $\frac{3}{5}$ **20.** 2 **21.** $2\frac{2}{3}$

22. multiply; ×; $\frac{2}{15}$; $\frac{2}{15}$; $\frac{1}{2}$; $\frac{1}{2}$; product; $\frac{1}{4}$ **23.** $\frac{7}{8}$

24. $\frac{2}{15}$ **25.** $\frac{3}{4}$ **26.** $1\frac{1}{2}$ **27.** $5\frac{5}{8}$ **28.** $9\frac{7}{12}$ **29.** $\frac{4}{21}$

30. $2\frac{1}{3}$ **31.** $1\frac{3}{8}$ **32.** $\frac{12}{23}$ **33.** $7\frac{19}{20}$ **34.** $3\frac{3}{5}$ **35.** $3\frac{1}{31}$

36. $8\frac{4}{15}$ **37.** $4\frac{1}{2}$ **38.** $5\frac{24}{35}$ **39.** *Sample answer:*

Multiply $1\frac{1}{8}$ by 2 to find the combined thickness

of the boards. Then subtract $\frac{5}{8}$ from the product

to find the length of the nail.

$1\frac{1}{8} \times 2 = 2\frac{1}{4}$ and $2\frac{1}{4} - \frac{5}{8} = 1\frac{5}{8}$, so the nail is

$1\frac{5}{8}$ inches long. **40.** *Sample answer:* Multiply

$\frac{2}{5}$ by 7 to find how many quarts of soup are in the

bowls. Then subtract the product from 5 quarts to

find how much is left. $7 \times \frac{2}{5} = \frac{14}{5}$ or $2\frac{4}{5}$ and

$5 - 2\frac{4}{5} = 2\frac{1}{5}$, so there are $2\frac{1}{5}$ quarts left.

Lesson 2-18, pp. 74–77
Try this: 1. 2 **2.** hundredths **3.** two hundred
forty-one and seven tenths **4.** five hundred
forty-nine thousandths **5.** 304.027 **6.** 0.82
Practice: 1. 0 **2.** 4 **3.** 8 **4.** 6 **5.** hundredths
6. hundred-thousandths **7.** tenths **8.** hundredths
9. thousandths **10.** tenths **11.** hundredths
12. ten-thousandths **13.** B **14.** A **15.** C
16. 0.0008 **17.** 200.3 **18.** 0.029 **19.** 41.05
20. 0.35 **21.** 6.007 **22.** three and forty-five
hundredths **23.** seventy-one and four hundred
four thousandths **24.** nine ten-thousandths
25. sixteen hundredths **26.** two hundred
fourteen and one hundredth **27.** three hundred
ninety-two and three tenths **28.** nineteen and
two thousandths **29.** six and three thousand
four hundred seventy-seven ten-thousandths
30. three and forty-eight hundredths seconds;
Sample answer: The 3 is in the ones' place. I
substituted "and" for the decimal. The 4 is in
the tenths' place, and the 8 is in the hundredths'
place. **31.** 2.562 mi; *Sample answer:* I need
to make sure that the final 2 lands in the
thousandths' place, so "two and five hundred

sixty-two thousandths" means "two point five,
six, two," or 2.562. **32.** 3; *Sample answer:* The
digit two places to the right of the decimal is 3.
33. one; right; decimal point **34.** 2.5
35. *Sample answer:* 0.065; sixty-five thousandths

Lesson 2-19, pp. 78–81
Try this: 1. 0.274 **2.** 22.7 **3.** 16.49 **4.** 0
Practice: 1. 18.22 **2.** 0.2 **3.** 2.011 **4.** 10.34
5. 1.0 or 1 **6.** C **7.** B **8.** A **9.** 3.4 **10.** 2.0, or
2 **11.** 0.713 **12.** 45 **13.** 25 **14.** 0.48 **15.** 31
16. 2.80 or 2.8 **17.** 5.6 **18.** 10 **19.** 0.245
20. 115.0 or 115 **21.** 5.7 **22.** 0.5 **23.** 7
24. 0.63 **25.** 1.8 **26.** 0.008 **27.** 8.6; *Sample
answer:* The digit to the right of 6 is 2, so 8.62
rounds down to 8.6. **28.** 0.88; *Sample answer:*
The digit to the right of 7 is 5, so 0.875 rounds
up to 0.88. **29.** 8 lb; *Sample answer:* The nearest
pound means the nearest whole number. The
digit to the right of 8 is 2, so 8.25 pounds rounds
down to 8 pounds. **30.** right **31.** *Sample answer:*
$1.77 \approx 1.8$;

$$\begin{array}{c}\text{1.77}\\ \vdash\!\!+\!\!+\!\!+\!\!+\!\!+\!\!+\!\!\bullet\!\!+\!\!+\!\!+\!\!+\!\!\dashv\\ \text{1.7}\qquad\qquad\text{1.8}\end{array}$$

32. *Sample answers:* 3.176 and 3.182

Lesson 2-20, pp. 82–85
Try this: 1. 2, 3, 3.3, 4.2, 4.9; Check students'
graphs. **2.** 1.66, 1.7, 1.79, 1.8, 1.92; Check
students' graphs. **3.** 12.87, 12.93, 13, 13.03,
13.06; Check students' graphs. **4.** 14.42 < 14.47
5. 0.31 > 0.29 **6.** 0.16 > 0.092 **7.** 3 > 2.99
Practice: 1. 4.82, 4.84, 4.94, 5; Check students'
graphs. **2.** 0.96, 0.98, 1, 1.08; Check students'
graphs. **3.** 5, 6.3, 7, 7.7; Check students' graphs.
4. A **5.** C **6.** B **7.** > **8.** < **9.** > **10.** < **11.** <
12. < **13.** > **14.** > **15.** > **16.** = **17.** < **18.** >
19. > **20.** > **21.** < **22.** Cole; *Sample answer:*
Since 5 < 9, 4.45 < 4.49. Cole jumped farther
than Mario. **23.** Check students' graphs. *Sample
answer:* The weights from least to greatest are
22.58, 22.6, 22.68, and 22.71, so the dogs from
lightest to heaviest are Clyde, Bonnie, Lisa, and
Mona. **24.** your friend; *Sample answer:* Since
8 > 0, 3.68 > 3.6. Your friend typed the same
paragraph in less time, so your friend types faster.
25. column; place values; left; right **26.** Check
students' work. **27.** *Sample answer:* 0.08

Lesson 2-21, pp. 86–89
Try this: 1. $\frac{3}{10}$ **2.** $\frac{27}{100}$ **3.** $\frac{23}{200}$ **4.** $\frac{3}{4}$ **5.** $7\frac{1}{2}$
6. $4\frac{9}{20}$ **7.** $\frac{1}{50}$

Answers *continued*

ANSWERS

Practice: **1.** D **2.** C **3.** A **4.** B **5.** C **6.** A
7. B **8.** D **9.** $\frac{3}{25}$ **10.** $\frac{2}{5}$ **11.** $\frac{5}{8}$ **12.** $\frac{7}{20}$ **13.** $\frac{9}{10}$
14. $\frac{23}{50}$ **15.** $\frac{19}{20}$ **16.** $\frac{7}{25}$ **17.** $\frac{1}{5}$ **18.** $\frac{51}{200}$ **19.** $\frac{7}{40}$
20. $\frac{3}{5}$ **21.** $9\frac{3}{20}$ **22.** $1\frac{1}{10}$ **23.** $3\frac{63}{200}$ **24.** $4\frac{1}{4}$
25. $2\frac{19}{25}$ **26.** $8\frac{1}{2}$ **27.** $2\frac{1}{50}$ **28.** $3\frac{1}{125}$ **29.** $\frac{9}{100}$
30. $\frac{1}{250}$ **31.** $7\frac{13}{20}$ **32.** $5\frac{21}{200}$ **33.** *Sample answer:*
$0.25 = $ twenty-five hundredths $= \frac{25}{100} = \frac{1}{4}$,
$0.75 = $ seventy-five hundredths $= \frac{75}{100} = \frac{3}{4}$
34. *Sample answer:* $3.04 =$ three and four
hundredths $= 3\frac{4}{100} = 3\frac{1}{25}$ **35.** *Sample*
answer: one and seven tenths $= 1.7$ or $1\frac{7}{10}$
36. place value; denominator **37.** no; *Sample*
answer: 0.08 is eight hundredths, not eight
tenths. You would write $\frac{8}{100}$ and then simplify
to $\frac{2}{25}$. **38.** *Sample answer:* $1.14, 1\frac{7}{50}$

Lesson 2-22, pp. 90–93
Try this: **1.** 0.35 **2.** 0.225 **3.** 5.75 **4.** 1.1875
5. $0.\overline{6}$ **6.** $1\frac{3}{8} > 1.36$

Practice: **1–4.** Check students' graphs. **1.** $\frac{9}{10} =$
0.9 **2.** $\frac{1}{2} = 0.5$ **3.** $1\frac{7}{10} = 1.7$ **4.** $2\frac{3}{5} = 2.6$ **5.** C
6. B **7.** D **8.** A **9.** 0.4 **10.** 0.09375 **11.** 1.275
12. 2.26 **13.** $0.08\overline{3}$ **14.** $0.291\overline{6}$ **15.** $4.\overline{6}$
16. $1.\overline{36}$ **17.** = **18.** < **19.** > **20.** < **21.** >
22. < **23.** $7 \div 8 = 0.875$ **24.** $5.41\overline{6}$; *Sample*
answer: I wrote $5\frac{5}{12}$ as $\frac{65}{12}$ and divided 65 by 12 to
get 5.416666…. The 6 repeats, so I wrote $5.41\overline{6}$.
25. *Sample answer:* I wrote $4\frac{7}{16}$ as a decimal
(4.4375) and compared the decimals.
$4.4375 > 4.35$, so the blue paper is wider.
26. terminating **27.** Check students' work.
28. $\frac{3}{12}, \frac{6}{12}$, and $\frac{9}{12}; \frac{3}{12} = 0.25, \frac{6}{12} = 0.5, \frac{9}{12} = 0.75$

Mixed Practice for Lessons 2-18 to 2-22, pp. 94–95
1. B **2.** A **3.** C **4.** repeating decimal **5.** place
value **6.** 14.065 **7.** one hundred five and sixty-
one hundredths **8.** 3; 2.84 **9.** 9; 2.0 or 2
10. 5.26, 5.268, 5.27, 5.271; Check students'
graphs. **11.** 0.45, 0.5, 0.52, 0.6; Check students'
graphs. **12.** < **13.** > **14.** < **15.** > **16.** = **17.** >

18. less; <; Meredith **19.** $\frac{3}{4}$ **20.** $\frac{1}{50}$ **21.** $\frac{29}{50}$
22. $3\frac{3}{5}$ **23.** $4\frac{3}{20}$ **24.** $2\frac{21}{25}$ **25.** $9\frac{9}{10}$ **26.** $\frac{1}{200}$
27. 0.73 **28.** 0.375 **29.** 0.08 **30.** 0.85
31. 3.125 **32.** 1.4 **33.** 5.61 **34.** 1.75 **35.** no;
Sample answer: Since $8\frac{2}{5} > 8.2$, the height of
the rolled poster is longer than the height of
the mailing tube. **36.** more; *Sample answer:* 4.25
rounded to the nearest tenth is 4.3, and $4.3 > 4.25$.

Lesson 2-23, pp. 96–99
Try this: **1.** 7.67 **2.** 17.792 **3.** 2.112 **4.** 8.9
5. 15.422 **6.** 2.54
Practice: **1.** C **2.** B **3.** D **4.** A **5.** 13.955
6. 5.03 **7.** 10.11 **8.** 37.1 **9.** 15.84 **10.** 2.489
11. 14.781 **12.** 5.985 **13.** 5.28 **14.** F **15.** G
16. E **17.** 5.231 **18.** 2.45 **19.** 2.3 **20.** 14
21. 56.4 **22.** 2.24 **23.** 6.23 **24.** 2.195 **25.** 2.38
26. *Sample answer:* To find the difference
between the lengths, subtract $7.4 - 4.18$ to get
3.22 ft. **27.** *Sample answer:* To find how much
you have now, add $10.74 + 4.75$ to get $15.49.
28. *Sample answer:* To find how much longer the
neighbor's driveway is, subtract $78.25 - 25.375$ to
get 52.875 ft. **29.** decimal points **30.** no; *Sample*
answer: She did not line up the decimal points,
and she added a zero to 1.03 to make 4 digits.
When you line up the decimal points correctly,
you do not need to add any zeros. The sum is
13.17. **31.** *Sample answer:* $1.4 - 0.52 = 0.88$

Lesson 2-24, pp. 100–103
Try this: **1.** 120 **2.** 0.07 **3.** 375; 2; 3.75
4. 0040; 3; 0.04
Practice: **1.** E **2.** D **3.** C **4.** A **5.** B **6.** 47.29
7. 779 **8.** 125 **9.** 29,930 **10.** 9520 **11.** 1440.3
12. 56,100 **13.** 9791.3 **14.** 840 **15.** 0.012
16. 1.12 **17.** 8.1 **18.** 0.08 **19.** 1.96 **20.** 36
21. 2.028 **22.** 8.058 **23.** 50.05 **24.** 11.2
25. 10.412 **26.** 0.16 **27.** 12.003 **28.** 27.672
29. 40.68 **30.** *Sample answer:* To find the cost
for a pack of 100 erasers, move the decimal
point 2 places to the right to get $3. **31.** *Sample*
answer: To find the total length across the spines
of 8 reference books, multiply 2.45 by 8 to get
19.6 in. **32.** *Sample answer:* To find the weight
that the crate will contain, multiply 0.8125 by 30
to get 24.375 lb. **33.** right; zero **34.** no; *Sample*
answer: Vladimir placed the decimal point one
decimal place to the right of the leftmost digit of
the answer. He should have placed the decimal

Math Intervention
Teacher's Edition
124

Answers

Answers *continued*

point one decimal place to the left of the rightmost digit of the answer. The correct answer is 138.6.

Activity 2-25, pp. 104–105
Practice: 1. 0.16;

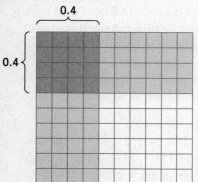

2. 0.45;

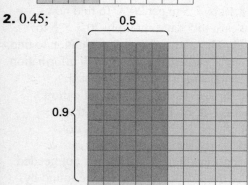

3. 0.12;

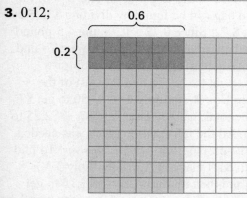

4. 0.12;

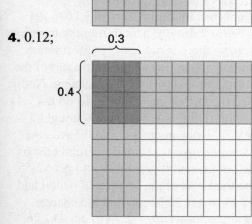

5. 0.35;

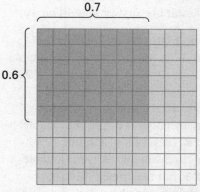

6. *Sample answer:* Multiply the numbers, placing the decimal point so that the product has the same number of decimal places as both factors combined.

Lesson 2-26, pp. 106–109
Try this: 1. 0.24 **2.** 2056.104 **3.** 0.056 **4.** 0.053
Practice: 1. 0.0992 **2.** 6.462 **3.** 45.236
4. 0.003342 **5.** 4.06 **6.** 2.25 **7.** 0.214
8. 301.595 **9.** C **10.** A **11.** D **12.** B **13.** 0.028
14. 0.0035 **15.** 0.0036 **16.** 0.182 **17.** 3.7
18. 0.06 **19.** 0.576 **20.** 7.056 **21.** 46.839
22. 9.723 **23.** 1.8288 **24.** 57.744 **25.** 4.5419
26. 52.563 **27.** 72.8832 **28.** *Sample answer:*
To find the number of ounces the machine can pour in 8.5 minutes, multiply 15.6 by 8.5 to get 132.6 oz. **29.** *Sample answer:* To find the weight that the kitten could gain in 4.25 months, multiply 4.25 by 0.6 to get 2.55 lb. **30.** *Sample answer:* To find how much I pay for the turkey, multiply 0.75 by 7.76 to get $5.82. **31.** decimal places; decimal places **32.** *Sample answer:*
$0.6 \times 0.7 = 0.42$;

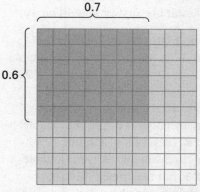

33. *Sample answer:* There are a total of 3 decimal places in the factors, so I place the decimal point between the first 4 and the 8: 24.840. Then I drop the final zero to get 24.84.

Answers *continued*

ANSWERS

Lesson 2-27, pp. 110–113

Try this: 1. 0.585 **2.** 46.772 **3.** 1.16 **4.** 0.561
5. 0.22 **6.** 2.08 **7.** 0.769 **8.** 0.55
Practice: 1. 1.145 **2.** 0.97 **3.** 24.785 **4.** 0.006
5. 0.5264 **6.** 44.976 **7.** 9.18 **8.** 0.000987
9. 0.0242 **10.** E **11.** D **12.** B **13.** C **14.** A
15. 0.08 **16.** 0.3 **17.** 0.1 **18.** 0.41 **19.** 0.01
20. 0.02 **21.** 0 **22.** 0.28 **23.** 1.46 **24.** 9.787
25. 0.576 **26.** 0.083 **27.** 0.479 **28.** 45.87
29. 3.894 **30.** *Sample answer:* To find the width
of each section, divide 8.5 by 5 to get 1.7 in.
31. *Sample answer:* To find the cost of 1 pencil,
divide 0.96 by 12 to get $.08. **32.** *Sample answer:*
To find the mass of one sugar cube, divide 16.7
by 10 to get 1.67 g. **33.** left; zero **34.** yes;
Sample answer: She uses long division, and she
places the decimal point correctly in her answer.

Lesson 2-28, pp. 114–117

Try this: 1. 1.4 **2.** 9 **3.** 20 **4.** 800 **5.** 375
6. 13.28
Practice: 1. C **2.** D **3.** A **4.** B **5.** 1.5 **6.** 0.8
7. 1.4 **8.** 3 **9.** 7.2 **10.** 1.2 **11.** 0.4 **12.** 1.9
13. 4 **14.** 5 **15.** 2.3 **16.** 0.3 **17.** 2.5 **18.** 8
19. 45 **20.** 10 **21.** 5 **22.** 600 **23.** 30 **24.** 70
25. 1200 **26.** 150 **27.** 60 **28.** 35 **29.** *Sample
answer:* To find the number of signs, divide 9
by 0.15 to get 60 signs. **30.** *Sample answer:* To
find the number of employees, divide 124.50 by
12.45 to get 10 employees. **31.** *Sample answer:*
To find the cost of each share, divide 150.94 by
31.35 to get $4.83. **32.** divisor; whole number
33. no; *Sample answer:* Maddox multiplied the
divisor by 100 to get 15, but he did not multiply
the dividend by 100. His division statement
should be 15)600, and his answer should be 40.

Lesson 2-29, pp. 118–121

Try this: 1. 6 **2.** 7 **3.** reasonable **4.** reasonable
Practice: 1. B **2.** A **3.** C **4.** 11 **5.** 4 **6.** 5 **7.** 6
8. 73 **9.** 12 **10.** reasonable **11.** reasonable
12. not reasonable **13.** reasonable **14.** not
reasonable **15.** reasonable **16.** not reasonable
17. reasonable **18.** reasonable **19.** not
reasonable **20.** not reasonable **21.** reasonable
22. reasonable **23.** not reasonable **24.** no;
Sample answer: It will cost about 3 × 3 = $9
to buy 3 packs of grape juice and 4 × 2 = $8 to
buy 2 packs of Sweet-and-Salty Mix. Since
$9 + $8 = $17 and $17 > $15, I do not have
enough money. **25.** yes; 40.4 ÷ 5.05 is 8. I can
check by rounding 40.4 ÷ 5.05 to 40 ÷ 5 = 8. The

answers are the same, so my mother was correct.
26. yes; *Sample answer:* When I fill two 1.5-quart
containers, I use 2 × 1.5 qt of iced tea. Because
2 × 2 = 4, I use about 4 qt of tea. Then I subtract
4 from 5.75 to find how much tea is left. I know
that 6 − 4 = 2, so I have about 2 qt of iced tea left.
Two quarts is enough to fill a 0.5-quart container.
27. decimal; whole number **28.** yes; *Sample
answer:* You can estimate that 12.78 − 5.94 is
about 13 − 6, which is 7. The given answer, 6.84,
is close to 7, so this answer is reasonable.

Lesson 2-30, pp. 122–125

Try this: 1. add; 104.29 + 25.60 = 129.89;
129.89 + 15.14 = 145.03; $145.03 **2.** *Sample
answer:* To find how much you earn each day,
multiply 8.12 by 2.5 to get 20.3. To find how
much you earn in 5 days, multiply 20.3 × 5 to
get $101.50. There was enough information to find
how much was earned, but not enough information
given to decide which days were worked.
Practice: 1. 2, 1 **2.** 1, 2 **3.** multiplication
4. subtraction **5.** division **6. a.** subtract; −;
34.98; 34.98; −; 32.23; $32.23; was not
b. $22.00; hours; cannot **7.** *Sample answer:*
The information about white flour is not needed.
The cost of the 2.5-pound bag can be found by
dividing $1.95 ÷ 2.5 to get $.78. The cost of the
4.5-pound bag can be found by dividing $3.25 by
4.5 to get $.72. Since 0.72 < 0.78, the 4.5-pound
bag is the better buy. **8.** *Sample answer:* To find
the cost of the items from Box A, multiply
3 × $.75 to get $2.25. To find the cost of the
items from Box B, multiply 2 × $3.50 to get $7.
To find the total that you earn, add $7 + $2.25 to
get $9.25. All the information given was needed
to solve the problem. **9.** *Sample answer:* To find
how much Karl made in April, multiply 3.5 × 8
to get 28 and then multiply 28 × $11.15 to get
$312.20. The amount he spent during the month
is not given, so there is not enough information
to find out how much he had left at the end of the
month. **10.** *Sample answer:* This morning, Neill
had $1.50. His brother gave him $3.40 on his
way to school. In the afternoon, Neill bought a
snack for $.79. How much does Neill have now?
11. yes; *Sample answer:* To find the total cost of
the puzzle books, multiply $.85 × 3 to get $2.55.
To find the total cost of the books and pencil add
$2.55 + $.19 to get $2.74. To find the change
he should get, subtract 20 − 2.74 to get $17.26.

Answers *continued*

Rounded to the nearest dollar, $17.26 is $17.00. My friend's answer is reasonable.

Mixed Practice for Lessons 2-23 to 2-30, pp. 126–127

1. A **2.** C **3.** B **4.** decimal places **5.** power of ten; whole number

6. 0.24;

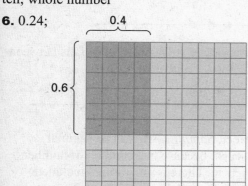

7. 0.25;

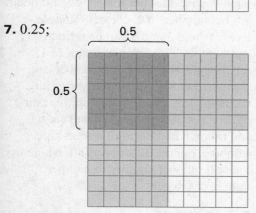

8. 0.84 **9.** 0.52 **10.** 5.65 **11.** 754.2 **12.** 1.787 **13.** 0.018 **14.** 1.72 **15.** 1.05 **16.** 48.072 **17.** 0.0489 **18.** 10.872 **19.** 14.982 **20.** divide; ÷; 12; 12; *Sample answer:* estimating shows that $600 \div 50 = 12$ **21.** 70.43 **22.** 4.7 **23.** 0.112 **24.** 0.5 **25.** 19.836 **26.** 145.48 **27.** 9.4 **28.** 0.9313 **29.** 20 **30.** 9 **31.** 7 **32.** 24 **33.** 3 **34.** 63 **35.** 11 **36.** 3 **37.** *Sample answer:* To find the weight of the large apple, subtract $3.48 - 3.13$ to get 0.35 lb. There is no information given about the smallest apple. You cannot determine its weight. **38.** *Sample answer:* The information about how often the company buys ink is not needed. To find how much the manager spent on the ink last week, multiply 200.65 by 1.4 to get $280.91.

Answers to Book 3 Integers and Rational Numbers

Lesson 3-1, pp. 2–5
Try this: 1. 92, 455, −672 **2.** −15, −19

3.

4. −19 in.
Practice: 1. B **2.** C **3.** A **4.** D **5.** 99, −37, 14 **6.** −1055, 7 **7.** 676, 12 **8.** −15 **9.** −1434, 0 **10.** 10,922, −5

11.

12.

13.

14.

15.

16.

17. decrease; −$14 **18.** decrease; −10 blocks **19.** increase; 3 gal **20.** decrease; −6 slices **21.** positive integers; negative integers **22.** *Sample answer:* A number is an integer if it is a positive whole number, the opposite of a positive whole number, or zero. **23.** *Sample answer:* Real-life increase: Adding 8 songs to your MP3 player can be described with the positive integer 8. Real-life decrease: A penalty in football means that a team loses yardage. Getting a 15 yard penalty in a football game can be described with the negative integer −15.

Lesson 3-2, pp. 6–9
Try this: 1. ② so, 4 units to the *left* ① 4 units to the *right* ; −4

2. ① 2 units to the *left* ② so, 2 units to the *right* ; 2

3. ; 7

4. ; 6; 6

Answers *continued*

Practice: 1. A **2.** D **3.** B **4.** D **5.** 7 **6.** −6
7. 9 **8.** 2 **9.** 1 **10.** −28 **11.** −44 **12.** 199
13. 50 **14.** 0 **15.** 762 **16.** −10 **17.** 78
18. −92 **19.** 31 **20.** 74 **21.** −936 **22.** 302
23. 4002 **24.** −76 **25.** −668 **26.** −65 **27.** 32
28. −8701 **29.** −15 or 15; *Sample answer:*
Both −15 and 15 are the same distance from 0 on
a number line, so each of them has an absolute
value of 15. **30.** *Sample answer:* They must each
determine how far from zero they are. Since they
are on opposite sides of 0, then if their distances
from zero are the same they are holding cards with
opposite numbers on them. **31.** absolute value; 0
32. −3; *Sample answer:* The opposite of −3 is 3,
and the opposite of 3 is −3. **33.** *Sample answer:*
Both the absolute value and opposite of a number
have to do with distance from 0 on a number line.
They are different in that the absolute value of a
number is always positive, while opposites can be
either positive or negative.

Lesson 3-3, pp. 10–13
Try this: 1. > **2.** < **3.** −7, −1, 3, 8 **4.** 8, 4,
−3, −6
Practice: 1–12. Check students' drawings.
1. 9, 4, 1, −2, −7 **2.** 10, 6, 3, −7, −8 **3.** 4, 1, 0,
−6, −12 **4.** 11, 10, 5, −3, −5 **5.** −1, −2, −6,
−8, −14 **6.** 0, −11, −13, −22, −25 **7.** −4, −2,
0, 3, 8 **8.** −10, −3, 0, 4, 10 **9.** −8, −7, 0, 7, 8
10. −10, −4, −2, 4, 8 **11.** −22, −15, −14, 0, 19
12. −30, −20, −18, −13, −2 **13.** Mackenzie;
Mackenzie, Jenna, Morgan **14.** 10°F, 5°F, −2°F,
−3°F, −12°F **15.** Paige; Paige, Bailey, Amber
16. right; left **17.** *Sample answer:* Any positive
integer is always greater than any negative integer.

Lesson 3-4, pp. 14–17
Try this: 1. 58, 1.77 **2.** −12.1, 0, 5.$\overline{6}$
3. 1.2; 1; 2; −2; −3; 3; 4;

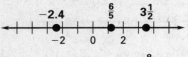

4.

$$-3.\overline{6} \quad -1 \quad \frac{8}{3}$$

Practice: 1. A **2.** C **3.** B **4.** R **5.** R **6.** N
7. R **8.** R **9.** R **10.** R **11.** N

12.

$$-2.5 \quad -1 \quad \frac{3}{5} \qquad 4.9$$

13.

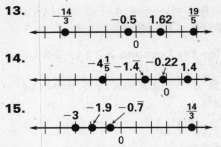

14.

$$-4\frac{1}{5} \quad -1.\overline{4} \quad -0.22 \quad 1.4$$

15.

$$-3 \quad -1.9 \quad -0.\overline{7} \qquad \frac{14}{3}$$

16. incorrect; *Sample answer:* −0.9 falls between
0 and −1, not −1 and −2.;

$$-0.9$$

17. incorrect; *Sample answer:* The decimal
does not repeat because the same set of numbers
does not repeat. There is one more 8 included
between each 9, so it does not repeat. The number
is not a rational number. **18.** correct; *Sample
answer:* Every whole number can be written
as a rational number with a denominator of 1.
19. correct; *Sample answer:* Each number can
be written as the quotient of two integers with a
nonzero denominator. **20.** terminating; repeating
21. *Sample answer:* All whole numbers are
integers and rational numbers; all integers are
rational numbers, but not all integers are whole
numbers; not all rational numbers are either
whole numbers or integers.

Lesson 3-5, pp. 18–21
Try this: 1. = **2.** > **3.** 2.43, 1.07, 0.12, $-2\frac{7}{10}$,
$-\frac{19}{5}$;

$$-\frac{19}{5} \quad -2\frac{7}{10} \quad 0.12 \quad 1.07 \quad 2.43$$

4. $\frac{17}{3}$, $3\frac{7}{20}$, −0.8, $-\frac{7}{2}$, −3.82;

$$-3.82 \quad -\frac{7}{2} \quad -0.8 \quad 3\frac{7}{20} \quad \frac{17}{3}$$

5. 4.31, $\frac{5}{2}$, −0.2, $-\frac{5}{4}$, −3, $-\frac{13}{3}$;

$$-\frac{13}{3} \; -3 \quad -\frac{5}{4} \; -0.2 \quad \frac{5}{2} \quad 4.31$$

Practice: 1. < **2.** > **3.** < **4.** < **5.** = **6.** >
7. $3\frac{7}{8}$, 2.08, −4.2, $-4\frac{2}{5}$ **8.** 4.1, 3.06, $-\frac{23}{3}$,
−8.9 **9.** $-\frac{9}{10}$, $-\frac{907}{1000}$, −0.97 **10.** $\frac{1049}{10}$, $104\frac{3}{16}$,
−10.99, −10.998 **11.** $-3\frac{2}{3}$, −3.66, 2.01, $\frac{21}{10}$

Answers continued

12. $-4.101, -4\frac{1}{100}, 4\frac{1}{100}, 4.101$ **13.** $\frac{33}{12}, \frac{17}{6}, \frac{27}{4},$ $\frac{26}{3}$ **14.** $-13\frac{2}{5}, -13.25, -13.09, -12.9$

15. yes; *Sample answer:* The piece that is $\frac{133}{10}$ feet long; $\frac{133}{10} = 13.3$ feet, which is greater than the 13.25 feet he needs. **16.** Tyrei, Samuel, Garrett, Keisha; *Sample answer:* I changed each fraction to a decimal and compared them. Keisha's $= 12.44$ pounds and Samuel's $= 11.8$ pounds, $10.9 < 11.8 < 12.14 < 12.44$ **17.** my friend; *Sample answer:* I changed yards to feet and compared the rope lengths. My rope is 4 feet long. My friend's rope is $1\frac{2}{3} \times 3 = 5$ feet long. Since $5 > 4$, my friend's rope is longer. **18.** right; left **19.** *Sample answer:* 1) You can change the numbers to fractions with common denominators and then compare the numerators. 2) You can place the numbers on a number line and then write them in order as they appear.

Mixed Practice for Lessons 3-1 to 3-5, pp. 22–23

1. C, Y **2.** A, Z **3.** B, X **4.** absolute value

5.

6.

7. $-16, 16$ **8.** $81, 81$ **9.** $28, 28$ **10.** $-72, 72$ **11.** not rational **12.** rational **13.** rational **14.** rational **15.** rational **16.** rational **17.** $\frac{51}{10}$ **18.** $\frac{33}{10}$ **19.** $-\frac{2}{5}$ **20.** $\frac{172}{25}$ **21.** $\frac{7}{10}$ **22.** $\frac{533}{100}$ **23.** $\frac{32}{5}$ **24.** $\frac{1977}{250}$ **25.** $-3, -1, 0, 1, 4$; Eli **26.** $80.01, $57.75

Activity 3-6, pp. 24–25

Practice: 1. -2 **2.** 1 **3.** 2 **4.** -4 **5.** *Sample answer:* When adding integers of opposite signs, take their absolute values, subtract the smaller from the larger, and give the result the sign of the integer with the larger absolute value. **6.** 1 **7.** 4 **8.** -6 **9.** -3 **10.** -3 **11.** -4 **12.** -8 **13.** -4 **14.** *Sample answer:* Add the absolute values of the integers and then make the sum negative. **15.** -6 **16.** -6 **17.** -12 **18.** -30 **19.** -8 **20.** -6 **21.** -2 **22.** -20

Lesson 3-7, pp. 26–29

Try this: 1. Check students' drawings; 1 **2.** Check students' drawings; -4 **3.** Check students' drawings; 0 **4.** Check students' drawings; -3 **5.** 7; 8; 15; -15
Practice: 1. B **2.** A **3.** C **4.** Check students' drawings; -3 **5.** Check students' drawings; -1 **6.** Check students' drawings; 5 **7.** -12 **8.** -23 **9.** -18 **10.** -25 **11.** -5 **12.** -158 **13.** -23 **14.** 0 **15.** $-10 + (-5) + (-8)$; absolute values; -23 in.; *Sample answer:* The hole is currently 23 inches below the surface of the ground. **16.** $3 + (-1)$; number line; 2; *Sample answer:* There are 2 gallons of water left in the can after Harley waters the flowers. **17.** number line; left; right **18.** *Sample answer:* It is easiest to use absolute values when all of the integers in the sum have the same sign.

Lesson 3-8, pp. 30–33

Try this: 1. Check students' drawings; -3 **2.** Check students' drawings; -4 **3.** 8 **4.** -11
Practice: 1. B **2.** C **3.** A **4.** Check students' drawings; -4 **5.** Check students' drawings; -3 **6.** Check students' drawings; 0 **7.** 4 **8.** 13 **9.** 0 **10.** -25 **11.** -7 **12.** 23 **13.** -26 **14.** -65 **15.** $84 - 14$; 70; *Sample answer:* The temperature at 8:00 P.M. was 70°F. **16.** $185 - 120$; 65; *Sample answer:* Brandon needs to save $65 more for the bike. **17.** $-65 - (-20)$; -45; *Sample answer:* The change in elevation of the elevator was -45 feet. **18.** left; right **19.** *Sample answer:* When subtracting integers, add the opposite of the integer being subtracted.

Lesson 3-9, pp. 34–37

Try this: 1. $8 + 8 + 8 + 8 + 8 = 40$ **2.** $-4 + (-4) = -8$ **3.** $6 + 6 + 6 + 6 = 24$ **4.** $-7 + (-7) + (-7) = -21$ **5.** negative **6.** positive **7.** negative **8.** positive **9.** -60 **10.** 32
Practice: 1. A **2.** C **3.** B **4.** 50 **5.** -32 **6.** -132 **7.** -100 **8.** 42 **9.** 0 **10.** -72 **11.** 120 **12.** -33 **13.** 6 **14.** -48 **15.** -180 **16.** 0 **17.** 24 **18.** -35 **19.** -192 **20.** $(-2)(12)$; negative; -24; *Sample answer:* The temperature dropped 24°F in 12 hours. **21.** $(-6)(15)$; negative; -90; *Sample answer:* Sylvia burns 90 calories running for 15 minutes. **22.** $20(5)$; positive; 100; *Sample answer:* Chandler drives 100 miles to and from work in 5 days. **23.** negative; positive **24.** *Sample answer:* Multiplication is like

Answers *continued*

repeated addition since $3(-2) = -2 + (-2) + (-2) = -6$.

Lesson 3-10, pp. 38–41
Try this: 1. $\underline{?} \times (-3) = 36$ **2.** $\underline{?} \times (-5) = -15$ **3.** 8 **4.** -8 **5.** 25 **6.** -12
Practice: 1. N **2.** P **3.** N **4.** P **5.** $\underline{?} \times (-5) = 105$ **6.** $\underline{?} \times (-12) = 156$ **7.** $\underline{?} \times 11 = -99$ **8.** $\underline{?} \times (-4) = -32$ **9.** 5 **10.** -7
11. -25 **12.** 8 **13.** 7 **14.** 12 **15.** 9 **16.** -6
17. $75 \div 5$; 15; *Sample answer:* Each person receives 15 pieces of strawberries. **18.** $675 \div 3$; 225; *Sample answer:* Each person can use 225 minutes on the cellular telephone each month.
19. positive; negative **20.** *Sample answer:* One method for finding a quotient is to begin by representing the quotient as a multiplication expression and then using mental math to solve it.

Lesson 3-11, pp. 42–45
Try this: 1. 35 ft; $140 \div 4 = 35$ **2.** 82°F; *Sample answer:* 5 days times an increase of 3° each day $= 5 \times 3 = 15°$ increase. Day zero had a high of 67°F. $67°F + 15°F = 82°F$
Practice: 1. B **2.** C **3.** D **4.** A
5. multiplication **6.** addition **7.** subtraction
8. *Sample answers:* division by 3 or multiplication by $\frac{1}{3}$ **9.** add; $+$; -7; $-7°F$
10. multiply; $\times$; 52; 52 **11.** *Sample answer:* Each of 3 curtains needs 4 yards of fabric. So, multiply 3 times 4 to get 12 yards. **12.** $6\frac{1}{4}$ yd of rope; *Sample answer:* 50 yd split or divided into $8 = 50 \div 8 = 6.25$. **13.** Division; 5 chaperones; *Sample answer:* Since a group is being divided into equal smaller groups, division must be performed, $75 \div 15 = 5$. **14.** Multiplication then addition; 55 baseball cards; multiplication must first be used to find how many cards Simon has, $15 \times 3 = 45$ baseball cards. Then 10 must be added to 45 to find how many baseball cards Garret has, $45 + 10 = 55$. **15.** Check students' work.
16. *Sample answer:* Look at what information is given and how the information is related.

Lesson 3-12, pp. 46–49
Try this: 1. $-1\frac{9}{10}$ **2.** 2.596 **3.** -12 **4.** $-\frac{1}{15}$
5. $\frac{70}{207}$ **6.** 9.9

Practice: 1. 2 **2.** $2\frac{1}{35}$ **3.** 47.6 **4.** -7.7 **5.** $-\frac{1}{6}$
6. $-\frac{6}{7}$ **7.** $81\frac{2}{3}$ **8.** $-\frac{25}{38}$ **9.** 12.61 **10.** $-\frac{7}{16}$
11. $9\frac{7}{12}$ **12.** -14.3 **13.** 80.691 **14.** $-9\frac{1}{45}$
15. $-4\frac{11}{12}$ **16.** -4.915 **17.** 11.271 **18.** 9.7
19. addition; *Sample answer:* $\frac{3}{10} + \frac{2}{5} = \frac{7}{10}$ of the pizza **20.** multiplication; *Sample answer:* $150 \times 0.2 = 30$ sheets **21.** division; *Sample answer:* $16.8 \div 4 = 4.2$ oz **22.** $\frac{a}{b}$ where $b \neq 0$
23. *Sample answer:* Rewrite the rational numbers so they are all in the same form, all decimals or all fractions. Then use the rules for performing operations with decimals or fractions.

Lesson 3-13, pp. 50–53
Try this: 1. $5 \times 5 \times 5 = 125$ **2.** $10 \times 10 \times 10 \times 10 = 10,000$ **3.** $1.8 \times 1.8 = 3.24$
4. $2.3 \times 2.3 \times 2.3 = 12.167$ **5.** $\frac{1}{4} \times \frac{1}{4} \times \frac{1}{4} = \frac{1}{64}$ **6.** $\frac{4}{5} \times \frac{4}{5} = \frac{16}{25}$
Practice: 1. C **2.** A **3.** 16 **4.** $\frac{4}{25}$ **5.** 132.651
6. 51.84 **7.** 144 **8.** $\frac{81}{256}$ **9.** $\frac{1}{32}$ **10.** 614.125
11. 2197 **12.** 23.04 **13.** 15,625 **14.** $\frac{1296}{2401}$
15. $(12.3)^2$; 151.29 ft² **16.** 3^3; 27 teammates
17. $\left(\frac{1}{2}\right)^2$, or $\frac{1}{4}$ cup **18.** exponent; base; multiply
19. *Sample answer:* When taking fractions to a power, the power is applied to the entire base, both the numerator and the denominator. The exponent tells how many times the entire fraction (the base) must be multiplied together.

Mixed Practice for Lessons 3-7 to 3-13, pp. 54–55
1. C, Z **2.** A, Y **3.** B, X **4.** positive, negative
5. -2 **6.** -24 **7.** 9 **8.** 12 **9.** 7 **10.** 15
11. -2 **12.** 84 **13.** -9 **14.** -1 **15.** -52
16. -30 **17.** subtraction and multiplication; $-$; $\frac{4}{5}$; $\times$; $\frac{1}{2}$, $\frac{1}{2}$ **18.** 125 **19.** 0.09 **20.** $\frac{81}{256}$
21. 1.44 **22.** division; \$1.34; *Sample answer:* Dividing the total amount, \$4.02, by the number of people, 3, gives the amount each person must pay, \$1.34. **23.** division; Emma had the fastest time; *Sample answer:* $\frac{19}{20} = 0.95$ minute, $\frac{11}{12} = 0.92$ minute, so Emma's time of 0.9 minute is the fastest.

Answers *continued*

Answers to Book 4 Ratios, Rates, Proportions, and Percents

Lesson 4-1, pp. 2–5

Try this: 1. $\frac{3}{8}$; 3:8; 3 to 8 **2.** $\frac{7}{12}$; 7:12; 7 to 12

3. basket with 5 oranges; *Sample answer:* Basket 1: $\frac{1}{5}$, Basket 2: $\frac{3}{4}$ **4.** Jamilla;

Kendra: $\frac{3}{7}$, Jamilla: $\frac{4}{7}$

Practice: 1. $\frac{3}{7}$; 3 to 7 **2.** 20 **3.** 14 **4.** 7 **5.** $\frac{36}{97}$

6. $\frac{33}{119}$ **7.** $\frac{29}{92}$ **8.** Best A; Worst B **9.** $\frac{221}{720}$

10. $\dfrac{\text{number of 6th grade students}}{\text{number of 8th grade students}} = \dfrac{76}{89}$ **11.** <

12. < **13.** < **14.** = **15.** Willis: $\frac{7}{10}$, Joe: $\frac{2}{3}$;

Willis; *Sample answer:* Willis had the better practice because his decimal equivalent is 0.7, and that is larger than Joe's, which is $0.\overline{6}$.

16. Hakim: $\frac{82}{157} \approx 0.52$, Juan: $\frac{54}{157} \approx 0.34$;

Sample answer: Hakim came closer to the ratio of 0.45. He is about 0.07 higher than the ratio, and Juan is about 0.11 lower. **17.** fractions; decimal **18.** Ty **19.** Michael's; *Sample answer:* $\frac{10}{6}$? $\frac{12}{8}$; $1.\overline{6} > 1.5$, so Michael's lap speed is greater.

Lesson 4-2, pp. 6–9

Try this: 1. 31 notecards per session **2.** 3 bird houses per day **3.** numerator; 60; 60, 180; 180 miles

Practice: 1. B; *Sample answer:* The other choices represent ratios, but not rates, because their units are of the same type. **2.** D; *Sample answer:* The denominator is not a single unit. **3.** 40 words per minute **4.** 60 miles per hour

5. 2 batches per hour **6.** $1\frac{1}{3}$ lawns per hour

7. $.50 per tomato **8.** $4.33 per cap **9.** $.21 per pencil **10.** 12 CDs for $64 **11.** 10 lb for $16.38

12. $\dfrac{8 \text{ min}}{1 \text{ km}}$; 80 min; *Sample answer:* I chose to multiply because the unknown value "minutes" is in the numerator of the unit rate. **13.** $\dfrac{50 \text{ envelopes}}{1 \text{ h}}$;

200 envelopes; *Sample answer:* I chose to multiply because the unknown value "envelopes" is in the numerator of the unit rate. **14.** $\dfrac{36 \text{ pages}}{1 \text{ h}}$;

8 h; *Sample answer:* I chose to divide because the unknown value "hours" is in the denominator of the unit rate. **15.** numerator; denominator **16.** 219 miles per hour **17.** *Sample answer:* $5.99; I chose to use multiplication because the unknown value "cost" is in the numerator of the unit rate. *Note:* If intermediate rounding is used, $6.12 is also correct.

Lesson 4-3, pp. 10–13

Try this: 1. divide; 100 **2.** divide; 1000 **3.** multiply; 10 **4.** 3650 g **5.** 710 mm **6.** 49.1 kL **7.** 9400 hm **8.** 137,000 cg **Practice: 1.** 1000 **2.** 1000 **3.** 10 **4.** 1000 **5.** *Sample answer:* 23 hm = (23 × 10,000) cm **6.** *Sample answer:* 1320 dag = (1320 ÷ 100) kg **7.** *Sample answer:* 37,500,000 mL = (37,500,000 ÷ 1000) L **8.** *Sample answer:* 2300 cm = (2300 ÷ 10) dm **9.** *Sample answer:* 32 km = (32 × 1,000,000) mm **10.** *Sample answer:* 230 dag = (230 × 10) g **11.** *Sample answer:* 1350 mL = (1350 ÷ 10) cL **12.** *Sample answer:* 97 dm = (97 × 100) mm **13.** *Sample answer:* 34,000,000 cg = (34,000,000 ÷ 10,000) hg **14.** *Sample answer:* 7500 L = (7500 ÷ 10) daL **15.** *Sample answer:* 272,000 mm = (272,000 ÷ 1000) m **16.** 3900 **17.** 52,000 **18.** 0.3 **19.** divide; length: 12.2 dm, width: 3.1 dm, height: 24.4 dm; *Sample answer:* Since the units were given in centimeters, and decimeters is larger, you divide by 10. **20.** divide; 2 L; *Sample answer:* Since the units were given in milliliters, and liters is larger, you divide by 1000. **21.** multiply; 180 cm; *Sample answer:* Since the units were given in meters, and centimeters are smaller, you multiply by 100. **22.** multiply; 1000 **23.** 230 g = (230 × 100) cg **24.** 0.237 L; *Sample answer:* Since the units were given in milliliters, and liters are larger, you divide by 1000.

Lesson 4-4, pp. 14–17

Try this: 1. 5 × 16 = 80; 80 **2.** 15,840 ÷ 5280 = 3; 3 **3.** 216 in. **4.** 2.25 gal **5.** 448 fl oz **Practice: 1.** divide by 16 **2.** multiply by 2 **3.** multiply by 60 **4.** multiply by 8 **5.** *Sample answer:* 3 × 24 **6.** *Sample answer:* 2 × 5280 **7.** *Sample answer:* 36 ÷ 8 **8.** *Sample answer:* 10 ÷ 4 **9.** *Sample answer:* 12 × 3 **10.** *Sample answer:* 32,000 ÷ 2000 **11.** *Sample answer:* (3 × 4) × 2 **12.** *Sample answer:* (12 × 60) × 60

Answers continued

13. *Sample answer:* 3.5×2000 **14.** *Sample answer:* 6×8 **15.** *Sample answer:* 2×1760 **16.** *Sample answer:* 13×16 **17.** divide; 4.5 mi; *Sample answer:* Since miles are larger than feet, divide by the conversion value 5280. **18.** multiply; 21,600 min; *Sample answer:* Since minutes are smaller than days, multiply by the conversion values for hours in a day and minutes in an hour. **19.** multiply; 128 c; *Sample answer:* Since cups are smaller than gallons, multiply by the conversion values for quarts in a gallon, pints in a quart, and cups in a pint. **20.** feet; multiply **21.** *Sample answer:* 41 yd = (41×3) ft = 123 ft **22.** 80 oz; *Sample answer:* Since ounces are smaller than pounds, multiply by the conversion value 16.

Lesson 4-5, pp. 18–21

Try this: 1. 53.81 ft **2.** 0.53 gal **3.** 3.50 kg **4.** 12.95; > **5.** 32 gal > 50 L **6.** 132 ft³ > 2 m³ **7.** 12 g < 2 oz

Practice: 1. multiplication **2.** multiplication **3.** division **4.** multiplication **5.** 85.71 ft³ **6.** 0.63 oz **7.** 25 **8.** 9.32 **9.** 15.62 **10.** 60.56 L **11.** 8.9 **12.** 15.62 m² **13.** 18 mi² **14.** 13 g **15.** 4 fl oz **16.** 7°C **17.** *Sample answer:* multiplication; 117 lb = 53.1 kg; Kevin weighs less because 53.1 > 51. **18.** *Sample answer:* division; 12 m³ = 428.57 ft³; The second container can hold the most liquid because 428.57 < 450. **19.** *Sample answer:* division; 40 km = 24.86 mi; The first path is longer because 24.86 > 24. **20.** liters; multiply **21.** *Sample answer:* 32 ÷ 2.59 = 12.36, so 32 km² = 12.36 mi² **22.** 14 kg; *Sample answer:* I converted 14 kg to 30.84 lb by dividing 14 by 0.454. 30.84 lb is less than 35 lb, so 14 kg is the lesser weight.

Activity 4-6, pp. 22–23

Practice: 1. $\frac{7}{8}$ in. by 1 in. **2.** $\frac{3}{4}$ in. by 1 in. **3.** 45 ft by 20 ft **4.** 25 ft by 20 ft **5.** Check students' work. **6.** 100 m by 350 m

Lesson 4-7, pp. 24–27

Try this: 1. 12 **2.** 24 **3.** $5 \cdot x = 7 \cdot 10$; $5 \cdot x = 70$; $\frac{5x}{5} = \frac{70}{5}$; $x = 14$ **4.** $x \cdot 3 = 2 \cdot 9$; $3 \cdot x = 18$; $\frac{3x}{3} = \frac{18}{3}$; $x = 6$

Practice: 1. $\frac{3}{10}$ **2.** $\frac{19}{6}$ **3.** $\frac{5}{7}$ **4.** $\frac{5}{9}$ **5.** $\frac{13}{1}$ **6.** $\frac{2}{1}$ **7.** $9x$, 4×7 **8.** $10x$, 7×13 **9.** C **10.** B **11.** 45 **12.** 4.5 **13.** 26 **14.** 4.5 **15.** *Sample answer:* Kendra should have used $\frac{14}{1}$ as the multiplicative inverse. She forgot to take the multiplicative inverse of the fraction with the variable. The correct answer is $x = 10$. **16.** $x = 16$ in.; yes; *Sample answer:* $\frac{8}{9}$ is the shorter side to the longer side, and the second fraction is set up the same way. **17.** multiply; diagonal **18.** 8 **19.** 6 ft × 9 ft; yes; *Sample answer:* His proportion is set up as $\frac{\text{shorter side}}{\text{longer side}}$.

Lesson 4-8, pp. 28–31

Try this: 1. 7; 4; 14 **2.** $4\frac{1}{3}$ **3.** $2\frac{2}{7}$ **4.** *Sample answer:* $10 \cdot x = 6 \cdot 22$; $x = 13.2$ **5.** *Sample answer:* $\frac{260 \text{ m}}{32.5 \text{ cm}} = \frac{x \text{ m}}{10 \text{ cm}}$; $32.5 \cdot x = 260 \cdot 10$; $x = 80$

Practice: 1. $7\frac{1}{2}$ **2.** 30 **3.** 3 **4.** 27 **5.** 34.6 min **6.** $44\frac{4}{9}$ min **7.** *Sample answer:* $\frac{3}{2} = \frac{15}{x}$ **8.** *Sample answer:* $\frac{1.5 \text{ in.}}{40 \text{ mi}} = \frac{13.5 \text{ in.}}{x \text{ mi}}$ **9.** *Sample answer:* $\frac{1 \text{ in.}}{200 \text{ ft}} = \frac{x}{8981 \text{ ft}}$; $x \approx 44.9$ in.; I wrote the scale 1 inch : 200 feet as $\frac{1 \text{ in.}}{200 \text{ ft}}$ and then set this equal to $\frac{\text{unknown length in inches}}{\text{given length: 8981 ft}}$, or $\frac{x}{8981 \text{ ft}}$. **10.** *Sample answer:* $\frac{30 \text{ pages}}{1 \text{ h}} = \frac{318 \text{ pages}}{x}$; 10.6 h; I wrote the unit rate of 30 pages in 1 hour as $\frac{30 \text{ pages}}{1 \text{ h}}$ and set this equal to $\frac{318 \text{ pages}}{\text{unknown length of time}}$, or $\frac{318 \text{ pages}}{x}$. **11.** *Sample answer:* $\frac{6 \text{ mi}}{1 \text{ h}} = \frac{x}{1.5 \text{ h}}$; 9 miles; I wrote Marco's rate on Tuesday, 15 miles in 2.5 hours, as $\frac{15 \text{ mi}}{2.5 \text{ h}} = \frac{30 \text{ mi}}{5 \text{ h}} = \frac{6 \text{ mi}}{1 \text{ h}}$, and set this equal to $\frac{\text{unknown distance}}{1.5 \text{ h}}$, or $\frac{x}{1.5 \text{ h}}$. **12.** fraction; same **13.** 2; *Sample answer:* Write the cross products: $3 \cdot 12 = k \cdot 18$. Multiply and simplify each side to get $36 = 18k$. Divide by 18 to get $2 = k$. **14.** no; *Sample answer:* The proportion for this problem is $\frac{15 \text{ mi}}{x} = \frac{35 \text{ mi}}{1 \text{ h}}$. When you solve this, you get about 0.43 hours, which is approximately 26 minutes.

Answers continued

Mixed Practice for Lessons 4-1 to 4-8, pp. 32–33

1. B, Z **2.** C, X **3.** A, Y **4.** Unit conversion

5. *Sample answer:* multiplicative inverse or reciprocal **6.** scale **7.** $\frac{28}{75}$ **8.** $\frac{15}{41}$ **9.** 54 miles per hour **10.** 2 cars per hour **11.** 6 × 60; 6 h = 360 min **12.** 7300 ÷ 100; 7300 cm = 73 m

13. 7.57 ÷ 3.785; 7.57 L = 2 gal **14.** 3.5 × 0.454; 3.5 lb = 1.589 kg **15.** 6 **16.** 6 **17.** 18 **18.** 12

19. $\frac{\$13}{24 \text{ bottles}}$; $.54 per bottle; $19.44; *Sample answer:* When you multiply the cost per bottle ($.54) by 36, you get $19.44 for a 36-bottle case.

20. $\frac{\$29.60}{10 \text{ gallons}}$; $2.96 per gallon; $44.40; *Sample answer:* When you multiply the cost per gallon ($2.96) by 15, you get $44.40 for 15 gallons of gasoline.

21. Warren: $\frac{1700}{31}$ words per minute, Cristina: $\frac{5000}{77}$ words per minute; *Sample answer:* Cristina types faster because the decimal conversion of her rate is about 64.9 words per minute. Warren's typing rate is about 54.8 words per minute.

Lesson 4-9, pp. 34–37

Try this: 1. 80; $\frac{4}{5}$ **2.** 65; $\frac{13}{20}$ **3.** 25; $\frac{1}{4}$ **4.** 10; $\frac{1}{10}$ **5.** 20; 20 **6.** 45; 45 **7.** 92; 92 **8.** 13; 13

9. *Sample answer:*

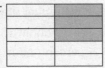

10. *Sample answer:*

11. *Sample answer:*

12. *Sample answer:*

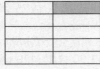

Practice: 1. $\frac{3}{20}$ **2.** $\frac{7}{20}$ **3.** $\frac{1}{2}$ **4.** $\frac{17}{20}$ **5.** $\frac{1}{20}$ **6.** $\frac{2}{5}$

7. $\frac{3}{5}$ **8.** $\frac{19}{20}$ **9.** 0.25 **10.** 0.10 **11.** 0.42 **12.** 0.87

13. 0.32 **14.** 0.09 **15.** 0.77 **16.** 0.53 **17.** B

18. *Sample answer:*

19. *Sample answer:*

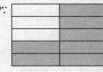

20. *Sample answer:*

21. *Sample answer:*

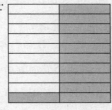

22. 50% **23.** 75% **24.** 0.40, $\frac{2}{5}$; *Sample answer:*

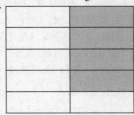

25. 0.25, $\frac{1}{4}$; *Sample answer:*

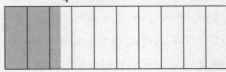

26. 0.70, $\frac{7}{10}$; *Sample answer:*

ANSWERS

27. 0.10, $\frac{1}{10}$;

Sample answer:

28. *Sample answer:*

29. fraction; numerator; 100; denominator

Lesson 4-10, pp. 38–41

Try this: **1.** 13 **2.** 91 **3.** 57 **4.** 8 **5.** 40 **6.** 90
7. 31.25 **8.** 87.5 **9.** *Sample answer:* $\frac{1}{3} \overset{?}{=} \frac{30}{100}$;
$1 \cdot 100 \overset{?}{=} 3 \cdot 30$; $100 \neq 90$ **10.** *Sample*
answer: $\frac{22}{100} \overset{?}{=} \frac{11}{50}$; $22 \cdot 50 \overset{?}{=} 11 \cdot 100$; $1100 = 1100$
Practice: **1.** 67% **2.** 30% **3.** 19% **4.** 26%
5. 55% **6.** 71% **7.** 33% **8.** 49% **9.** 80%
10. 25% **11.** 30% **12.** 57% **13.** $83.\overline{3}$%
14. $85.\overline{45}$% **15.** $46.\overline{6}$% **16.** $36.\overline{36}$% **17.** B
18. D **19.** A **20.** C **21.** D **22.** B **23.** A **24.** C
25. Abby; *Sample answer:* $\frac{18}{20} = 0.90 = 90\%$.
90% is greater than 87%. **26.** Adam; *Sample*
answer: $\frac{67}{100} = 67\%$. This is less than 70%.
27. Beatrice; *Sample answer:* $\frac{3}{5} = 60\%$. This is
greater than 55%. **28.** divide; denominator; right
29. 20 **30.** Jordan; *Sample answer:* Kelly ran $\frac{4}{5}$,
or 80%, of the race at her fastest pace. Since
$80 < 96$, Jordan ran her fastest pace for more
of the race.

Lesson 4-11, pp. 42–45

Try this: **1.** 5.4 **2.** 4.5 **3.** 7 **4.** 3.2 **5.** 9 **6.** 3.6
7. 60 tickets **8.** 18 pages
Practice: **1.** C **2.** A **3.** D **4.** B **5.** 3.5 **6.** 9
7. 2 **8.** 6 **9.** 1 **10.** 12 **11.** 6 **12.** 28.5
13. *Sample answer:* $\frac{25}{100} = \frac{x}{132}$ **14.** *Sample*
answer: $\frac{20}{100} = \frac{x}{10}$ **15.** *Sample answer:* $\frac{25}{100} = \frac{x}{8}$
16. *Sample answer:* $\frac{10}{100} = \frac{x}{30}$; $x = 3$; When
Veronica sells 10% of 30 signatures, she sells

3 signatures. **17.** *Sample answer:* $\frac{75}{100} = \frac{x}{40}$;
$x = 30$; When Hyun washes 75% of 40 cars, he
washes 30 cars. **18.** *Sample answer:* $\frac{65}{100} = \frac{x}{20}$;
$x = 13$; When Cora makes 65% of 20 shots, she
makes 13 shots. **19.** *Sample answer:* $\frac{25}{100} = \frac{x}{16}$;
$x = 4$; When Isaac buys lunch 25% of 16 days,
he buys lunch 4 days. **20.** percent; proportion;
percent; numerator **21.** *Sample answer:* $\frac{40}{100} = \frac{x}{30}$
22. 20 pages

Lesson 4-12, pp. 46–49

Try this: **1.** $\frac{102 - 85}{85} = \frac{17}{85} = 20\%$ increase
2. $\frac{51 - 45}{51} = \frac{6}{51} \approx 12\%$ decrease
Practice: **1.** increase **2.** decrease **3.** decrease
4. increase **5.** ≈18% **6.** ≈30% **7.** 100%
8. 80% **9.** 60% **10.** ≈23% **11.** 24% **12.** ≈57%
13. increase; ≈60%; *Sample answer:* The number
of books Olivia read increased by $\frac{40 - 25}{25} = 60\%$
from last summer to this summer. **14.** decrease;
≈6%; *Sample answer:* The number of sixth grade
students decreased by $\frac{250 - 234}{250} =$ about 6% from
last year to this year. **15.** increase; ≈15%; *Sample*
answer: The number of plants the garden center
sold increased by $\frac{132 - 115}{115} =$ about 15% from last
weekend to this weekend. **16.** decrease; ≈13%;
Sample answer: The number of balls Ralph hit
decreased by $\frac{32 - 28}{32} =$ about 13% from last week
to this week. **17.** percent; numerator; increase;
decrease; original **18.** 20% increase

Lesson 4-13, pp. 50–53

Try this: **1.** $28.00 **2.** $56.25 **3.** $65.00
4. $96.00
Practice: **1.** add **2.** add **3.** subtract **4.** $14.00
5. $72.00 **6.** $66.00 **7.** $102.00 **8.** $64.90
9. $44.16 **10.** $200.00 **11.** $60.00 **12.** $220.00
13. $350.00 **14.** $165.00; *Sample answer:*
$100 + ($100 × 0.65) = $165 **15.** $52.50;
Sample answer: $75 − ($75 × 0.30) = $52.50
16. $280.00; *Sample answer:* $3500 × 0.08 =
$280.00 **17.** $140.50; *Sample answer:* $194.25 −
$53.75 = $140.50 **18.** add; tip; bill **19.** $25.50
20. $231.25

Lesson 4-14, pp. 54–57

Try this: **1.** 550; 0.07; 4; $154.00 **2.** 870; 0.037;
2.5; $80.48 **3.** $43.55 **4.** $355.86 **5.** $832.00

Answers continued

Practice: 1. $\frac{1}{3}$ year **2.** $\frac{1}{2}$ year
3. *Sample answer:* $\frac{7}{4}$ or $1\frac{3}{4}$ years **4.** *Sample*
answer: $\frac{8}{3}$ or $2\frac{2}{3}$ years **5.** $14.51 **6.** $49.34
7. $114.00 **8.** $195.08 **9.** $42.00
10. $2111.50 **11.** $66.41 **12.** $297.60
13. $212.00 **14.** $1082.73 **15.** $825.60
16. $1728.13 **17.** 0.032; $73.60; *Sample*
answer: $460 \times 0.032 \times 5 = 73.6$ **18.** 0.057;
$32.06; *Sample answer:* $375 \times 0.057 \times 1.5 =$
32.06 **19.** 0.05; $15.00; *Sample answer:* $300 \times$
$0.05 \times 1 = 15$ **20.** 0.045; $264.38; *Sample*
answer: $2350 \times 0.045 \times 2.5 = 264.38$
21. principal; decimal; time **22.** $590.70

Lesson 4-15, pp. 58–61
Try this: 1. $624.00; $648.96; $674.92
2. $870.40; $891.29; $912.68; $934.58 **3.** 285;
0.019; 6; $319.07 **4.** 1200; 0.087; 2; $1417.88
Practice: 1. $600; 0.04; $624.00; $624.00;
$648.96; $648.96; $674.92 **2.** $421.82
3. $1141.46 **4.** $158.29 **5.** $282.47
6. $1462.08 **7.** $897.82 **8.** $514.87
9. $1119.15 **10.** 4; $389.81 **11.** 2; $703.04
12. Monty; *Sample answer:* The amount in
Jong's account is $538.45, and the amount in
Monty's account is $552.30. **13.** principal;
interest; previously **14.** $506.65

Activity 4-16, pp. 62–63
Practice: 1. $\frac{4}{25}$ **2.** $\frac{6}{25}$ **3.** $\frac{1}{25}$ **4.** $\frac{1}{5}$ **5.** $\frac{7}{50}$
6. $\frac{11}{50}$ **7.** *Sample answer:* 24 green marbles;
$\frac{6}{25}(100) = 24$

Lesson 4-17, pp. 64–67
Try this: 1. 10; $\frac{1}{5}$ **2.** $\frac{13}{50}$ **3.** frog; pencil **4.** $\frac{7}{8}$
5. $\frac{5}{6}$

Practice: 1. C **2.** A **3.** B **4.** $\frac{6}{25}$ **5.** $\frac{2}{5}$ **6.** $\frac{1}{5}$
7. marbled **8.** $\frac{1}{5}$ **9.** $\frac{1}{4}$ **10.** $\frac{3}{10}$ **11.** $\frac{4}{5}$ **12.** $\frac{3}{4}$
13. $\frac{3}{4}$ **14.** $\frac{4}{9}$; *Sample answer:* There are 4 blue
squares out of 9 total squares. **15.** $\frac{11}{12}$; *Sample*
answer: There is one 10 side on a 12-sided
number cube, and $\frac{12}{12} - \frac{1}{12} = \frac{11}{12}$. **16.** yellow;
green; $\frac{1}{5}$; *Sample answer:* There are more yellow

marbles in the box than any other color, so
that color has the greatest probability of being
pulled. There are fewer green marbles in the box
than any other color, so that color has the least
probability of being pulled. The probability of a
blue marble being pulled is $\frac{15}{75}$, or $\frac{1}{5}$. **17.** number
of favorable outcomes; total number of possible
outcomes **18.** $\frac{8}{15}$ **19.** $\frac{7}{15}$; *Sample answer:* The
probability of pulling a pink ribbon is $\frac{8}{15}$. The
probability of not pulling a pink ribbon is one
minus the probability of pulling a pink ribbon,
or $1 - \frac{8}{15} = \frac{7}{15}$.

Mixed Practice for Lessons 4-9 to 4-17, pp. 68–69
1. B, Z **2.** C, Y **3.** A, X **4.** compound interest
5. percent **6.** probability **7.** $\frac{7}{25}$, 0.28 **8.** 40%, 0.4
9. 45%, $\frac{9}{20}$ **10.** $\frac{3}{10}$, 0.3 **11.** 35%, $\frac{7}{20}$ **12.** 12.5%,
0.125 **13.** $\frac{3}{4}$, 0.75 **14.** 42.86%, 0.4286 **15.** $\frac{1}{50}$,
2% **16.** 30 **17.** 32.5 **18.** 3.75 h **19.** $5.85 tip
20. 150%; increase **21.** ≈29.34%; decrease
22. $85.10 **23.** $464.60 **24.** $\frac{5}{6}$ **25.** $\frac{1}{6}$ **26.** add;
$371.25; *Sample answer:* $275 + ($275 \times 0.35) =$
$371.25 **27.** calculate, then add; $711.80; *Sample*
answer: ($3530 \times 0.06) + $500 = $711.80

Answers to Book 5 Algebraic Thinking

Lesson 5-1, pp. 2–5
Try this: 1.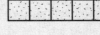

2.

3. 3; 3; 16; 19; 22 **4.** multiply; 48; 96; 192
5. $\times 3, \times 3, \times 3$; Multiply each number by 3 to
get the next number. **6.** 2; 4; 6; Add 2 to each
term to get the next term.
Practice: 1. A **2.** B **3.** $\times \times$

4.   **5.** 25, 31

Answers continued

6. 256, 1024 **7.** *Sample answer:* Start with 2 and add 2 to each term to get the next term. **8.** *Sample answer:* Starting with 2 ounces, the amount in the cup is increased by 2 ounces each time. **9.** *Sample answer:* circle, 1 triangle, circle, 2 triangles, circle, 3 triangles, circle, and so on **10.** *Sample answer:* Start with 2. Add 8 to each number to get the next number. **11.** 25; *Sample answer:* Four is being added each time, so the fifth number will be 25. **12.**

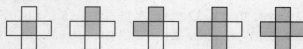

;

Sample answer: First the corners are shaded and then the square between them, so the fifth term will have the square in the middle right also shaded as well as the squares shaded in the fourth figure. **13.** M; *Sample answer:* Each time 2 letters of the alphabet are skipped. After J, K and L will be skipped, so the next letter will be M for the fifth term.

14. *Sample answer:*

15. *Sample answer:* You see if the numbers have been increased by a given number or multiplied by a given number each time. Then you continue to add that same number or multiply by that number.

Lesson 5-2, pp. 6–9

Try this: 1. 5; 5; 5; 10; 5; 5; 10; 15; 20 **2.** 2; 4; 6; 8 **3.** Starting with 100, subtract 25 from each term to get the next term. **4.** Starting with 1, add 0.5 to each term to get the next term.
5. subtract; 4; −; 4; 42; 34; 30; 26 **6.** 10; 34
Practice: 1. 4; 8; 12; 16 **2.** 2; 4; 6; 8 **3.** 10; 20; 30; 40 **4.** 8; 8; 8; 8; 8; 16; 24; 32 **5.** 60; 60; 60; 60; 60; 120; 180; 240 **6.** 7; 7; 7; 7; 7; 14; 21; 28
7. 77; *Sample answer:* Starting with 11, add 11 to each term. **8.** 37; *Sample answer:* Starting with 19, add 2 to each term. **9.** 93; *Sample answer:* Starting with 100, subtract 1 from each term.
10. 50; *Sample answer:* Starting with 300, subtract 50 from each term. **11.** *Sample answer:* You add 2 to each term to get the next term. Therefore, the 5th term is 11 + 2, or 13. Adding 13 + 2 gives 15, which is the 6th term. The 7th term is 15 + 2, or 17, and the 8th term is 17 + 2, or 19. **12.** added; add; next **13.** yes; *Sample*

answer: Each cube has 6 faces. Count by 6s or multiply the number of cubes by 6. This will generate the terms 6, 12, 18, 24, ...

Lesson 5-3, pp. 10–13

Try this: 1. $\frac{3}{4}$; $\frac{1}{8}$; $\frac{7}{8}$ **2.** 3; 9; 4; 13 **3.** 2; 3; 2; 5; 4; 15; 19
Practice: 1. 12 **2.** 16 **3.** 6 **4.** 7 **5.** 9.68 **6.** $4\frac{1}{3}$
7. 4 **8.** 120 **9.** division; 4 **10.** multiplication; 9
11. 20 **12.** 30 **13.** 1 **14.** 17 **15.** 177 **16.** 9
17. 58 **18.** 90 **19.** 24 **20.** 2 **21.** 10
22. 22.476 **23.** *Sample answer:* He multiplied 4 by 3 and then divided 12 by 12 instead of dividing 12 by 4 and then multiplying by 3. The correct answer is 9. **24.** letter; symbol; number
25. replace; number **26.** *Sample answer:* Substitute 1 for a and 2 for b, getting $(3 + 1)^2 - 7 \times 2$. Simplify in the parentheses to get $4^2 - 7 \times 2$. Next simplify the power to get $16 - 7 \times 2$. Then multiply 7 times 2 to get $16 - 14$. Finally, subtract 14 from 16 to get 2.

Lesson 5-4, pp. 14–17

Try this: 1. $n \div 5$ or $\frac{n}{5}$ **2.** 5; f; −; 6 **3.** *Sample answer:* sixteen more than twice the number of T-shirts sold **4.** *Sample answer:* 5 less than the quotient of the number of rabbits and 4
Practice: 1. addition **2.** division
3. multiplication **4.** subtraction **5.** addition
6. multiplication **7.** division **8.** subtraction
9. addition **10.** C **11.** A **12.** Let f represent the number of fish; $f + 20$ **13.** Let n represent the number; $12n$ **14.** Let h represent the number of helicopters; $h + 5$ **15.** Let n represent the number; $\frac{3n}{2}$ **16.** Let z represent the number of zebras; $2z - 6$ **17.** Let t represent the number of trees; $7t - 24$ **18.** *Sample answer:* 4 more than the number of bicycles **19.** *Sample answer:* the difference of 22 and the number of kittens
20. *Sample answer:* 8 more than twice the number of potatoes in the bag **21.** *Sample answer:* the number of roses divided by 5
22. *Sample answer:* Let c represent the number of cars. Since the number of cars is multiplied by 6 and then decreased by 24, you would write $6c$ for "six times the number of cars." Then you would subtract 24 for "decreased by 24." An expression is $6c - 24$. **23.** variable; symbols
24. +; p **25.** *Sample answer:* If n represents the number, then $5n$ represents 5 times the number.

Answers *continued*

Two less than $5n$ means 2 is subtracted from $5n$, or $5n - 2$.

Lesson 5-5, pp. 18–21

Try this: 1. 10; 8; Associative property of addition **2.** 5; Inverse property of multiplication **3.** -5; Associative property of addition; 0; Inverse property of addition; 8; Identity property of addition **4.** 9; Commutative property of multiplication; $\frac{9}{1}$; Associative property of multiplication and write 9 as $\frac{9}{1}$; 6; Multiply; 60; Multiply

Practice: 1. $+$; Associative property of addition **2.** 3; Commutative property of multiplication **3.** 2; Identity property of addition **4.** $\times$; Inverse property of multiplication **5.** 4; Commutative property of addition **6.** 1; Identity property of multiplication **7.** 12; Inverse property of addition **8.** 3; Associative property of multiplication **9.** $+$; 5; Commutative property of addition **10.** 1; Inverse property of multiplication **11.** 0 **12.** 1 **13.** 9 **14.** $\frac{2}{3}$ **15.** 15 **16.** 20 **17.** 45 **18.** 252 **19.** 56; 11; -11; 0; 56; Identity property of addition **20.** 16; $\frac{1}{9}$; 9; 16; Associative property of multiplication; 1; Inverse property of multiplication; 16 **21.** Associative property of multiplication; 2; 5; 17; 2; 5; Associative property of multiplication; 10; 170; Multiply **22.** zero; the number **23.** *Sample answer:* You could use the commutative property of addition to change $(56 + 74)$ to $(74 + 56)$ and then use the associative property of addition to group the 56 and -56 together to get 0. Finally, use the identity property of addition to get $0 + 74 = 74$. **24.** *Sample answer:* 2×7 multiplies the same two numbers as 7×2, but the order of the numbers has been changed. The commutative property of multiplication says you can change the order of two numbers in a multiplication problem.

Lesson 5-6, pp. 22–25

Try this: 1. A **2.** 8; 2; 10; 190 **3.** $\frac{1}{2}$; 8; 8; 6; 4; 6; 48; 58

Practice: 1. C **2.** 140 **3.** 0 **4.** 31 **5.** -22 **6.** 0 **7.** 18 **8.** -60 **9.** 11 **10.** $15(2 + 5 + 3) = 150$ **11.** $19(11 + 9 + 10) = 570$ **12.** $9\left(\frac{1}{2} + \frac{1}{2} + 4\right) = 45$ **13.** $0.1(4 + 1 + 5) = 1$ **14.** $2(9) + 2(50) + 2(100) = 318$ **15.** $4(25) + 4(3) + 4(1) = 116$ **16.** $6(-5) + 6(10) = 30$ **17.** $12\left(\frac{3}{4}\right) + 12\left(\frac{1}{6}\right) + 11$

18. $+$; 100; 36; 136 **19.** Distributive property; 12; Associative property of addition; 0; Inverse property of addition; 5; Identity property of addition; 4 **20.** 3; 7 **21.** Answers may vary; $2(3 + 5) = 2(3) + 2(5) = 6 + 10 = 16$; $2(3 + 5) = 2(8) = 16$ **22.** *Sample answer:* The expression $37(95 + 5)$ is easier because $95 + 5 = 100$ and $37(100)$ is 3700.

Lesson 5-7, pp. 26–29

Try this: 1. 4; 6; 6; x^2; -1; constant **2.** $2m$; $+$; 15; $30m$; $+$; $15n$ **3.** $2y^2 + 7y$ **4.** $13a + 3$

Practice: 1. 6 **2.** -13 **3.** -2 **4.** 19 **5.** 5 **6.** -17 **7.** 1 **8.** -45 **9.** B **10.** 11; $+$; 2 **11.** 3; a; $-$; 3; b **12.** 12; $+$; 12; y **13.** m^3; $-$; 3 **14.** $20x$ **15.** $8a + 10b$ **16.** $5y^2 - y + 7$ **17.** $b^2 + 4b - 16$ **18.** $34x + 14y$ **19.** $39x - 26y$ **20.** *Sample answer:* Rewrite $7x + 15x$ as $(7 + 15)x$. Then add. $(7 + 15)x = 22x$. **21.** *Sample answer:* The variables are not raised to the same power. **22.** $-2y^2 + 17y + 11$ **23.** C; *Sample answer:* $6(x + 8) = 6(x) + 6(8) = 6x + 48 \neq 6x + 8$ **24.** coefficient; constant term **25.** $4a - a = 3a$, not 3, and $2b + 10b = 12b$, not $12b^2$. **26.** *Sample answer:* You can rewrite $6x + 2y$ as $2 \cdot 3x + 2 \cdot y$. Then, applying the distributive property gives $2 \cdot 3x + 2 \cdot y = 2(3x + y)$.

Lesson 5-8, pp. 30–33

Try this: 1. $-$; 1; $-$; 1; -11 **2.** $-$; 15; $-$; 15; 10 **3.** $+$; 11; $+$; 11; 9 **4.** $+$; 3; $+$; 3; 9 **5.** Subtract 2 from each side; $y = -7$ **6.** Add 12 to each side; $b = 29$

Practice: 1. Subtract; 15 **2.** 2; Add **3.** Subtract 17 from each side. **4.** Subtract 5 from each side. **5.** Subtract 10 from each side. **6.** Add 11 to each side. **7.** Add 18 to each side. **8.** Add 9 to each side. **9.** 6 **10.** -12 **11.** -3 **12.** 17 **13.** -35 **14.** 9.65 **15.** $\frac{1}{2}$ **16.** $\frac{1}{3}$ **17.** 20 **18.** 39 **19.** 73 **20.** -4 **21.** 4.5 **22.** 12.1 **23.** $-\frac{1}{5}$ **24.** $\frac{5}{8}$ **25.** *Sample answer:* Because 17 is added to x, Marty should have subtracted 17, instead of 9, from each side. **26.** 18 **27.** *Sample answer:* Add 2 to each side of the equation. Then simplify to get $y = -3 + 2$ or $y = -1$. **28.** yes; *Sample answer:* The solution of both equations is 2.

Lesson 5-9, pp. 34–37

Try this: 1. 8; 8; 1; 7; 7 **2.** 5; 5; 1; -4; -4 **3.** -7; -7; 1; 9; 9 **4.** 9; 9; 1; -45; -45

Answers continued

Practice: **1.** C **2.** A **3.** 2 **4.** 8 **5.** −4 **6.** −5 **7.** 9 **8.** −5 **9.** 6 **10.** −3 **11.** 15; 3; 3 **12.** 9 **13.** −2 **14.** −0.4 **15.** 10 **16.** 9 **17.** 16 **18.** 80 **19.** −57 **20.** 24 **21.** 98 **22.** −72 **23.** −3.2 **24.** no; He should have divided each side by $\frac{2}{3}$ or multiplied each side by $\frac{3}{2}$. **25.** multiply; 9 **26.** divide; −5 **27.** *Sample answer:* Dividing each side by 6 gives the equivalent equation $-x = 2$. To solve the equation, you must find the value of x, not $-x$. To solve the equation you should divide both sides by −6.

Lesson 5-10, pp. 38–41

Try this: **1.** Let h represent the number of horses in the barn; $4h = 28$; $h = 7$; There are 7 horses in the barn. **2.** Let q represent Bette's quiz grade; $100 = 14 + q$; $86 = q$; Bette's quiz grade is 86. **3.** Let b represent Bob's amount; $b = 83 − 20$; $b = 63$; Bob has 63 cents. **4.** yes; *Sample answer:* If Cammy has 7 stuffed dogs, when you add 5 to that you get 12, which is the correct number of bears.

Practice: **1.** Let n represent the number; $n + 36 = 79$; $n = 43$; The number is 43. **2.** Let g represent the number of girls in the choir; $6g = 90$; $g = 15$; There are 15 girls in the choir. **3.** Let a represent the number of apples; $\frac{a}{5} = 35$; $a = 175$; There are 175 apples in the basket. **4.** Let t represent the temperature now; $t − 7 = -2$; $t = 5$; The temperature now is 5° F. **5.** Let q represent the number of quarters; $0.25q = 2.75$; $q = 11$; Martha has 11 quarters. **6.** Let n represent a number; $n − \frac{2}{3} = \frac{1}{2}$; $n = \frac{7}{6}$; The number is $\frac{7}{6}$ or $1\frac{1}{6}$. **7.** Let l represent the number of letters; $l = 24 \cdot 6$; $l = 144$; The employees wrote 144 letters. **8.** Let k represent the number of kittens; $k + 20 = 33$; $k = 13$; There are 13 kittens in the shelter. **9.** no; *Sample answer:* Since 18 is two-thirds of the total number of students, the number of students must be more than 18, not less. **10.** variable; equation **11.** $\frac{3}{5}n = 30$ **12.** no; *Sample answer:* Nanette should have written $6 = t − 8$. The number of roses is 8 less than the number of tulips, so we can subtract 8 from the number of tulips to find the number of roses.

Lesson 5-11, pp. 42–45

Try this: **1.** $x > 2$;

2. $m > −6$;

3. at least $40

Practice: **1.** A **2.** C

3. $x < −7$;

4. $a \geq −12$;

5. $d > 9$;

6. $e \leq 35$;

7. $h > 4$;

8. $j < −3$;

9. $n < 54$;

10. $p \leq −3$;

11. $g \leq −2.25$;

12. $w > −5$;

13. $5d \geq 18$; $d \geq 3\frac{3}{5}$; *Sample answer:* Ramon must run at least $3\frac{3}{5}$ miles each day. This makes sense because $5\left(3\frac{3}{5}\right) \geq 18$. **14.** $15 + x < 80$; $x < 65$; *Sample answer:* Jen needs less than 65 ft³ of topsoil; This makes sense because $15 + 65 = 80$. **15.** $x − 25 > 180$; $x > 205$; *Sample answer:* Kinsley could have 206 cards now. This makes sense because $205 − 25 = 180$ and $206 − 25 > 180$. **16.** $358 + x \geq 450$; $x \geq 92$; *Sample answer:* Tyler must score at least 92 more points. This makes sense because $358 + 92 = 450$.

17. Divide each side by $\frac{2}{3}$ or multiply each side by $\frac{3}{2}$. **18.** divide; reverse **19.** The solution is $y > −5$. The graph has an open circle on −5 and is shaded to the right. **20.** no; *Sample answer:* The graph should be shaded to the right of 3 because the solution is the numbers greater than 3.

Mixed Practice for Lessons 5-1 to 5-11, pp. 46–47

1. E **2.** D **3.** A **4.** B **5.** C **6.** distributive

Answers continued

7. commutative; addition **8.** inverse; multiplication
9. 27, 33, 39 **10.** Start with 3. Each term is 3 more than in the previous term. **11.**

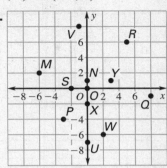

12. Start with 36. Then divide each term by 2 to get the next term. **13.** *Sample answer:* Start with 4, the number of leaves on 1 clover. Continue the pattern by counting by 4s. The pattern is 4, 8, 12, 16, 20, ... **14.** 22 **15.** $\frac{4}{3}$ **16.** $6 + 2s$

17. seven less than the number of monkeys in the zoo **18.** $8(-4) + 8(4) = 8(-4 + 4) = 8(0) = 0$
19. $16a - 8b$ **20.** 37 **21.** -27 **22.** 16
23. -2 **24.** -52 **25.** $\frac{5}{4}$ **26.** 14 **27.** $-\frac{5}{2}$
28. $p < -1$ **29.** $y \geq -7$ **30.** $g \leq -3$ **31.** $x > 6$

32. *Sample answer:* Let x represent the number of cards in the package she bought. $104 + x = 129$; $x = 25$. There were 25 cards in the package Miranda bought. **33.** *Sample answer:* Let x represent the number of inches the tree grew the first year. $7x = 84$; $x = 12$; The tree grew 12 inches the first year.

Lesson 5-12, pp. 48–51
Try this: 1. $-4, 0, 2, 8$ **2.** 2, 4, 7, 9
3. $(-15, -3), (-5, -1), (0, 0), (10, 2)$
4. $y = 3x$ **5.** $y = x - 3$
Practice: 1. 4, 8, 20, 28 **2.** 20, 22, 23, 25
3. $(-6, -8), (-2, -4), (1, -1), (4, 2)$ **4.** $(-3, 4), (-2, 5), (-1, 6), (0, 7)$ **5.** $y = -4x$ **6.** $y = x - 1$ **7.** $y = \frac{x}{3}$ **8.** *Sample answer:* The input values are the first values in each ordered pair. The input values are -2, 7, and 10.
9. *Sample answer:* (1, 50), (2, 100), (3, 150)
10. x; y **11.** *Sample answer:* Look for a relationship between the x-values and the y-values. In the table each y-value is 4 times the corresponding x-value, so the rule is $y = 4x$.
12. yes; 52 weeks in 1 year, so $w = 52y$

Lesson 5-13, pp. 52–55
Try this: 1. right, 0, G, G **2.** 3, down, D, D
3.

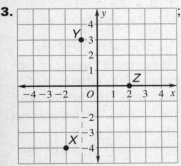

; *(continued)*

2; down; left; 3; right; 2; up; down
Practice: 1. $(1, -6)$ **2.** $(4, 1)$ **3.** 3; up; (3, 3)
4. 5; left; 2; down; $(-5, -2)$ **5.** 4; down; $(0, -4)$
6. $(-3, 5)$ **7.** $(-3, 0)$

8–19.

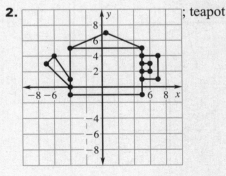

20. *Sample answer:* A point that lies on the x-axis has y-coordinate 0. A point that lies on the y-axis has x-coordinate 0. **21.** x-axis; y-axis
22. *Sample answer:* Start at the origin and move 6 units right and then 1 unit down. **23.** Vicki is correct. *Sample answer:* To get to M you move left 2 units and then up 4 units.

Activity 5-14, pp. 56–57
Practice: 1.

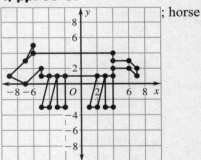

; horse

2.

; teapot

Lesson 5-15, pp. 58–61
Try this: 1. *(continued on next page also)*

x	-2	0	1
y	$y = 2x + 1$	$y = 2x + 1$	$y = 2x + 1$
	$y = 2 \cdot -2 + 1$	$y = 2 \cdot 0 + 1$	$y = 2 \cdot 1 + 1$
	$= -3$	$= 1$	$= 3$
(x, y)	$(-2, -3)$	$(0, 1)$	$(1, 3)$

Answers *continued*

$-2; -3; 0; 1; 1; 3;$

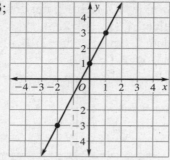

2. $-15; -8; 1$ **3.** vertical **4.** horizontal

Practice: 1.

x	−2	−1	0
y	$y = x - 1$	$y = x - 1$	$y = x - 1$
	$y = -2 - 1$	$y = -1 - 1$	$y = 0 - 1$
	$= -3$	$= -2$	$= -1$
(x, y)	$(-2, -3)$	$(-1, -2)$	$(0, -1)$

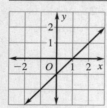 **2.** $5, 7, 9;$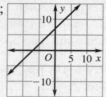

3. $-1, 1, 3;$

4. $-2, 2, 6;$

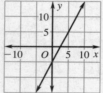

5. $2, -1, -4;$

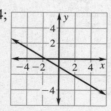

6. $5, 4, 3;$

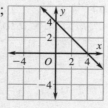

7. $3, 0, -3;$

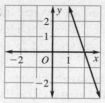

8. *Sample answer:* $1, 2, 3;$

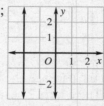

9. *Sample answer:* $1, 2, 3;$

10. The *y*-values are the same for each *x*-value, so the line is horizontal. **11.** The *x*-values are the same for each *y*-value, so the line is vertical. **12.** The *x*-values are different for each different *y*-value, so the line is diagonal. **13.** horizontal; vertical; diagonal **14.** *Sample answer:* Make a table of values choosing at least 3 numbers for *x*. To make the arithmetic easier, use even numbers for *x*. Substitute them in the equation for *x* to find the *y*-values. Then graph the ordered pairs and draw a line through them. **15.** no; *Sample answer:* For every ordered pair on the graph of $x = 2$, the value of *x* is 2. This means the graph goes through the points $(2, -1)$, $(2, 0)$, and $(2, 1)$, for example. This describes a vertical line 2 units to the right of the *y*-axis.

Lesson 5-16, pp. 62–65
Try this: 1. run; 6; 3; 3 **2.** vertical; 0; 0; 0
3. $2; 6; 7; -22; -\frac{7}{22}; -\frac{7}{22}$ **4.** $23; 8; \frac{21}{0};$
undefined
Practice: 1. zero **2.** positive **3.** undefined
4. negative **5.** rise; 2; 1; 2 **6.** horizontal; 0; 0; undefined **7.** -4 **8.** 0 **9.** 4 **10.** $5; -1; -1; -1;$ 1; 1 **11.** $6; 8; 0; -5; 0; 0$ **12.** undefined **13.** 2
14. 5 **15.** $-\frac{3}{5}$ **16.** -1 **17.** 1 **18.** rise; run

19. *Sample answer:* He put the difference of the *x*-values in the numerator and the difference of the *y*-values in the denominator. He should have put the difference of the *y*-values in the numerator and the difference of the *x*-values in the denominator. **20.** *Sample answer:* You are both correct. The order you subtract the coordinates of the points does not matter as long as you are consistent and subtract the coordinates in the numerator and denominator in the same order.

Lesson 5-17, pp. 66–69

Try this: **1.** 12; 3; 84; 12; 3; 7; 84;

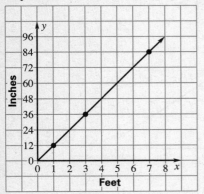

2. 12; 3; 84; 12; 12 **3.** 12; y; 12

Practice: **1.** 2 **2.** -3 **3.** 60 **4.** 4 **5.** 5 **6.** 16
7. $\frac{1}{5280}$ **8.** $\frac{4}{9}$ **9.** 3; 60; 360; 60; 3; 6; 360; 60; m;
60; *Sample graph:*

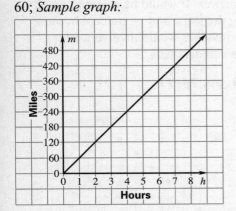

10. *Sample answer:* $w = 50m$; *Sample graph:*

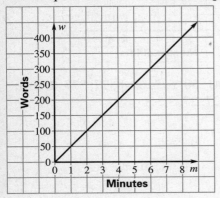

11. *Sample answer:* $y = 0.3x$; *Sample graph:*

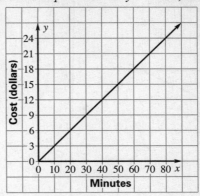

12. same; slope **13.** *Sample answer:* the distance traveled at a given speed for a number of hours; For example, $d = 55h$. **14.** yes; *Sample answer:* The graph contains (0, 0), and as the number of people increases, the cost increases at a constant rate.

Lesson 5-18, pp. 70–73

Try this: **1.** b; b; b; $\frac{3}{4}$; $+$; $\frac{3}{4}$; -2; $\frac{3}{4}$; -2
2. y-intercept; $+$; $+$; -1; $-\frac{1}{2}$; -1; 0; -1; rise;
-1; 1; 2; 2; -2; 2; -2;

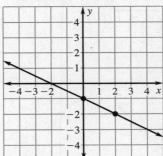

Practice: **1.** b; b; b; 8; $+$; 8; 2; 8; 2
2. slope $= \frac{1}{5}$, y-intercept $= -3$ **3.** slope $= -7$,
y-intercept $= -4$ **4.** slope $= -\frac{2}{3}$, y-intercept $= \frac{1}{2}$
5. slope $= 1$, y-intercept $= -10$ **6.** 3; 0; 3; run;
-4; 4; down; right; 0; 3

7.

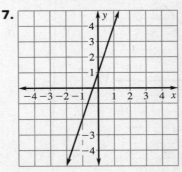

ANSWERS

8.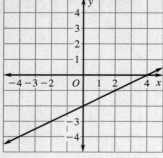

9.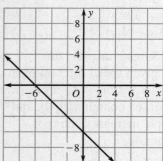

10.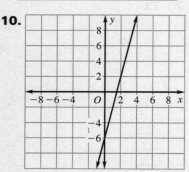

11.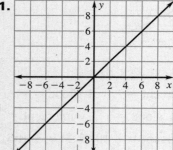

12.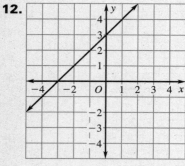

13.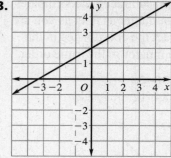

14.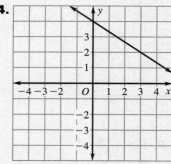

15. slope; *y*-intercept; slope-intercept
16. *Sample answer:* It would be easier to graph this line using the slope and *y*-intercept because using a table of values would involve working with fractions and decimals.

Lesson 5-19, pp. 74–77
Try this:

1.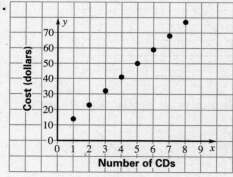

14; 23; 3; 32; 41; 50; 6; 7; 68; 8; 77; $77 **2.** 9; 5; 9; 8; 5; 77 **3.** 27; 27; 3.5

Answers *continued*

Practice: 1. 10; $60; 50; 10; 70; 50; 10; 80; 60; 70; 3; 80; 100; $100;

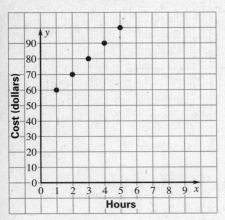

2. $68;

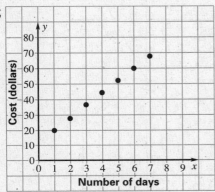

3. $220 **4.** After 15 weeks, Steve owes $100.

5. after 4 weeks **6.** about 2.5 ft³ **7.** $y = \frac{1}{2}x = \frac{1}{2}(5) = 2.5$ **8.** $10; $50 **9.** $y = 0.10x + 20$, where x is the number of minutes and y the total cost. **10.** *Sample answer:* The graph appears to contain the point (500, 350). This means the cost of printing 500 calendars is about $350.

Lesson 5-20, pp. 78–81
Try this: 1. -4; -1; 0; -1; -4;
Sample graph:

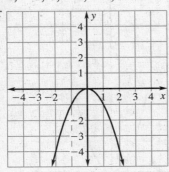

2. *Sample graph:*

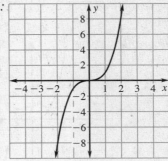

3. 10; 300; 300; 10
Practice: 1. A **2.** *Sample answer: x:* $-2, -1, 0, 1, 2; y:$ 4, 1, 0, 1, 4;

Sample graph:

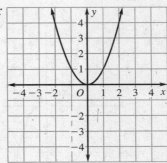

3. *Sample answer: x:* $-2, -1, 0, 1, 2; y:$ $-\frac{4}{3}, -\frac{1}{3}, 0, -\frac{1}{3}, -\frac{4}{3}$;
Sample graph:

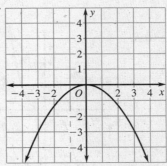

4. *Sample answer: x:* $-2, -1, 0, 1, 2; y:$ 12, 3, 0, 3, 12;

Sample graph:

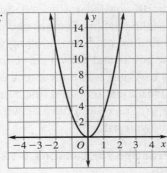

Answers *continued*

5. *Sample answer:* x: $-2, -1, 0, 1, 2$; y: $16, 2, 0,$ $-2, -16$;

Sample graph:

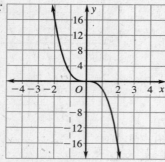

6. *Sample answer:* x: $-2, -1, 0, 1, 2$; y: $8, 1, 0,$ $-1, -8$;

Sample graph:

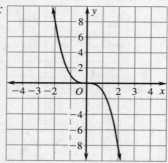

7. *Sample answer:* x: $-2, -1, 0, 1, 2$; y: $-4, -\frac{1}{2},$ $0, \frac{1}{2}, 4$;

Sample graph:

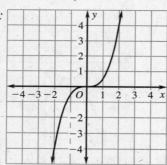

8. 400 m² **9.** nonlinear; line **10.** *Sample answer:* Make a table of values choosing values for x and finding the corresponding values for y. Plot the points and draw a curve through the points. **11.** Angus was not correct. *Sample answer:* This equation is not linear so its graph is not a line. Angus should have drawn a parabola opening downward.

Mixed Practice for Lessons 5-12 to 5-20, pp. 82–83

1. C **2.** A **3.** D **4.** B **5.** x; y **6.** y-intercept; slope **7.** $-10, -4, -1, 5, 14$

8. *Sample answer:* $y = 5x$

9.

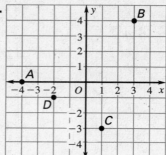

10.

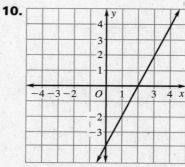

11.

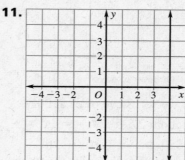

12.

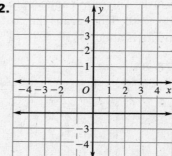

13.

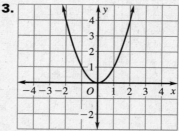

Answers continued

14. slope $= \frac{1}{2}$, y-intercept $= 3$ **15.** slope $= -1$, y-intercept $= 8$ **16.** $y = 500x + 1000$
17. $y = \frac{1}{30}x$ **18.** *Sample answer:* Put the difference of the y-values over the difference of the x-values. $\frac{-2-8}{7-2} = \frac{-10}{5} = -2$ **19.** B; *Sample answer:* The slope of this equation is negative, so its graph slopes downward from left to right.

Answers to Book 6 Data Analysis and Geometry

Lesson 6-1, pp. 2–5
Try this: 1. Large group: basketball, football, soccer ball, baseball bat, tennis racket; Small group: tennis ball **2.** *Sample answer:* Younger than my age: 2, 4, 5, 7, 9, 12; My age: 13; Older than my age: 20, 31, 32, 36, 45, 50
Practice: 1. 5, 7, 39, 23, 19, 99 **2.** 4, 8, 10, 16, 36, 44, 28, 56, 66 **3.** dinner plate, baseball, soup can, dartboard **4.** 45, 75, 25, 10, 30, 100
5. 20, 50, 110, 230, 70, 90 **6.** tennis ball, balloon, banana, golf ball, pen, pencil, watch **7.** 3, 42, 8, 48, 82, 97, 33, 21, 47, 52, 65 **8.** cereal box, cell phone, fork, picture frame **9.** *Sample answer:* 1, 2, 3, 4, 5, 6; odd numbers, even numbers; odd 1, 3, 5, even 2, 4, 6 **10.** objects **11.** numbers **12.** objects or numbers **13.** things you can touch and feel **14.** numbers

Lesson 6-2, pp. 6–9
Try this: 1. 2; 5, 10 **2.** 10 **3.** < 50 points: 8 times; 50 points: 2 times; > 50 points: 14 times
Practice: 1. 11, 19, 25, 28, 36, 39, 53, 64, 67, 73, 88, 98, 99 **2.** 11, 19, 25, 39, 53 **3.** 64, 88, 98 **4.** 25 (3), 18 (3), 30 (4), 32 (1), 24 (2)
5. The number 25 occurs 3 times; The number 18 occurs 3 times; The number 30 occurs 4 times; The number 32 occurs 1 time; The number 24 occurs 2 times. **6.** 3 (4), 21 (4), 42 (4) **7.** 3, 21
8. 8, 42, 120 **9.** 5 **10.** 98 (2), 256 (2), 120 (3), 82 (2) **11.** 82, 82, 98, 98, 120, 120, 120, 256, 256 **12.** occurs **13.** record **14.** order
15. collect

Lesson 6-3, pp. 10–13
Try this:
1.

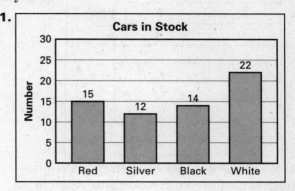

2. 5 **3.** 2, 32, 50

Practice: 1.

blue	卌 IIII
red	卌 卌 卌 I
green	卌 I
silver	卌

2.

Color	Number of Cars
blue	10
red	6
green	6
silver	7

3. *Sample answer:*

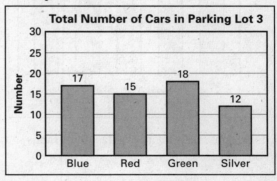

4. red: 37; green: 30; silver: 24
5.

CD A	卌 IIII
CD B	卌 III
CD C	卌 IIII
CD D	卌 卌
CD E	卌 卌 II

; 48 songs

6. 8 numbers; 2, 3, 4, 5, 6, 7, 8, 9

Answers continued

7.

Number	Frequency
2	7
3	1
4	2
5	3
6	2
7	6
8	3
9	1

8. 6; 7 **9.** *Sample answer:* Determine how many different numbers are in the data list. Add 1 to get the number of rows. Count how many of each number there are. Make a table with column headings "number" and "frequency". List the number in the number column and the frequency of each number in the frequency column.

10.

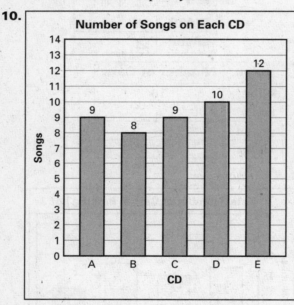

Number of Songs on Each CD

11. lists, graphs, tally charts, tables, bar graphs, and so on **12.** frequency

Lesson 6-4, pp. 14–17

Try this: 1. sandals **2.** $\frac{5}{10} = 0.5 = 50\%$

Practice: 1. 20% **2.** $\frac{200}{600}$ or $\frac{1}{3}$ **3.** $\frac{25}{30} = 0.83\overline{3} =$ 83.3% **4.** $\frac{47}{124} = 0.379 = 37.9\%$ **5.** $\frac{30}{124}$ or $\frac{15}{62}$; $\frac{22}{124}$ or $\frac{11}{62}$ **6.** 75% **7.** $\frac{12}{20}$ or $\frac{3}{5}$ **8.** $\frac{90}{360}$ or $\frac{1}{4}$

9. Box 2, which contains 126 marbles
10. *Sample answer:* Add up the total for each box, or 121, 126, and 113. Then add the totals of the boxes, or 360. Divide the number in Box 2 by

the total, or $\frac{126}{360}$. This reduces to $\frac{7}{20}$.

11.

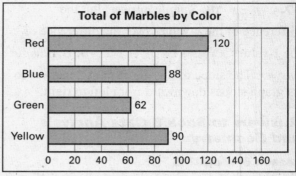

Total of Marbles by Color

Lesson 6-5, pp. 18–21

Try this: 1. *Sample answer:* There were 51 heads, so the probability is $\frac{51}{100}$, or 0.51. The result is close to the theoretical probability 0.5.
2. $\frac{6}{50} = \frac{3}{25}$, or 0.12; The experimental probability is slightly less than the theoretical probability of $\frac{1}{6}$. **3.** $\frac{26}{50} = \frac{13}{25}$, or 0.52; The experimental probability is close to the theoretical probability of $\frac{3}{6} = \frac{1}{2}$, or 0.5.

Practice: 1. a. 1, 3, 5 **b.** Check students' work.
c. *Sample answer:* 14 **d.** *Sample answer:* $\frac{14}{20} = 0.7$ **2.** $\frac{61}{120}$ **3.** $\frac{59}{120} = 0.49$ **4.** *Sample answer:* The experimental probability $\frac{59}{120}$ is slightly less than the theoretical probability of $\frac{60}{120}$, or $\frac{1}{2}$.
5. $\frac{42}{120}$ or $\frac{7}{20}$; *Sample answer:* The probability of rolling a 4 or a 6 is found by adding up the tallies for 4 and 6, or $22 + 20 = 42$. Then divide by the total number of rolls, 120. **6.** Check students' tally charts and answers. **7.** *Sample answer:* The actual probability of getting 2 heads is 0.25. Since there are 4 outcomes, the probability of getting one of them, heads-heads, is $\frac{1}{4}$, or 0.25.
8. $\frac{40}{121}$ **9.** Check students' answers; $\frac{1}{6}$
10. probability; outcome; probability of 0.5

Mixed Practice for Lessons 6-1 to 6-5, pp. 22–23

1. B, X **2.** A, Y **3.** object **4.** attribute **5.** numbers
6. 5, 17, 35, 39, 27, 99 **7.** 5 **8.** 2 **9.** 4 **10.** 7
11. 4 **12.** 2

Answers *continued*

13.

Number	Frequency
17	1
25	4
28	3
30	3
32	1
33	1

14. football, baseball bat, tennis racquet
15. tennis ball, soccer ball, basketball
16. *Sample answer:* $\frac{9}{20}$; The theoretical probability is $\frac{1}{2}$, so $\frac{9}{20}$ is close. **17.** $\frac{45}{100}$ or $\frac{9}{20}$
18. $\frac{35}{100}$ or $\frac{7}{20}$ **19.** 50%; *Sample answer:* To find the percentage, you divide the number of shoes by the total footwear. $200 + 500 + 300 = 1000$; $500 \div 1000 = 0.5$, or 50%. **20.** about 57%; *Sample answer:* Since she has 160 CDs with fewer than 14 songs, divide 160 by 280 to get 0.57, or 57%.

Lesson 6-6, pp. 24–27
Try this: 1. 8 cm **2.** 10.16 cm
Practice: 1. 4 in. **2.** 10.2 cm **3.** 2 in.
4. 5.1 cm **5.** 3 in. **6.** 7.62 cm **7.** 5 in. **8.** 6 in.
9. Answers will vary. *Sample answer:* The centimeter measurement is more accurate because a centimeter is a smaller unit than an inch. **10.** millimeters, centimeters, meters
11. inches, feet, yards **12.** *Sample answer:* There are 2.54 centimeters in 1 inch, so an inch is larger than a centimeter. **13.** *Sample answer:* The metric ruler may give a more accurate answer, but it depends on how closely the measure of the segment corresponds to a unit of measurement on the ruler.

Lesson 6-7, pp. 28–31
Try this: 1. 6; 6; 4; 4; 20 **2.** 3; 4; 4; 11
3.

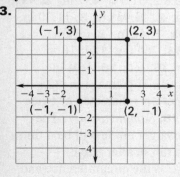

4. 14 units
Practice: 1. 30 in. **2.** 11 in. **3.** 27.94 cm
4. 20 in. **5.** 16 in. **6.** 26 in. **7.** 22 units
8.

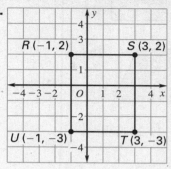

9. 18 cm **10.** *Sample answer:* Determine the lengths of all 5 sides. Add. **11.** *Sample answer:* Determine the lengths of all sides of the polygon. Add. **12.** *Sample answer:* Find the lengths of all vertical segments by taking the difference of the *y*-coordinates. Find the lengths of the horizontal segments by taking the difference of the *x*-coordinates. Add the lengths of the vertical segments and of the horizontal segments.
13. polygons **14.** *x*-; *y*-

Lesson 6-8, pp. 32–35
Try this: 1. *Sample answer:* 10.2 cm by 3.2 cm; 32.64 cm² **2.** Check students' drawings; 5; 4; 20; 12.7; 10.16; 129.032
Practice: 1. *Sample answer:* 3 in. by 1 in.; 3 in.²
2. 19.3548 cm² **3.** *Sample answer:* 10 cm by 4 cm; 40 cm² **4.** Check students' drawings; 7 in.²
5. Check students' drawings; 40.05 cm² **6.** 3.5 × 2.54 = 8.89 cm; 2 × 2.54 = 5.08 cm; 8.89 cm × 5.08 cm = 45.1612 cm² **7.** 12,395 in.² **8.** 86 ft²
9. 200.66 ft² **10.** *Sample answer:* Multiply the length by 2.54 and multiply the width by 2.54. Then multiply the new length by the new width to get the area in square centimeters. **11.** 9
12. length; width **13.** square; 2-dimensional

Lesson 6-9, pp. 36–39
Try this: 1. *l*; *w*; *b*; 18 **2.** *b*; 0.5; 0.3; 0.15
Practice: 1. 3 in.²
2.

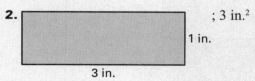

; 3 in.²

1 in.

3 in.

3. 34.2 cm²

Answers *continued*

4. 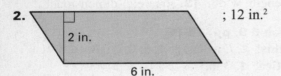 ; 34.2 cm²

3.8 cm

9 cm

5. ; 10 in.²

2 in.

5 in.

6. ; 11.25 cm²

4.5 cm

2.5 cm

7. 27.2 cm² **8.** 31.5 ft² **9.** 36 m² **10.** 53.125 in.²
11. *Sample answer:* The error was to multiply the base times the other side length instead of times the height. The area should be 8 × 4 = 32 square units. **12.** *Sample answer:* The area can be found by multiplying the base 60 times the height to that base, 36, or by multiplying the other base 40 by the height to that base, 54. 60 × 36 = 2160 = 40 × 54 **13.** both; parallel; equal **14.** base; height **15.** *Sample answer:* Since the area is base times height, to find the height you would divide the area by the base. The height is 24 ÷ 6 = 4 cm. **16.** *Sample answer:* Since a rectangle is also a quadrilateral and it has opposite sides parallel and equal, it is a parallelogram.

Lesson 6-10, pp. 40–43
Try this: 1. 32; 16 cm² **2.** 60 cm² **3.** 2.07 m²
Practice: 1. 6 in.²

2. 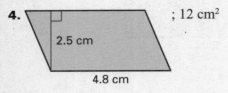 ; 12 in.²

2 in.

6 in.

3. 6 cm²

4. ; 12 cm²

2.5 cm

4.8 cm

5. *Sample answer:* 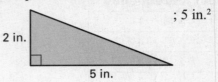 ; 5 in.²

2 in.

5 in.

6. *Sample answer:* 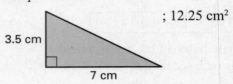 ; 12.25 cm²

3.5 cm

7 cm

7. 7.2 cm² **8.** 12.8 ft² **9.** 10.5 m² **10.** 19.6875 in.²
11. *Sample answer:* The error was to multiply the wrong side times the height. The area should be one-half of the height times the base it is perpendicular to, or $\frac{1}{2} \times 5 \times 9 = 22.5$ square units. **12.** 32; 16; 32; 8; 4 **13.** 3 **14.** $\frac{1}{2}$; base; height **15.** *Sample answer:* Method 1: Use $b = 50$ and $h = 12$, so $\frac{1}{2} \times 50 \times 12 = 300$. Method 2: Use $b = 30$ and $h = 20$, so $\frac{1}{2} \times 30 \times 20 = 300$. Both methods give the same result. **16.** *Sample answer:* Since a rectangle is also a parallelogram, and a triangle is one-half a parallelogram, you can say that a triangle is one-half a rectangle.

Activity 6-11, pp. 44–45
Example: Step 1. *Sample answer:* 4
Step 3. *Sample answer:* 12.6 **Step 4.** *Sample answer:* $\frac{12.6}{4} = 3.15$
Game: The winning answer should be 3.1416 or the closest one to 3.1416.
Practice: 1. 18.84 in. **2.** 31.40 cm **3.** 2 in.; 6.28 in. **4.** 8 cm **5.** 4 in. **6.** Circumference = $2\pi r$

Lesson 6-12, pp. 46–49
Try this: 1. 3.14; 8; 25.12 cm **2.** 3.14; 5.8; 18.21 cm **3.** 2; 3.14; 8.2; 51.5 ft **4.** 7 in. **5.** 9 cm
Practice: 1. 9.42 in. **2.** 23.93 cm **3.** 11.30 in.
4. 8π **5.** 5π **6.** 9.4π **7.** 44 in. **8.** 66 cm
9. 88 ft **10.** 88 m **11.** 264 cm **12.** 110 in.
13. 5 in. **14.** 12 cm **15.** 6 ft **16.** 16.4 in.
17. yes; *Sample answer:* If you take $\pi \cdot (2 \cdot$ diameter), you will get $2\pi \cdot$ diameter, or twice the circumference. **18.** *Sample answer:* The circumference of the larger circle will be 4 times the circumference of the smaller circle.
19. $C = \pi d$ (where C is the circumference and

Answers *continued*

d is the diameter) **20.** $C = 2\pi r$ (where *C* is the circumference and *r* is the radius) **21.** same; $\frac{1}{2}$
22. Divide the circumference by π, or 3.14.
23. yes; *Sample answer:* If you take $\pi \cdot (3 \cdot$ diameter), you will get $3\pi \cdot$ diameter, or three times the circumference.

Lesson 6-13, pp. 50–53
Try this: 1. 3.14; 8; 200.96 **2.** 25π ft^2
3. 49π cm^2; 154 cm^2 **4.** 4.41π ft^2; 13.86 ft^2
5. 3 in. **6.** 1 cm
Practice: 1. 1.77 in.^{2} **2.** 31.75 cm^2 **3.** 113.04 ft^2
4. 64π cm^2 **5.** 25π in.^{2} **6.** 23.04π ft^2 **7.** 154 in.^{2}
8. 616 cm^2 **9.** $\frac{22}{7}$ ft^2 **10.** 19.64 cm^2 **11.** 52.83 in.^{2}
12. 38.5 cm^2 **13.** 4 in. **14.** 11 cm **15.** 7 ft
16. 5 in. **17.** 3 cm **18.** 8 cm **19.** *Sample answer:* The area would be 4 times as large. If the radius is multiplied by 2, 2^2 is a factor of 4. You can also say that $A = \pi (2 \cdot \text{radius})^2 = \pi \cdot 4 \cdot \text{radius}^2 = 4\pi \cdot \text{radius}^2$. **20.** *Sample answer:* The larger circle will have an area 16 times as large.
21. *Sample answer:* The larger circle will have a radius that is 2 times the length of the smaller circle. **22.** *Sample answer:* Divide the diameter by 2 to get a radius of 6 cm. Then use the area formula $A = \pi r^2$ to get $3.14(6^2) = 113.04$ cm^2.
23. $A = \pi r^2$ (where *A* is the area and *r* is the radius) **24.** square; 16 **25.** no; *Sample answer:* The area will be 9 times as much because you square the factor of 3 to find the area.

Mixed Practice for Lessons 6-6 to 6-13, pp. 54–55
1. A, Y **2.** B, X **3.** metric **4.** customary
5. quadrilateral **6.** 3.5 cm; 3.5 cm; 5 cm
7. 2 cm; 4 cm; 4.5 cm **8.** Perimeter = 12 cm
9. Perimeter = 16 in.; Area = 15 in.^{2}
10. Perimeter = 20 cm; Area = 16 cm^2
11. Perimeter = 19.6 m; Area = 22.8 m^2
12. Perimeter = 8 cm; Area = 3.75 cm^2
13.

14. $AB = 7$, $BC = 5$, $CD = 7$, $AD = 5$
15. 35 in.^{2} **16.** 28 in.^{2} **17.** 72 cm^2 **18.** 216 m^2
19. 18 cm^2 **20.** 44 in.^{2} **21.** 10 m^2
22.

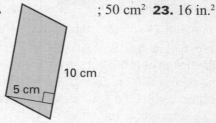

; 50 cm^2 **23.** 16 in.^{2}

24. 6 cm^2 **25.** 28 m^2 **26.** 10 m^2 **27.** 18 in.^{2}
28. 27 cm^2 **29.** 28.26 in. **30.** 37.68 m
31. 37.68 ft **32.** 18.84 ft **33.** 12.56 in.
34. 25.12 m **35.** 50.24 in.^{2} **36.** 314 m^2
37. 200.96 ft^2 **38.** 78.5 cm^2 **39.** 153.86 in.^{2}
40. 3.14 m^2 **41.** about 6.28 mi; 3.14 mi^2;
Sample answer: $C = \pi d$ is the formula for the circumference of a circle, which is the distance around the circle ($6.28 = 3.14 \cdot 2$). $A = \pi r^2$ gives the area of a circle ($3.14 = 3.14 \cdot 1$).
42. 15,000 yd^2; *Sample answer:* $A = lw$ gives the area the park ($15,000 = 150 \cdot 100$).

Activity 6-14, pp. 56–57
Example: Step 3. 2; 2; 4
Step 4. 4; 4; 4; 4; 4; 4; 24
Practice: 1. 1.5 in.^{2} **2.** 6; (0.5); 6; (0.5); 1.5 in.^{2}
3. *Sample answer:* The surface area of a cube is $6s^2$ where *s* is the length of one edge. **4.** 28 in.^{2}
5. 108 cm^2 **6.** *Sample answer:* Find the area of the 6 rectangular faces and add them up.

Lesson 6-15, pp. 58–61
Try this: 1. 340 cm^2 **2.** 64 in.^{2}
Practice: 1. yes **2.** yes **3.** no **4.** no **5.** *TUVW, TUQP, PQRS, WVRS, UVRQ, TWSP* **6.** 358 in.^{2}
7. 188 cm^2 **8.** 54 ft^2 **9.** 22 m^2 **10.** 1188 in.^{2};
Sample answer: Find the surface area of the box. Two faces are 24 by 15, two are 24 by 6, and two are 15 by 6. Find those areas, double each, and add them together. **11.** two; rectangles; faces **12.** *Sample answer:* Find the area of each face and add them together. Two are 8 by 10 or 80 cm^2, two are 8 by 12 or 96 cm^2, and two are 10 by 12 or 120 cm^2. The surface area is $2(80) + 2(96) + 2(120) = 592$ cm^2.

Lesson 6-16, pp. 62–65
Try this: 1. 24 cm^3 **2.** 144 ft^3
Practice: 1. 12 cubic units **2.** 648 cm^3
3. 421.875 m^3 **4.** 150 in.^{3} **5.** 5610 ft^3

Answers _continued_

6. 48.75 yd³ **7.** 40 cm³ **8.** 168 in.³ **9.** 288 cm³
10. 65 m³ **11.** 717.75 ft³ **12.** 48 bags;
Sample answer: The volume of the sandbox is
$4(6)(1) = 24$ ft³. Dividing 24 by $\frac{1}{2}$ gives 48.
13. space; contain **14.** divide; one; count
15. area; base; height **16.** _Sample answer:_ The
volume of the first pool is 6480 ft³, and the volume
of the second pool is 5600 ft³. The first pool will
hold more water. It will hold 880 cubic feet more.
I found that by subtracting 5600 from 6480.

Lesson 6-17, pp. 66–69
Try this: 1. C **2.** 72 in.³ **3.** 360 ft³
Practice: 1. yes **2.** no **3.** yes **4.** no **5.** yes
6. no **7.** 105 cm³ **8.** 144 in.³ **9.** 75 m³
10. 5040 in.³ **11.** _Sample answer:_ Both volumes
are found by multiplying the area of the base
times the height. The base of a rectangular prism
is a rectangle so its area is length times width,
while the base of a triangular prism is a triangle
so its area is one-half base times height.
12. _Sample answer:_ The volume of the
rectangular prism is twice the volume of
the triangular prism because the area of
the rectangular base is twice the area of the
triangular base. Both have the same height.
13. two; triangles **14.** area; base; height
15. _Sample answer:_ Find the area of the
triangular base by taking one-half times 10 times
8, which is 40 cm². Then multiply this times the
height of 15. The volume is 600 cm³.

Lesson 6-18, pp. 70–73
Try this: 1. C **2.** 100π cm³ or about 314 cm³
Practice: 1. yes **2.** no **3.** no **4.** yes **5.** 588π
in.³ or about 1846.32 in.³ **6.** 198π cm³ or about
621.72 cm³ **7.** 506.25π ft³ or about 1589.625 ft³
8. 529.984π m³ or about 1664.15 m³ **9.** 432π in.³
or about 1356.48 in.³ **10.** 400π cm³ or about
1256 cm³ **11.** 1125π cm³ or about 3532.5 cm³
12. 112π in.³ or about 351.68 in.³ **13.** _Sample
answer:_ The volume of the box is 51.84 in.³ and
the volume of the cylinder is about 31.4 in.³
When you divide 51.84 by 31.4 you get about
1.65, so Marie can fill 1 container. **14.** two;
circles **15.** _Sample answer:_ Multiply π by
3 by 1 squared, which is 3π or about 9.42 ft³.
16. _Sample answer:_ The volume of the cylinder
is 2835π, or about 8901.9 cm³. The volume of
the prism is 9450 cm³. The prism has the greater
volume.

Mixed Practice for Lessons 6-15 to 6-18, pp. 74–75
1. C, Y **2.** A, Z **3.** D, X **4.** B, W **5.** area; base
6. cylinder **7.** rectangular prism **8.** triangular
prism **9.** 370 cm² **10.** 336 in.² **11.** 384 m²
12. 92 in.² **13.** 121.2 ft² **14.** 90 in.³
15. 254.3 cm³ **16.** 132 mm³ **17.** 5400 in.³;
5595.48 in.³; cylinder; 195.48 in.³ **18.** the box;
Sample answer: The surface area of the box is
15.5 ft³, while the surface area of the triangular
prism is 13.33 ft³. **19.** _Sample answer:_ The toy
box is a rectangular prism plus half a cylinder. The
volume of the box is 10,368 in.³ The volume of
the half cylinder is about 8138.88 in.³ The total is
about 18,506.88 in.³

Lesson 6-19, pp. 76–79
Try this: 1. ∠U, ∠TUV, ∠VUT **2.** ∠X, ∠WXY,
∠YXW **3.** 40° **4.** 110°
5.

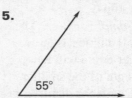

Practice: 1. ∠J, ∠HJK, ∠KJH **2.** ∠M, ∠LMN,
∠NML **3.** ∠Q, ∠PQR, ∠RQP **4.** 90° **5.** 150°
6. **7.**

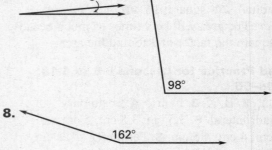

8.

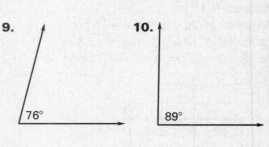

9. **10.**

11.

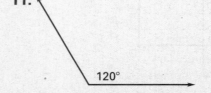

Answers *continued*

12.

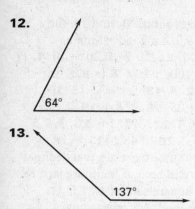

64°

13.

137°

14. *Sample answer:* There are three angles in the figure each with vertex *B*, so you would not know which angle she was referring to.
15. ∠*ABD*, ∠*ABC*, ∠*CBD* **16.** 70°, 30°, 40° **17.** two rays; same endpoint **18.** *Sample answer:* He read the wrong scale on the protractor; 40°.

Lesson 6-20, pp. 80–83

Try this: 1. right **2.** acute **3.** straight **4.** obtuse **5.** 70°; acute **6.** 115°; obtuse **7.** straight **8.** right **9.** acute **10.** obtuse
Practice: 1. acute **2.** obtuse **3.** obtuse **4.** right **5.** straight **6.** acute **7.** obtuse **8.** acute **9.** right **10.** acute **11.** straight **12.** obtuse **13.** acute **14.** obtuse **15.** right **16.** *Sample answer:* If you hold the corner of a sheet of paper at the vertex of an obtuse angle and line one side of the angle up with one side of the paper, the angle will extend beyond the edge of the other side of the paper. **17.** *Sample answer:* A straight angle looks like a straight line. **18.** *Sample answer:* pencil or book **19.** acute; obtuse

20.

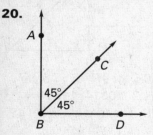

21. right; *Sample answer:* *m*∠*ABD* is equal to *m*∠*ABC* and *m*∠*CBD* together, and 45 + 45 = 90. Therefore, the measure of ∠*ABD* is 90°, so it is a right angle.

Lesson 6-21, pp. 84–87

Try this: 1. complementary **2.** neither **3.** supplementary **4.** supplementary **5.** 75°, 165° **6.** 19°, 109° **7.** no complement, 60° **8.** 48°, 138°

Practice: 1. neither **2.** complementary **3.** supplementary **4.** supplementary **5.** complementary **6.** neither **7.** complementary **8.** neither **9.** 64°, 154° **10.** 89°, 179° **11.** 6°, 96° **12.** no complement, 70° **13.** yes; *Sample answer:* Each angle can measure 45°. **14.** no; *Sample answer:* If each angle has measure less than 90°, their sum cannot equal 180°. **15.** no; *Sample answer:* Nothing greater than 90 can add to a positive value to get 90. **16.** complementary **17.** supplementary **18.** no; *Sample answer:* She subtracted from 180° instead of 90°. She found the supplement not the complement. **19.** *Sample answer:* Two right angles cannot be complementary because if each has measure 90° they cannot add up to 90°. They are, however, always supplementary.

Lesson 6-22, pp. 88–91

Try this: 1. right **2.** acute **3.** scalene **4.** equilateral
Practice: 1. acute **2.** obtuse **3.** obtuse **4.** right **5.** isosceles **6.** equilateral **7.** scalene **8.** isosceles

9. *Sample answer:*

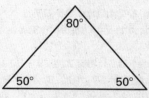

10. *Sample answer:*

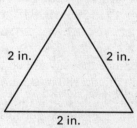

11. *Sample answer:*

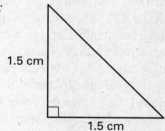

12. yes; *Sample answer:* One angle can be more than 90°, and the two sides forming it can be equal. **13.** *Sample answer:* When all the sides are equal, a triangle is called equilateral. Since all the angles in the triangle in Exercise 10 are equal,

this triangle might be called equiangular.
14. *Sample answer:* Two of the angles of an isosceles right triangle must be equal, and one of the angles must equal 90°; 45°, 45°, and 90°
15. 3 equal; at least 2 equal; one; more; 90°
16. *Sample answer:* Since each angle has measure less than 90°, the triangle is acute.
17. *Sample answer:* no; *Sample answer:* The triangle would look like this:

So the second and third sides cannot meet to form the third angle.

Activity 6-23, pp. 92–93
Example: Step 3. straight angle, 180°
Practice: 1. 40°, 60°, 80°, 180° **2.** 35°, 50°, 95°, 180° **3.** The sum of the angles of a triangle is 180°. **4.** 360° **5.** The sum of the angles of a quadrilateral is 360°.

Lesson 6-24, pp. 94–97
Try this: 1. 64° **2.** 96° **3.** yes **4.** no **5.** 32°
6. 146°
Practice: 1. 100° **2.** 129° **3.** 14° **4.** 156°
5. 86° **6.** 81° **7.** 40° **8.** 43° **9.** 60° **10.** 80°
11. 140° **12.** 102° **13.** 120° **14.** 76° **15.** 134°
16. 125° **17.** 158° **18.** 31° **19.** 90° **20.** 70°
21. no **22.** yes **23.** yes **24.** no **25.** yes
26. no **27.** no **28.** yes **29.** 60°; *Sample answer:* Since they all add up to 180° and they are equal, divide 180 by 3, and each angle is 60°. **30.** 180°; 360° **31.** *Sample answer:* Add 90° and 48° together to get 138°. Subtract 138° from 180°. The result is the measure of the third angle, or 42°. **32.** *Sample answer:* When he divided the quadrilateral into triangles he did not just connect vertices. Therefore, the triangles contain angles that were not part of the angles of the original quadrilateral. So the sum of the angles of the triangles is more than the sum of the angles of the quadrilateral.

Lesson 6-25, pp. 98–101
Try this: 1. 9, −9 **2.** 7, −7 **3.** 4 **4.** −10
5. 12, 12.2 **6.** 1, 1.4 **7.** −4, −4.4 **8.** 81; 100
9. *Sample answer:* Since 81 < 85 and 85 < 100, $\sqrt{81} < \sqrt{85}$ and $\sqrt{85} < \sqrt{100}$, $\sqrt{85}$ must be

between 9, the square root of 81, and 10, the square root of 100. 9.3 is a good estimate.
Practice: 1. 11, −11 **2.** 2, −2 **3.** 20, −20 **4.** 1, −1 **5.** 14, −14 **6.** 100, −100 **7.** 0 **8.** 8 **9.** −5
10. 25 **11.** −12 **12.** 4 **13.** 9 **14.** −13 **15.** 19
16. 2, 2.2 **17.** 13, 13.5 **18.** 9, 8.6 **19.** 4, 3.6
20. 10, 9.7 **21.** 6, 6.4 **22.** 32, 31.6 **23.** 3, 2.5
24. −9.8 **25.** −25.2 **26.** −48.1 **27.** −18.5
28. *Sample answer:* Since there are two decimal places in 1.21 there will be one decimal place in its square root. The square root of 1.21 is 1.1.
29. *Sample answer:* Find the square root of 4 and of 9. The square root is $\frac{2}{3}$. **30.** *Sample answer:* Since the square root squared gives you the number, $\sqrt{3} \cdot \sqrt{3}$ must equal 3.
31. *Sample answer:* When you square a number you multiply two identical numbers with the same sign. You cannot multiply two numbers with the same sign and get a negative number.
32. 15; 15^2; 225 **33.** *Sample answer:* Since 81 < 93 and 93 < 100, $\sqrt{93}$ must be between 9, the square root of 81, and 10, the square root of 100. 9.4 is a good estimate. **34.** *Sample answer:* Because 3^2 is 9 and 4^2 is 16 and 15 is between 9 and 16, $\sqrt{15}$ must be between $\sqrt{9}$ and $\sqrt{16}$.
35. *Sample answer:* Both 2 squared and negative 2 squared gives 4 so they are both square roots of 4. However, when the square root symbol is written it means the positive square root only, so $\sqrt{4}$ means just 2.

Lesson 6-26, pp. 102–105
Try this: 1. 13 **2.** 8 **3.** 9.9 m;

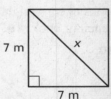

Practice: 1. 8 **2.** 20 **3.** 8.5 **4.** 9.7 **5.** 17.5 cm
6. 5.2 **7.** 7.2 **8.** 6.9 **9.** 11.2 **10.** 14 **11.** 34
12. 6 **13.** 5.7 **14.** 8.9 **15.** The triangle is not a right triangle. **16.** right; 6^2; c^2; Pythagorean
17. *Sample answer:* He took the square roots of each term individually. This is not correct. Instead, he must evaluate 6^2 and 10^2 and add them together before taking the square root of their sum. **18.** *Sample answer:* You should use the second equation because the 12 is the length of the hypotenuse so it should be alone on one side of the equation.

Answers continued

Lesson 6-27, pp. 106–109

Try this: 1. If John has orchestra practice, then today is Monday. **2.** If a number is even, then it is a multiple of 2. **3.** no; $15^2 = 225$, $18^2 = 324$, and $20^2 = 400$. $225 + 324 \neq 400$, or $15^2 + 18^2 \neq 20^2$. **4.** yes; $10^2 = 100$, $24^2 = 576$, and $26^2 = 676$. $100 + 576 = 676$, so $10^2 + 24^2 = 26^2$.

Practice: 1. If Lois does not have school, then today is Saturday. **2.** If a triangle is equilateral, then it has three equal sides. **3.** If a quadrilateral is a rectangle, then it has four right angles. **4.** If $x = 9$, then $x + 6 = 15$. **5.** yes **6.** no **7.** yes **8.** yes **9.** no **10.** no **11.** yes **12.** no **13.** yes **14.** no; $9^2 + 11^2 = 81 + 121 = 202$, $14^2 = 196$; $202 \neq 196$ **15.** *Sample answer:* Measure 6 inches on one edge and 8 inches on an adjacent edge. Move the endpoints until they are 10 inches apart. This makes a right triangle. Therefore the angle is a right angle. **16.** no; *Sample answer:* $8^2 + 12^2 = 64 + 144 = 208 \neq 15^2$ **17.** yes; *Sample answer:* $90^2 + 400^2 = 8100 + 160,000 = 168,100 = 410^2$ **18.** converse; right **19.** *Sample answer:* If $x = 1$, then $x > 0$. Converse: If $x > 0$, then $x = 1$. **20.** yes; *Sample answer:* It is a right triangle because $8^2 + 15^2 = 64 + 225 = 289 = 17^2$.

Lesson 6-28, pp. 110–113

Try this: 1. perpendicular **2.** parallel

3–4.

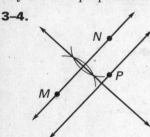

Practice: 1. parallel **2.** perpendicular **3.** neither **4.** perpendicular **5.** parallel

6. **7.**

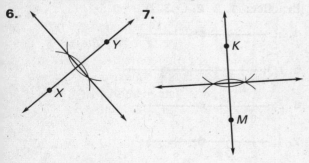

8.

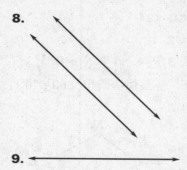

9.

10. *Sample answer:* Make congruent arcs on each side of B on the line. From the points where those arcs intersect the line, make congruent arcs with larger radii that intersect on one side of the line. Draw a line through that intersection point and B. This line is perpendicular to $\overleftrightarrow{BC}$. **11.** 1; *Sample answer:* There is only 1 line perpendicular to line BC that passes through point B. Any other perpendicular line would pass through a point other than B. **12.** *Sample answer:* Mark off congruent distances with your compass on each perpendicular line from B and from C. Draw a line through those two points. This line is parallel to $\overleftrightarrow{BC}$. **13.** intersect; right angles **14.** *Sample answer:* Mark two points on the line. Open your compass more than half the distance between the two points. Make congruent arcs from those points that intersect on each side of the line. Draw a line through the intersection points of the arcs. **15.** *Sample answer:* Trudy is not correct. The lines could intersect at an angle other than 90°.

Lesson 6-29, pp. 114–117

Try this: 1. C **2.** $\overline{GH} \cong \overline{QR}$, $\overline{GK} \cong \overline{QP}$, $\overline{HK} \cong \overline{RP}$, $\angle G \cong \angle Q$, $\angle H \cong \angle R$, $\angle K \cong \angle P$ **3.** 120°; 7

Practice: 1. no **2.** yes **3.** yes **4.** no **5.** $\overline{AC} \cong \overline{MP}$, $\overline{AB} \cong \overline{MQ}$, $\overline{BC} \cong \overline{QP}$ **6.** $\overline{ZE} \cong \overline{TH}$, $\overline{ZR} \cong \overline{TK}$, $\overline{ER} \cong \overline{HK}$ **7.** $\angle A \cong \angle M$, $\angle B \cong \angle Q$, $\angle C \cong \angle P$ **8.** $\angle Z \cong \angle T$, $\angle E \cong \angle H$ $\angle R \cong \angle K$ **9.** 15°; 135° **10.** 8, 10, 6, 10 **11.** no; *Sample answer:* They do not have to be the same size. **12.** yes; *Sample answer:* They will be the same size and have the same shape. **13.** size; shape **14.** length; measure **15.** *Sample answer:* $\angle R \cong \angle L$ because R is the middle letter in triangle PRQ and L is the middle letter in triangle KLM.

Answers continued

Lesson 6-30, pp. 118–121

Try this: 1. $26\frac{2}{3}$ min **2.** 12

Practice: 1. 3 **2.** 18 **3.** 9 **4.** no **5.** yes **6.** 5; 18; $\frac{3}{1}$ **7.** $2\frac{2}{3}$; $5\frac{1}{4}$; $\frac{4}{3}$ **8.** 7.5; 5 **9.** 70°; 50°; 60°; 70°
10. *Sample answer:*

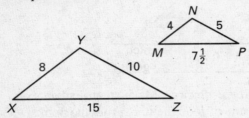

11. no; *Sample answer:* If they are congruent they are the same shape and same size, so they must be similar. **12.** shape **13.** proportional; congruent **14.** *Sample answer:* Corresponding sides have the same length so their ratio is 1 to 1. **15.** *Sample answer:* Because the triangles are similar and *ST* is greater than *YZ*, *WT* will be greater than *ZY*.

Mixed Practice for Lessons 6-19 to 6-30, pp. 122–123

1. C, X **2.** A, Z **3.** B, Y **4.** complementary; supplementary **5.** ∠N, ∠MNP, ∠PNM **6.** 40°
7. acute **8.** obtuse **9.** straight **10.** right
11. acute **12.** obtuse **13.** supplementary
14. neither **15.** complementary
16. complementary **17.** 73°; 163° **18.** acute
19. obtuse **20.** right **21.** equilateral
22. scalene **23.** isosceles **24.** 4 **25.** −12
26. 9.6 **27.** 2, −2 **28.** 35 **29.** 20 in. **30.** yes; *Sample answer:* $16^2 + 30^2 = 256 + 900 = 1156 = 34^2$ **31.** B; A; *Sample answer:* The first two are similar because they are the same shape but not the same size. The second two are congruent because they are the same shape and the same size.

Answers to Book 7 Getting Ready for Algebra

Lesson 7-1, pp. 2–5

Try this: 1. $6r = 90$ **2.** $8x - 3 = 21$ **3.** $x - \frac{1}{2} = 7$ **4.** $2b + 4 = 16$ **5.** $x + (x + 1) = 25$
6. $x - \frac{1}{3}x = 18$

Practice: 1. B **2.** C **3.** A **4.** $x + 4 = 7$
5. $x - 5 = 16$ **6.** $\frac{3}{8}x = 24$ **7.** $\frac{x}{3} = 10$ **8.** $x + (x + 2) = 66$ **9.** $x - \frac{2}{3}x = 50$ **10.** $4x - 3 = 12$

11. $x + 8 = 2x - 3$ **12.** $4(x + 2) = 5x$
13. $x + 5x = 36$ **14.** $x + (x - 8) = 42$; *Sample answer:* One sack contains x apples and the other contains 8 fewer apples, so that is $x - 8$. The two sacks added together must equal 42, so the equation is $x + (x - 8) = 42$. **15.** $\frac{1}{5}x = 48$; *Sample answer:* Let x represent the number of bulbs in the box, since one-fifth of the bulbs were damaged, that would be represented by $\frac{1}{5}x$. Since the number of bulbs that were damaged is 48, the equation is $\frac{1}{5}x = 48$. **16.** $x + (x - 2) = 30$; *Sample answer:* Let x be Jim's age. Then $x - 2$ is Chris's age. The sum of these two ages is 30. **17.** sentence, symbols **18.** *Sample answer:* When multiplication is seen you can say *times*, when there is an equals sign that means *is*, and the subtraction symbol means you say *less than*. So $2x = 5x - 4$ as a word sentence is *2 times a number is 4 less than 5 times the number*. **19.** No; *Sample answer:* Since the 8 and the 10 are switched around, the equations are different. The first equation $2x + 8 = 10$ means *eight more than twice a number is ten*, while $2x + 10 = 8$ means *ten more than twice a number is eight*.

Lesson 7-2, pp. 6–9

Try this: 1. 5;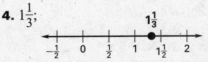

2. −2;

3. 1.8;

4. $1\frac{1}{3}$;

5. −22;

Practice: 1. A **2.** C **3.** B

4. 3;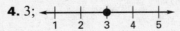

5. 1.5;

6. 2;

7. 4;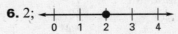

Answers *continued*

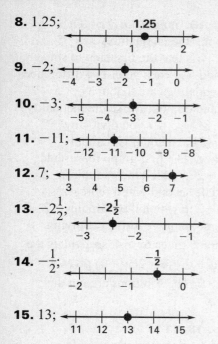

8. 1.25;

9. −2;

10. −3;

11. −11;

12. 7;

13. $-2\frac{1}{2}$;

14. $-\frac{1}{2}$;

15. 13;

16. $32x + 50 = 530$; 15 days; *Sample answer:* Let x represent the number of days. Then $32x$ is the number of pages read in x days. You also have to add the 50 pages he has already read to get a total of 530 pages. So the equation is $32x + 50 = 530$. To solve it, subtract 50 from each side then divide by 32 to get 15 days. **17.** $11 + 3w = 6 + 4w$; 5 weeks; *Sample answer:* Let w represent the number of weeks. Since Kyle runs an additional 3 miles a week, $11 + 3w$ is how many miles he runs per week in w weeks. Similarly Sara runs an additional 4 miles per week so $6 + 4w$ is how many miles she runs per week in w weeks. Since you want to know when they will be running the same number of miles per week, the expressions must be set equal to each other. This gives $11 + 3w = 6 + 4w$. To solve the equation, subtract $3w$ from each side, then subtract 6 from each side to get $w = 5$ weeks. **18.** variable, itself **19.** *Sample answer:* First distribute the 3 and −1 (understood) to get $3x + 15 − x + 7 = 14$. Combine the x terms and the 15 and 7 to get $2x + 22 = 14$. Subtract 22 from each side to get $2x = -8$, then divide by 2 to get $x = -4$. **20.** yes; *Sample answer:* Solving $5x + 8 = -17$ by subtracting 8 and dividing by 5 results in an answer of −5. Solving $-5x - 8 = 17$ by adding 8 and dividing by −5 results in the answer of −5. The answers are the same.

Lesson 7-3, pp. 10–13

Try this: **1.** w; w; $16w$; 329; $16w$; 89; 15 **2.** 8; 6; 24

Practice: **1.** $\times$ **2.** $\div$ **3.** −, + **4.** + **5.** Subtract 7 from each side. **6.** Add 8 to each side. **7.** Add 4 to each side. **8.** add; subtract; +; −; adding; subtract; 560 **9.** $700d + 900 = 3000$; $d = 3$ days; *Sample answer:* Since the family already traveled 900 miles and they are traveling 700 per day, which is represented by $700d$, this needs to be added together to get 3000, or $700d + 900 = 3000$. Solve by subtracting 900 from each side to get $700d = 2100$. Divide each side by 700 to get $d = 3$ days. **10.** $10h + 7 + 9 = 68.50$; $h = 5\frac{1}{4}$ hours; *Sample answer:* Since Brent receives $10 an hour plus $7 for transportation and $9 for meals if he works on Saturdays, this needs to be added together to get 68.50, so $10h + 7 + 9 = 68.50$. Solve by subtracting 7 and 9 from 68.50 to get $10h = 52.50$. Divide each side by 10 to get $h = 5.25$, or $5\frac{1}{4}$ hours. **11.** $4000 + 500w = 10,000$; $w = 12$ weeks; *Sample answer:* Since Mr. Johnson already provided the outlet store with 4000 golf balls and he finds 500 golf balls per week, which is represented by $500w$, this needs to be added together to get 10,000, or $4000 + 500w = 10,000$. Solve by subtracting 4000 from each side to get $500w = 6000$. Divide each side by 500 to get $w = 12$ weeks. **12.** *Sample answer:* A farmer has a herd of 458 sheep. He needs to shear all his sheep before summer. He has 178 sheep already sheared. He shears 70 sheep a day. How many days will it take him to get all the sheep sheared? Answer: 4 days; I was looking for a situation where 70 was multiplied by a number so I came up with a person shearing 70 sheep per day. Then 178 needed to be added, so I said he already sheared 178 sheep. Since it was set equal to 458, I made 458 be the number of sheep in his herd. **13.** no; *Sample answer:* The equation is $190 + 28d = 638$. To solve it, you need to subtract 190 from each side and then divide by 28, which results in 16 days. If you add 190 and then divide by 28, you get about 30, which is probably what my friend did.

Lesson 7-4, pp. 14–17

Try this: **1.** $x < \frac{1}{2}$;

Answers *continued*

ANSWERS

2. $x > 1\frac{2}{3}$;

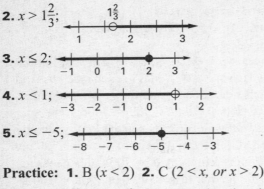

3. $x \le 2$;

4. $x < 1$;

5. $x \le -5$;

Practice: 1. B $(x < 2)$ **2.** C $(2 < x, \text{ or } x > 2)$

3. A $(x > -2)$ **4.** $x < 4$;

5. $x \ge 6$;

6. $x > 4$;

7. $q < -\frac{6}{7}$;

8. $p > 4$;

9. $t \ge 10$;

10. $x \le 3$;

11. $p \le -1.5$;

12. $r < -1.2$;

13. $n < 5$;

14. $x \ge 15$;

15. $x \le -3$;

16. $25h + 35 < 85$; less than 2 hours; *Sample answer:* Let *h* represent hours worked, so $25h$ represents the wages. Also add the service fee, which gives the inequality $25h + 35 < 85$. To solve the inequality, subtract 35 from each side. Then divide by 25 to get $h < 2$ hours. **17.** $30h + 25 < 115$; less than 3 hours; *Sample answer:* Let *h* represent hours worked, so $30h$ represents the wages. Also add the service fee, which gives the inequality $30h + 25 < 115$. To solve the inequality, subtract 25 from each side. Then divide by 30 to get $h < 3$ hours. **18.** multiply, divide,

negative, reverse **19.** *Sample answer:* The similarity in solving the inequalities $3x - 5 < 7$ and $-3x - 5 < 7$ is that the first step to solve them both is to add 5 to each side. The differences in solving the inequalities are that in $3x - 5 < 7$ you divide by 3 and do not reverse the inequality symbol, but in $-3x - 5 < 7$ you divide by -3 and you do reverse the inequality symbol.
20. *Sample answer:* The first graph represents the solution $x > -2$ in which the endpoint -2 is not included. The second graph represents the solution $x \ge -2$ in which the endpoint -2 is included. **21.** no; *Sample answer:* Solving $-3x + 1 > -9x + 5$ gives $6x > 4$, so $x > \frac{2}{3}$ is the solution. Solving $-x + 6 > 2(x + 4)$ gives $-3x > 2$, so $x < -\frac{2}{3}$. The solutions are not the same.

Lesson 7-5, pp. 18–21
Try this: 1. 4 or fewer bracelets; *Sample answer:* Write the inequality $12 + 2x \le 20$. Subtract 12 from each side to get $2x \le 8$. Divide each side by 2 to get $x \le 4$. To buy 4 bracelets at \$2 each, she pays \$8. Add the first item she bought for \$12, and the total is \$20. So, the answer that Jackie can buy 4 or fewer bracelets with the money she has seems reasonable.
2. 4 or fewer checks; *Sample answer:* Write the inequality $1025 + 1000 - 375x \ge 500$. Simplify to get $2025 - 375x \ge 500$. Subtract 2025 from each side to get $-375x \ge -1525$. This simplifies to $x \le 4$ when you divide each side by -375, reverse the inequality symbol, and round down. He has \$2025 in the bank and must keep \$500, so that leaves \$1525 for checks. 4 checks at \$375 each is \$1500. So, the answer that Dave can write 4 or fewer checks for \$375 seems reasonable.
Practice: 1. $\le$ **2.** $>$ **3.** $<$ **4.** $\ge$ **5.** Add 6 to each side. **6.** Add 2 to each side. **7.** Subtract 4 from each side. **8.** $\ge$; $\ge$; subtracting; divide; 25; 25 **9.** $700 + 3m \le 2650$; $m \le 650$ miles; *Sample answer:* Since Bob already traveled 700 miles and he is traveling 3 more days with the same number of miles each day, which is represented by $3m$, this needs to be added together to get at most 2650, or $700 + 3m \le 2650$. Solve by subtracting 700 from each side to get $3m \le 1950$. Divide each side by 3 to get $m \le 650$ miles. **10.** $n + (n + 1) \ge 47$; *Sample answer:* The smallest two numbers are 23 and 24; Two consecutive integers are represented

Answers continued

by n and $n + 1$ and *at least* means *greater than or equal to*. So the equation for the sum of two consecutive integers to be at least 47 is $n + (n + 1) \geq 47$. Begin solving by combining like terms to get $2n + 1 \geq 47$. Then subtract 1 from each side to get $2n \geq 46$. Next divide each side by 2 to get $n \geq 23$. $n + 1 \geq 24$, so the two smallest integers that satisfy the conditions are 23 and 24.
11. $29 + 5h \leq 54$; $h \leq 5$ hours; *Sample answer:* Gary plays 5 holes of golf in an hour, which is represented by $5h$, and he has already played 29 holes. These must be added together to be at most 54, so the equation is $29 + 5h \leq 54$. Solve by subtracting 29 from each side to get $5h \leq 25$. Divide each side by 5 to get $h \leq 5$ hours.
12. *Sample answer:* Brandon bought a pig that weighed 50 pounds. He will sell the pig when it weighs at least 200 pounds. If the pig gains 25 pounds a month, in how many months can Brandon sell the pig? Answer: $m \geq 6$ months; I was thinking of a situation where 25 had to be multiplied by some number, then 50 more was added on, and the sum had to be greater than or equal to 200. **13.** yes; *Sample answer:* The inequality is $31 + 3m \geq 85$. To solve the inequality, subtract 31 from each side, which gives $3m \geq 54$. Divide each side by 3 to get $m \geq 18$. So Jessica must run at least 18 miles a day the next 3 days.

Mixed Practice for Lessons 7-1 to 7-5, pp. 22–23

1. B, X **2.** C, Z **3.** A, Y **4.** other **5.** subtract **6.** reverse **7.** $n - 7 < 20$, $n < 27$ **8.** $2n + 5 = 8$, $n = 1.5$ **9.** $200 + 30w \geq 500$, $w \geq 10$ weeks

10. $x = 3$;

11. $x = 40$;

12. $x = 13$;

13. $x = 5$;

14. $x = 3$;

15. $x = 1$;

16. $x < 2$;

17. $x \leq -4$;

18. $\leq$; 45; $\leq$; subtracting; divide; 15; less
19. $x = 24$ **20.** $x = 3$ **21.** $x < 1$ **22.** $x = -5$
23. $x > 5$ **24.** $x = 6$ **25.** $12 + 8r = 52$;
5 rounds; *Sample answer:* 8 rows per round means $8r$. 12 rows were already planted so $12 + 8r$ should be set equal to the number of rows he wants, which is 52. Solving $12 + 8r = 52$, you subtract 12 from each side to get $8r = 40$. Divide by 8 to get $r = 5$ rounds. **26.** $n + (n + 4) \leq 42$; Trevor's sister is at most 19 years old. Trevor is at most 23 years old; *Sample answer:* Since Trevor is 4 years older than his sister and the sum of their ages is at most 42, the inequality is $n + (n + 4) \leq 42$. Simplifying gives $2n + 4 \leq 42$. Subtract 4 from each side to get $2n \leq 38$. Dividing by 2 gives $n \leq 19$ and $n + 4 \leq 23$, so Trevor's sister is at most 19 and Trevor is at most 23.

Activity 7-6, pp. 24–25
Example: *Sample answer:* The pattern is to divide by 10 each time the exponent is decreased by one. The last two values in the table are $\frac{1}{1000}$ and $\frac{1}{10,000}$.
Practice: 1. 16 **2.** $\frac{1}{16}$ **3.** $\frac{1}{4}$ **4.** 4 **5.** 1 **6.** $\frac{1}{64}$

7. *Sample answer:* When x is a positive integer, the value of the expression x^0 is 1. Any positive integer to the zero power is always 1. **8.** *Sample answer:* When x and n are positive integers, the value of the expression x^{-n} is always $\frac{1}{x^n}$. When a positive integer is raised to a negative integer power, the result is always a fraction with 1 in the numerator and the positive integer raised to a positive integer power in the denominator.
9. 1 **10.** $\frac{1}{9}$ **11.** $\frac{1}{8}$

Lesson 7-7, pp. 26–29
Try this: 1. $\frac{1}{3}$ **2.** $\frac{1}{64}$ **3.** $\frac{1}{16}$ **4.** 7^{-2} **5.** 2^{-5} **6.** 3^{-3}
7. 1 **8.** $\frac{b^5}{c^2}$ **9.** $\frac{4}{c^3 b}$ **10.** 1 **11.** $\frac{k^3}{h^5}$ **12.** $\frac{2a^3}{c^2}$ **13.** $<$
14. $>$ **15.** $=$ **16.** $<$ **17.** $<$ **18.** $=$
Practice: 1. B **2.** C **3.** A **4.** 5^{-2} **5.** 6^{-3} **6.** 5^{-3}
7. $\frac{z^3}{x^2}$ **8.** $\frac{b^2}{a^3}$ **9.** $\frac{16}{27}$ **10.** $\frac{4}{9}$ **11.** 1 **12.** $\frac{3n^3}{m^4}$ **13.** $\frac{1}{9}$
14. 1 **15.** $\frac{1}{x^3}$ **16.** $\frac{1}{125}$ **17.** $\frac{1}{y}$ **18.** 1 **19.** True
20. False **21.** True **22.** C **23.** B **24.** A
25. 2^{-5} **26.** 10^{-3} **27.** 7^2 **28.** 40^{-2} **29.** 12^{-2}
30. zero, reciprocal **31.** $4^{-2} = \frac{1}{16}$; *Sample answer:* $4^3 = 64$, $4^2 = 16$, $4^1 = 4$, $4^0 = 1$,

ANSWERS

$4^{-1} = \dfrac{1}{4}$, $4^{-2} = \dfrac{1}{16}$, $4^{-3} = \dfrac{1}{64}$; The pattern shows that each time the exponent is decreased by 1, you divide the value by 4, so to get 4^{-2}, divide $\dfrac{1}{4}$ by 4 to get $\dfrac{1}{16}$. **32.** no; *Sample answer:*

$3^{-1} + 3^{-6} + 4^{-2} = \dfrac{1}{3} + \dfrac{1}{729} + \dfrac{1}{8}$ is not correct

because $4^{-2} = \dfrac{1}{16}$, not $\dfrac{1}{8}$. The other two values that were substituted were correct.

Lesson 7-8, pp. 30–33
Try this: 1. 9 **2.** 10 **3.** 10 **4.** 15 **5.** 6 **6.** 13 **7.** 8; 5 **8.** 9; 3 **9.** 11; 1 **10.** 5^6 **11.** 2^4 **12.** $c^{10}d^8$ **13.** 3^3
Practice: 1. C **2.** A **3.** B **4.** False **5.** False **6.** True **7.** x^8 **8.** x^4 **9.** z^3 **10.** a^5b^3 **11.** n^2m^3 **12.** c^4b^{10} **13.** a **14.** b^3c^3 **15.** x^7y^2 **16.** n^{10} **17.** df^5 **18.** a^6b^2 **19.** 2^5 **20.** x^3 **21.** c^7 **22.** 3^8 **23.** 4^2 **24.** b^{10} **25.** 8, B **26.** 16, C **27.** 4, A **28.** 2700 bacteria; *Sample answer:* Substitute 2 for h in the formula $B = 300 \cdot 3^h$. Since $3^2 = 9$, multiply $300 \cdot 9 = 2700$. **29.** 2^{32}, or 4,294,967,296 kg; *Sample answer:* Substitute 21 for x and 11 for y in the equation $M = 2^x \cdot 2^y$. Then simplify $M = 2^{21} \cdot 2^{11} = 2^{32}$, or 4,294,967,296 kg. **30.** add, base **31.** *Sample answer:* Use the product of powers property to simplify $6^3 \cdot 6^{-3} \cdot 6^2$ to get $6^{3+(-3)+2}$, or $6^2 = 36$. **32.** no; *Sample answer:* You do not multiply exponents. According to the product of powers property, if the bases are the same you add exponents, so $x^3 \cdot x^4 = x^7$, not x^{12}.

Lesson 7-9, pp. 34–37
Try this: 1. x^{10} **2.** k^{27} **3.** x^{33} **4.** t^{32} **5.** p^{28} **6.** m^{20} **7.** b^2 **8.** c^0 or 1 **9.** g^{36} **10.** 4; 7 **11.** 3; 23 **12.** 6; 28 **13.** 2^{16} **14.** $21p^{12}$ **15.** x^6 **16.** $20t^{24}$ **17.** 6^{16} **18.** $72x^{13}$
Practice: 1. C **2.** B **3.** A **4.** A **5.** C **6.** B **7.** False **8.** True **9.** True **10.** m^{28} **11.** p^{18} **12.** z^{20} **13.** t^9 **14.** x^0 or 1 **15.** s^8 **16.** $3v^7$ **17.** $8t^{25}$ **18.** $6n^{40}$ **19.** 4096 **20.** 32 **21.** 3072 **22.** 3^{12} **23.** x^{14} **24.** $27b^8$ **25.** a^{40} **26.** $5x^{16}$ **27.** $16p^6$ **28.** $(2^x)^3$ or 2^{3x}; 512 cubic units; *Sample answer:* Since the length, width, and height are all 2^x and they all need to be multiplied together, take $2^x \cdot 2^x \cdot 2^x$. This equals $(2^x)^3$. Use the power of a power property to multiply exponents. The expression is 2^{3x}. When $x = 3$, $2^{3x} = 2^{3(3)} = 2^9 = 512$. **29.** $(3^x)^3$ or 3^{3x}; 729 cubic units; *Sample answer:* Since the length, width, and height are all 3^x and they all need to be multiplied together, take $3^x \cdot 3^x \cdot 3^x$. This equals $(3^x)^3$. Use the power of a power

property to multiply exponents. The expression is 3^{3x}. When $x = 2$, $3^{3x} = 3^{3(2)} = 3^6 = 729$. **30.** power; multiply **31.** *Sample answer:* To simplify $[(x^3)^2]^4$, work from the inside out. Use the power of a power property to get $(x^3)^2 = x^6$ or $[(x^3)^2]^4 = (x^6)^4$. Then use the power of a power property again to get $(x^6)^4 = x^{24}$. **32.** no; *Sample answer:* $(x^5)^2 = x^{10}$, not x^7, because by the power of a power property, the exponents are multiplied not added. The result is $7x^{10}$, not $7x^7$.

Lesson 7-10, pp. 38–41
Try this: 1. 5; 5 **2.** 4; 2 **3.** 81; 4 **4.** 10; 10 **5.** 8; 8 **6.** 8; 3 **7.** $a^2b^2c^2$ **8.** $24y^3$ **9.** 15 **10.** 648 **11.** 7 **12.** 324
Practice: 1. C **2.** A **3.** B **4.** True **5.** False **6.** True **7.** $16m^4$ **8.** g^3t^6 **9.** a^3d^3 **10.** $a^5b^5c^{10}$ **11.** $16x^6$ **12.** $c^{16}x^{24}$ **13.** $2b^{18}n^7$ **14.** $5m^2s^8$ **15.** $9r$ **16.** 2916 **17.** 144 **18.** 15 **19.** $81x^{12}$ **20.** b^3x^6 **21.** $8a^5b^{10}$ **22.** $216a^3f^3$ **23.** $3c^3x^7$ **24.** $5p^2t^7$ **25.** B **26.** A **27.** C **28.** $(4n)^2 = 16n^2$; *Sample answer:* Length times width is $4n \cdot 4n = (4n)^2$. By the power of a product, $(4n)^2 = 16n^2$. **29.** 8 times; *Sample answer:* The volume of the smaller cube is c^3. The volume of the larger cube is $(2c)^3$, which equals $8c^3$. $8c^3$ is 8 times as large as c^3. **30.** product; parentheses **31.** *Sample answer:* In $2(x)^2$ only the x is squared, so $2(x)^2 = 2x^2$. In $(2x)^2$ both the 2 and the x are squared, so $(2x)^2 = 4x^2$. **32.** no; *Sample answer:* $(x^3y)^2 = x^6y^2$, but $(x^2y)^3 = x^6y^3$. In the first equation, y is to the second power, but in the second equation, y is to the third power.

Lesson 7-11, pp. 42–45
Try this: 1. positive **2.** negative **3.** positive **4.** 5 **5.** 8 **6.** -4 **7.** $\dfrac{2x}{3}$ **8.** $\dfrac{d}{f^5}$ **9.** $\dfrac{cd}{2}$
Practice: 1. B **2.** C **3.** A **4.** positive **5.** negative **6.** negative **7.** False **8.** False **9.** True **10.** $\dfrac{a}{2}$ **11.** $\dfrac{2}{3d^2}$ **12.** b^5 **13.** c^2f^3 **14.** $2n^4$ **15.** $\dfrac{1}{r^4}$ **16.** $7bc$ **17.** $\dfrac{r}{s^5}$ **18.** $\dfrac{3ad^3}{b^3}$ **19.** 5 **20.** 64 **21.** $\dfrac{1}{9}$ **22.** 9 **23.** 64 **24.** 8 **25.** 8; 2 · 2 · 2; 3; 8; 8; 3; 8; 3; 5; $32; *Sample answer:* Step 1 is 8 because you add 1 (for Sam) to the 7 friends; Step 2 is 2^3 because $2 \cdot 2 \cdot 2 = 8$; Step 3 is 2^8 because $2 \cdot 2 \cdot 2 \cdot 2 \cdot 2 \cdot 2 \cdot 2 \cdot 2 = 256$; Step 4 is $\dfrac{2^8}{2^3} = 2^{8-3} = 2^5$ by the quotient of powers property; Step 5 is $32 by simplifying. **26.** 9; *Sample answer:* $243 = 3^5$ and $27 = 3^3$. Divide $\dfrac{3^5}{3^3}$. By the quotient of powers property, subtract exponents to get $3^{5-3} = 3^2 = 9$, so Jane's

Answers *continued*

answer is 9. **27.** positive; denominator **28.** yes; *Sample answer:* Since any positive integer to the zero power is 1, dividing by n^0 is dividing by 1, which is possible. **29.** no; *Sample answer:* Since the larger exponent is in the denominator, the result must be c to a negative power. $\frac{c^5}{c^8} = c^{-3}$. Subtract exponents $5 - 8 = -3$.

Lesson 7-12, pp. 46–49

Try this: 1. $\frac{5^2}{8^2}$; $\frac{25}{64}$ **2.** $\frac{1}{81}$ **3.** $\frac{27x^3}{64}$ **4.** $\frac{c^2}{2d^2e^2}$
5. a^4 **6.** $\frac{8}{27}$ **7.** $\frac{100}{49}$ **8.** $\frac{27}{8}$

Practice: 1. C **2.** A **3.** B **4.** True **5.** True
6. False **7.** $\frac{a^7b^7}{128}$ **8.** $\frac{m^3}{64}$ **9.** $\frac{81}{n^4}$ **10.** c^8 **11.** a
12. $4t^4$ **13.** $\frac{8}{27}$ **14.** 243 **15.** 36 **16.** $\frac{729}{1000}$ **17.** $\frac{225}{64}$
18. $\frac{1296}{625}$ **19.** $\left(\frac{2}{3}\right)^2$; *Sample answer:* Since she reduces the page to $\frac{2}{3}$ of its original size and then reduces it again to $\frac{2}{3}$ of that size, you multiply $\frac{2}{3} \cdot \frac{2}{3}$ or $\left(\frac{2}{3}\right)^2$. **20.** $\left(\frac{3}{8}\right)^3 = \frac{27}{512}$ ft³; *Sample answer:* Since volume equals length times width times height, the volume is $\left(\frac{3}{8}\right)^3 = \frac{3}{8} \cdot \frac{3}{8} \cdot \frac{3}{8} = \frac{27}{512}$ ft³. **21.** numerator; denominator **22.** *Sample answer:* Any positive integer raised to the zero power is 1, so $\left(\frac{c}{d}\right)^0 = 1$ no matter what the values of the positive integers c and d are. **23.** no; *Sample answer:* $\left(\frac{b}{6}\right)^2$, by the power of a quotient property, means both the numerator and the denominator are taken to the second power, which is $\frac{b^2}{36}$, not $\frac{b^2}{6}$.

Lesson 7-13, pp. 50–53

Try this: 1. 8 **2.** 12 **3.** $\frac{5}{7}$ **4.** $\sqrt{51}$ **5.** 60 **6.** 27
Practice: 1. B **2.** C **3.** A **4.** False **5.** False
6. True **7.** 2 **8.** 54 **9.** $\frac{4}{5}$ **10.** $\frac{6}{11}$ **11.** 28 **12.** 36
13. $\sqrt{15}$ **14.** $\frac{7}{4}$ **15.** $\sqrt{47}$ **16.** 1 **17.** $\sqrt{23}$
18. 14 **19.** 125 **20.** 64 **21.** 32 **22.** $36^{\frac{1}{2}} = x$; $x = 6$ in.; *Sample answer:* Area is equal to the length of the side squared, so $x^2 = 36$, which means $x = \sqrt{36}$, or $x = 36^{\frac{1}{2}}$. Therefore $x = 6$.
23. $49^{\frac{1}{2}} = y$; $y = 7$ ft; *Sample answer:* Area is equal to the length of the side squared, so $y^2 = 49$, which means $y = \sqrt{49}$, or $y = 49^{\frac{1}{2}}$. Therefore $y = 7$. **24.** $2500^{\frac{1}{2}} = z$; $z = 50$ in.;

Sample answer: Area is equal to the length of the side squared, so $z^2 = 2500$, which means $z = \sqrt{2500}$, or $z = 2500^{\frac{1}{2}}$. Therefore $z = 50$.
25. square; whole **26.** *Sample answer:* $81^{\frac{1}{2}} = \sqrt{81}$ because in the fractional exponent $\frac{1}{2}$, 1 is the power and 2 is the root, so you take $\sqrt[2]{81^1} = \sqrt{81} = 9$. **27.** yes; *Sample answer:* $4^{\frac{1}{2}} = \sqrt{4^1} = \sqrt{4} = 2$. Take the square root of 4 to the first power which is 2.

Lesson 7-14, pp. 54–57

Try this: 1. 5 **2.** 2 **3.** $\sqrt[4]{27}$ **4.** 8 **5.** 4 **6.** 9 **7.** 15
8. 12 **9.** 7

Practice: 1. C **2.** A **3.** B **4.** True
5. False **6.** False **7.** 3 **8.** 0 **9.** 10 **10.** 3
11. 400 **12.** $\frac{3}{4}$ **13.** 30 **14.** 36 **15.** 6 **16.** $\sqrt[3]{28}$
17. 5 **18.** $\frac{\sqrt[4]{33}}{2}$ **19.** $t^3 = 512$, $t = 8$ in.; *Sample answer:* The volume of a cube is equal to the length of the side cubed, so $t^3 = 512$, which means $t = \sqrt[3]{512}$, or $t = 512^{\frac{1}{3}}$. Therefore $t = 8$.
20. $m^3 = 27$, $m = 3$ ft; *Sample answer:* The volume of a cube is equal to the length of the side cubed, so $m^3 = 27$ and $m = \sqrt[3]{27}$, or $m = 27^{\frac{1}{3}}$. Therefore $m = 3$. **21.** power; root **22.** *Sample answer:* $64^{\frac{2}{3}}$ means $\left(\sqrt[3]{64}\right)^2$. Find the cube root of 64 to get 4. Then square 4 to get 16. **23.** John; *Sample answer:* When simplifying $16^{\frac{3}{4}}$, if you take the root first you get $\left(\sqrt[4]{16}\right)^3$ which is $(2)^3$, or 8. This can be done using mental math. If you take the power first to get $\sqrt[4]{16^3}$, you have to take 16^3, which is 4096, and then you have take the fourth root of 4096, which is 8. The second way, taking the power first and then the root, is more difficult because it involves working with larger numbers.

Mixed Practice for Lessons 7-6 to 7-14, pp. 58–59

1. C, Z **2.** A, Y **3.** B, X **4.** zero **5.** add
6. square **7.** 3; 4; 7 **8.** 2; 3; 3; 8 **9.** $\frac{n^2 m}{nm^2} = \frac{n}{m}$
10. $\left(\frac{2}{3}\right)^4 = \frac{2^4}{3^4}$ **11.** x^8 **12.** x^2 **13.** $\frac{a}{b}$ **14.** 1 **15.** x^6
16. x^8 **17.** $8r^3$ **18.** x^4y^2 **19.** b^2 **20.** r^{12}
21. a^6 **22.** b^{27} **23.** h; 3; 3200; 3200 **24.** $\frac{1}{25}$

Answers *continued*

25. 1 **26.** $\dfrac{c^2}{p^2}$ **27.** $\dfrac{b^6}{d^3}$ **28.** 3 **29.** 4 **30.** 2

31. 20 **32.** $x^2 = 100$, $x = 10$ ft; *Sample answer:* Since the area of a square is side times side, the area 100 is equal to x^2. To solve for x, take the square root of each side, which gives $x = 10$ or -10. Since length must be a positive number, the answer is 10 ft. **33.** $y^3 = 216$, $y = 6$ cm; *Sample answer:* Since the volume of a cube is length times width times height, the volume 216 is equal to y^3. To solve for y, take the cube root of each side, which gives $y = 6$.